The Elements of Formal Logic

THE ELEMENTS OF
Formal Logic

G. E. HUGHES
PROFESSOR OF PHILOSOPHY
VICTORIA UNIVERSITY OF WELLINGTON

D. G. LONDEY
SENIOR LECTURER IN LOGIC
UNIVERSITY OF NEW ENGLAND

HARPER & ROW, PUBLISHERS, NEW YORK

Library of Congress Catalog Card Number: 66-11461

Contents

PART I

The Propositional Calculus:
Elements and Decision Procedures

PART II

The Propositional Calculus:
Axiomatic Systems

PART III
The Lower Predicate Calculus

PART IV
Syllogistic

Contents

APPENDICES

Preface

This book is designed as an introduction to some of the most central and important branches of modern Formal Logic. We set out explicitly to write a text-book which would start at the start, achieve a substantial penetration into its field, and at the same time provide a sound training in technique as well as in theory. We believe that the book is suitable both for class-room use and for solitary study, and that it can provide a text for a variety of differently constructed courses. (Some suggestions on such courses follow the Preface).

While writing the book, we have had in mind primarily the needs of University students of philosophy; but we have tried to meet these needs by keeping a constant eye on the perplexities and stumbling-blocks which our own students have encountered in logic itself, rather than by excursions into philosophical questions or the superficial device of using 'philosophical' examples. In fact, questions of philosophical logic have been deliberately avoided as far as possible, and the book could equally well be used apart from any philosophical context.

The topics treated are, briefly, the Propositional Calculus (Parts I and II), the more elementary parts of the Lower Predicate Calculus (Part III), and Syllogistic Logic from a modern point of view (Part IV). We have chosen to give a more intensive treatment of this relatively narrow range of topics rather than a more superficial survey of a wider field, because we believe that this will give a clearer insight into the nature of logic and a surer foundation for more advanced work. The Propositional Calculus and Lower Predicate Calculus have been chosen as being the most fundamental parts of logic; the discussion of Syllogistic has been included partly because of its historical importance and partly because modern developments in logic have cast a great deal of new light on it. In treating each system, our two main concerns are with Decision Procedures and Axiomatization. We have tried to justify as well as describe the techniques used, and, within the limits of difficulty suggested by what our students have been able to achieve, we have acted on the principle that whatever can be proved should be proved. In consequence, this book contains more meta-logic than many other introductory texts. That is, it contains more results about logical systems as wholes, as distinct from results obtained within some system.

Since we aim to give a training in *doing* logic, and not merely to provide information *about* the subject, the exercises appended to most chapters are an essential part of the book and should be worked through with care. Indeed, the constant use of pen and paper is indispensable in studying logic. Equally indispensable is recognition of the fact that one of the things that give formal logic its value as an intellectual discipline is that it has standards of exactness and completeness in statement and in proof which are hardly ever attained, and seldom even aimed at, in any other subject. In the text, we have tried to meet these standards as far as is compatible with writing for beginners.

Our thanks are due to the Victoria University of Wellington for assistance in meeting the cost of typing, and to our typists for their patience in coping with a difficult manuscript.

G. E. H.
D. G. L.

Wellington, New Zealand
Armidale, N.S.W., Australia

Some Suggestions on the Use of this Book

The whole book should be adequately covered by a class of beginners in logic meeting for about four hours a week throughout one academic year. It has however been so designed that it could be abridged or divided in several different ways, to provide either a shorter course than this or two successive courses.

Here are some suggestions. In each case the chapters indicated would give a self-contained first course; the rest of the book could then be used for a second course presupposing familiarity with the first.

1. The simplest method would be to stop at the end of any of the first three Parts. Another possible halting-place is the end of Chapter 30 in Part III.

2. A course concentrating on Decision Procedures and omitting Axiomatic Systems can be obtained by using the following: the whole of Part I; Part III, Chapters 23–28, 31–34, 37–41; Part IV, Chapters 42–47. (The Part IV chapters could be omitted or postponed.)

3. A course concentrating on methods and minimizing justifications (thus omitting most of the meta-logical arguments) is given by the following: Part I; Part II, Chapters 12–17, plus 20 and 21 if desired; Part III, Chapters 23–27 (omitting the last few pages of 26), 29, 31–33, 35, 37–41; Part IV, Chapters 42, 43, 45, 46, 48. (The Part IV chapters could again be omitted or postponed.)

4. A sketchier course than either 2 or 3 would be found by using only those chapters common to both.

Other schemes are possible; but in the planning of any division of the material it should be borne in mind that each Part *as a whole* presupposes the previous Part or Parts. A partial exception is that while Part IV draws heavily on Chapters 23–30, it does not use the later chapters of Part III at all. One consequence of this is that in schemes 2, 3 and 4 the Part III chapters from Chapter 31 onwards could be omitted without loss of consecutiveness.

CHAPTER 1

Validity

Everyone knows that Formal Logic has something to do with argument or reasoning. Some think that it is a sophistic art, an art of winning arguments; others, nearer the mark, think that it is the more reputable sophistic art of reasoning correctly and spotting fallacious arguments when others use them; others, still nearer the mark, think of it less as an art or technique and more as an intellectual study of the structures of arguments or inferences, classifying them as sound or fallacious. We can get a good deal nearer the mark still by saying that Formal Logic is the study of the structures of propositions and deductive inferences. This remark is not offered as a definition of 'formal logic', but rather as an indication of the sort of subjects discussed in this book. Indeed it is not clear that any adequate definition of 'formal logic' (let alone 'logic') is possible – if you want to know what Logic is about, then you must set to work and do some. Let us get down to it.

Our subject revolves round the notion of *validity*, and the main purpose of this chapter is to give some explanation of this notion. But before we can address ourselves directly to this task, we need to introduce a few other terms. Since we shall be thus steadily building up a precise technical language you should make quite sure that you have understood and learned the explanation of each new term as it appears.

Propositions and propositional schemata

A *proposition* is a statement. It is either true or false. The following are propositions:

> Today is Tuesday
> 7 is a prime number
> If he goes to town, he will buy some sugar
> Socrates was not the brother of Plato.

A propositional *form* or *schema* (plural: *schemata*) is an expression containing blanks, such that if these blanks are filled in an appropriate way, the result is a proposition. Thus:

All —— are . . .

is a propositional schema. However, for reasons of convenience, we shall use letters instead of dots and dashes to mark the blanks. Such letters are known as *variables*. The following are propositional schemata:

(i) All S are P
(ii) n is a prime number
(iii) If n is a prime number greater than 2, then n is odd
(iv) If p, then q.

In order to get a proposition from a propositional schema we must fill in the blanks *appropriately*, or, as we say, make appropriate *substitutions* for the variables. Thus, in (ii) it is no use replacing 'n' by a proposition – only a number will do. And the same holds for (iii). Similarly we can get a proposition from (iv) only by replacing 'p' and 'q' by propositions. So we say that 'n' in (ii) and (iii) is a *numerical variable*, and that 'p' and 'q' in (iv) are *propositional variables*. A numerical variable like 'n' is said to *take numbers as values*, while a propositional variable like 'p' is said to *take propositions as values*.

We shall reserve the letters 'p', 'q', 'r', 's', 't', . . . for propositional variables. Where no ambiguity will result we shall occasionally use the word 'proposition' to mean 'propositional schema'.

Inferences and inferential schemata

An *inference* is the passage from the assertion of one proposition (the *premiss*) or group of propositions (*premisses*) to the assertion of another proposition (the *conclusion*). The following are inferences:

(i) All kangaroos eat grass, therefore some kangaroos eat grass.
(ii) Every kangaroo I have observed eats grass, therefore some kangaroos eat grass.
(iii) Every kangaroo I have observed eats grass, therefore kangaroos generally eat grass.
(iv) Every kangaroo I have observed eats grass, therefore all kangaroos eat grass.
(v) Some kangaroos eat grass, therefore all kangaroos eat grass.
(vi) Some kangaroos eat grass, therefore there is a man on the moon.

(vii) Kangaroos have such and such a sort of teeth, therefore they probably eat grass.

(viii) All kangaroos are marsupials and some grass-eaters are kangaroos; but Charlie is a grass-eater – so Charlie must be a marsupial.

Inferences are commonly classified into *deductive* and *inductive* inferences. Either sort may be sound or unsound. Of the examples given, (i), (ii), (v) and (viii) would usually be regarded as deductive inferences, the rest as inductive. (Go through these examples deciding which are sound and which are unsound inferences, and why. In the light of your conclusions, try to formulate some basis for the deductive/inductive classification.) In this book we shall be concerned only with various forms of deductive inference, and as you work through it your insight into the nature of this type of inference will grow.

It is perhaps going a little beyond ordinary usage to say that (vi) is an inference at all, since we tend to demand some connection of content between the premisses and the conclusion before we are willing to use the word 'inference'. But it is extremely difficult to make this demand precise; and even if we were to succeed in doing so we would be likely to succeed too well, limiting the meaning of 'inference' to that of 'sound inference' – and we know only too well that there is such a thing as an unsound inference! It is for this reason that we have adopted a very general account of the nature of an inference, even though this means that we must accept as inferences such queer fish as (vi).

A *form of inference* or *inferential schema* is an expression containing blanks, such that if these blanks are filled appropriately the result is an inference. Or, alternatively, it is an expression containing variables, such that if appropriate substitutions are made for the variables, the result is an inference.

The most general forms of inference are:

(i) p, therefore q   (single premiss)

(ii) (p, q, . . .), therefore r (more than one premiss)

Convenient alternative ways of writing these schemata are:

$$(i) \quad \frac{p}{\therefore q} \qquad (ii) \quad \begin{array}{c} p \\ q \\ \cdot \\ \cdot \\ \cdot \\ \hline \therefore r \end{array}$$

There are of course infinitely many specialized forms of these most general forms. For example,

$$\frac{\text{All S are P}}{\therefore \text{ Some S are P}}$$

is a special case of (i).

We are now in a position to begin on our main task of explaining validity, and we begin by introducing the notion of a *valid deductive inference*. An inference is a valid deductive inference if and only if the conclusion logically follows from the premiss(es); that is, if and only if the truth of the premiss(es) gives an absolute guarantee of the truth of the conclusion. It can be seen that a valid inference is a sound inference, and that the heart of this notion of validity is that the combination of true premisses and false conclusion is ruled out.

An inferential schema is, as it were, a pattern for a set of inferences, and we extend the notion of validity to cover such a schema by requiring that every inference constructed on that pattern should be valid. To state it more precisely, *an inferential schema is valid* if and only if every set of appropriate and uniform substitutions for all its variables yields a valid inference. The substitutions must be appropriate in the sense described earlier – i.e. we must substitute the *type* of expression appropriate to the variable – and they must also be *uniform* in the sense that, if a variable appears twice in a given schema, we must make the same substitution for it in each case. Consider the schema

(p, q), therefore q.

For the substitutions to be uniform we must put the same proposition for 'q' in the conclusion as in the premiss. But of course we may substitute a different proposition for 'p' from the one we substitute for 'q', although it is not necessary to do so.

Classification of propositions

A proposition may be either *necessarily true, contingent* or *necessarily false*. Every proposition is of one of these kinds.

A proposition is *necessarily true* if there is no conceivable circumstance in which it would be false – or, as Leibniz[1] put it, if it is true in all possible worlds.

A proposition which is not necessarily true may be either *contingent*

[1] G. W. Leibniz (1646–1716) – a famous German philosopher, logician, mathematician, natural scientist and diplomat.

(true or false, but not necessarily so) or *necessarily false* ('impossible'). Thus:

(i) A brown cow is a cow

(ii) If all triangles are equilateral, then some triangles are equilateral

are necessarily true.

(iii) England is a monarchy

is contingent – it happens to be true, but we could imagine circumstances in which it would be false.

(iv) France is a monarchy

is contingent – it happens to be false.

(v) All round objects are square

is *necessarily* false – we could imagine no set of circumstances in which it would be true.

Classification of propositional schemata

The classification of propositional schemata is analogous to that of propositions. A propositional schema may be either *valid*, *contingent* or *inconsistent*. Every propositional schema is of one of these kinds.

A propositional schema is valid if and only if every set of appropriate and uniform substitutions for all its variables yields a true proposition.

Thus: (i) 'If p, then p' is a valid schema

but   (ii) 'If p, then q' is not a valid schema.

But since *some* substitutions in (ii) will yield a true proposition, we say that (ii) is a *contingent schema*. For example, if we put 'all whales are caught in the Antarctic' for 'p', and 'some whales are caught in the Antarctic' for 'q', we get the *true* proposition:

If all whales are caught in the Antarctic, then some whales are caught in the Antarctic.

But if we reverse these substitutions, we get the *false* proposition:

If some whales are caught in the Antarctic, then all whales are caught in the Antarctic.

It is worth noting that by suitable choice of substitutions we can obtain from a contingent schema any sort of proposition – necessarily true, contingently true, contingently false or necessarily false.

This point can be illustrated by considering the schema:

p and q.

By substituting necessarily true propositions for both variables we obtain a necessarily true proposition; by substituting contingently true propositions for both variables we obtain a contingently true proposition; and so on.

(iii) 'p and not-p' is not a valid schema,

but it differs from (ii) in that every substitution will yield a false proposition. We shall say that any propositional schema which shares this characteristic is *inconsistent*. (We might have used the term 'necessarily false' by analogy with the propositional case, but it seems better to avoid this here, since, strictly speaking, a propositional *schema* is neither true nor false – it is just a skeleton which can be fleshed-out to yield something true or false.)

Now if a proposition can be obtained by substitutions in a valid schema, we might say that it is true by reason of its form, or because it has the sort of form or structure which it has. Similarly, if an inference can be obtained by substitutions in a valid schema, we might say that it is valid by reason of its form. It is precisely these forms, structures or schemata with which formal logic is concerned. In this field we are concerned not with truth and falsity as springing from agreement or disagreement with the facts, but with truth and falsity as springing from form. And we are concerned not with the force of inferences as springing from their plausibility or persuasiveness, but with their soundness or unsoundness as springing from the forms of inference.

In a word, we are concerned with validity and invalidity.

PART I

The Propositional Calculus:
Elements and Decision Procedures

CHAPTER 2
Some Simple Forms of Inference

Let us try our teeth on some simple inferences and see what we can learn from them.

Consider first the inference:

> If it is 3 p.m., then school is out.
>
> It is 3 p.m.
>
> ∴ School is out.

Common-sense tells us that this inference is valid. If it is the case both that if it is 3 p.m. then school is out, *and* that it is 3 p.m., then it *can't* be false that school is out. And this is just what we want in a valid inference – the impossibility of getting a false conclusion from true premisses.

This is a simple inference – so simple in fact that no-one would produce it in full in conversation without adopting a now-I'm-speaking-to-a-child-of-five tone of voice. Usually we would content ourselves with stating the first premiss, if someone were to ask whether school was out yet. But in that case, we are just using the shortened form to convey the whole of the inference set out above.

Now look at the structure of this inference. The first premiss (often called the *major* premiss) is a compound proposition in the sense that it is built from simpler propositional elements, viz. 'It is 3 p.m.' and 'School is out', connected by 'If . . . then . . .'. That is to say, it has the form:

> If p then q.

Any proposition of this form is known as a *hypothetical proposition*, and the first of its constituent propositions is known as its *antecedent*, the second as its *consequent*. Similarly

> If p then q

is called *a hypothetical propositional schema*, 'p' and 'q' being antecedent and consequent, respectively.

9

[There is, of course, nothing sacred about the letters 'p' and 'q' here – the following are also hypothetical propositional schemata:

If q then p
If r then s

as are:

If p and q, then r
If (if q then r) then not-p.]

You will notice that the second (or *minor*) premiss is the same proposition as the antecedent of the major premiss, viz. 'It is 3 p.m.'; and that the conclusion is identical with the consequent of the major premiss, viz. 'School is out'.

Thus, the form of the inference (i.e. the inferential schema from which the inference can be obtained by appropriate substitutions) is:

$$\text{If p then q}$$

$$\frac{\text{p}}{\therefore \quad \text{q}}$$

Now a deductive inference with two premisses is called a *syllogism*;[1] and since one of the premisses in the case we are considering is a hypothetical proposition, it is known as a *hypothetical syllogism*. Since only one of the premisses is hypothetical, we may call it a *mixed hypothetical syllogism*.

It is easy to see that there are just four forms of hypothetical syllogism of this sort. For if the major premiss is of the form 'If p then q', we can have as minor premiss either the affirmation of the antecedent (as in the case above) or the denial of the antecedent, 'not-p'; or the affirmation of the consequent, 'q'; or the denial of the consequent, 'not-q'.

These are the only possible minor premisses, since the minor premiss must bear some clear relation to the major premiss. Obviously nothing follows from the premisses

If it is 3 p.m. then school is out
China is in Asia

except whatever would follow from either premiss on its own.

---

[1] Note that this is a wider use of 'syllogism' than you will find in some books in which the term is reserved for cases in which the two premisses are of special forms. But our use is also narrower than that of some authors who allow a syllogism to have more than two premisses.

For similar reasons the conclusion can only be either the affirmation or denial of either the antecedent or the consequent.

We thus have the four schemata[1]:

I	II	III	IV
If p then q	If p then q	If p then q	If p then q
p	not-p	q	not-q
∴ q	∴ not-q	∴ p	∴ not-p

[You should construct inferences with these forms for yourself.]

These four schemata are called the four *figures* of the mixed hypothetical syllogism, and are given names according to the nature of the minor premiss.

> I Affirming the Antecedent
> II Denying the Antecedent
> III Affirming the Consequent
> IV Denying the Consequent.

It is easy to see that II and III are invalid, since we can find substitutions for 'p' and 'q' which yield an invalid inference, e.g. in II put: 'The authors of this book speak Portuguese' for 'p', and 'The authors of this book speak an Indo-European language' for 'q'.' Then we have:

If the authors of this book speak Portuguese, then they speak an Indo-European language.

The authors of this book do not speak Portuguese.
∴ They do not speak an Indo-European language.

The major premiss is certainly true, and so is the minor premiss, since it happens that the authors know no Portuguese. But it is false to say that they do not speak an Indo-European language, since they speak English. Thus we have true premisses and a false conclusion, so the inference must be invalid. And since the inferential schema, II, has an invalid instance, it must also be invalid.

The same substitutions will serve to demonstrate that III is not a valid form of inference. For then we have two true premisses yielding the false conclusion that the authors speak Portuguese.

However, reflection on the structures of the other two figures, I

[1] Strictly speaking, there are eight of this sort; but we omit four of these since no-one would be tempted to draw the conclusion 'not-q' from the premisses of I, or the conclusion 'q' from the premisses of II, or 'not-p' from those of III, or 'p' from those of IV.

and IV, will convince us that they are valid. If we have both that if p is true then q is true, and that p *is* true, then q must be true. So we conclude that I (Affirming the Antecedent) is a valid form of inference. And so is IV (Denying the Consequent). For if we have both that if p is true then q is true, and that q is *not* true, then p cannot be true either - i.e. not-p must be true.

CHAPTER 3

Establishing Validity (Theory)

We found it easy to prove that two forms of the mixed hypothetical syllogism were invalid, that they could not be relied on to give us a true conclusion from true premisses. But although easy, the proof is none the less watertight. Since, in order for the form to be valid, *every* proper set of substitutions must yield a valid inference, to show that a form is invalid it suffices to find one set of substitutions which does not yield a valid inference. But it is quite impossible to prove that a form of inference is *valid* by this means. Even a long series of sets of substitutions which yield valid inferences does not provide us with a proof that the form of inference is valid. So far we have relied on our logical intuitions, our *sense* of what follows and what doesn't, to convince us that Affirming the Antecedent and Denying the Consequent are valid forms of inference. But just seeing that . . . is not the same as proving that . . . ; and it is clear that if we want to prove that an inferential schema is valid we shall have to devise some general method for doing so, which will not depend either on intuition or on the result of assigning particular values to the variables.

Now someone might say, 'But surely, common-sense is a good enough guide to validity. If you can just *see* that the conclusion follows, you don't need to worry about proof.' Well, in the first place, common-sense isn't always good enough – people do make mistakes about what follows from what, especially with more complicated sorts of inference. In the second place, 'You can just see it' is theoretically unsatisfying if a rigorous proof is available. And in the third place, if we can devise a sufficiently general sort of proof it may suggest ways of tackling other problems of a related sort.

Now consider the inferential schema

$$\text{If } p \text{ then } q$$
$$\frac{p}{\therefore \qquad q} \qquad (1)$$

13

If we assert that this is valid, we are asserting that whenever we have premisses of the forms 'If p then q' and 'p', the conclusion of the form 'q' follows; that is, that if these premisses are true, then that conclusion is also true; or, to state it in a way that is strictly inaccurate but a convenient shorthand locution, that if *If p then q* and *p* are true, then *q* is also true. But this is just what is expressed by the *propositional* schema

$$\text{If (if p then q, and p), then q} \qquad (2)$$

This makes it clear that if (2) is valid then (1) must also be valid, and vice versa. But it must be stressed that (1) and (2) are *not the same*. They are schemata of different sorts; (1) is an inferential schema, (2) is a propositional schema. Nevertheless there is a strong structural similarity between them, since the antecedent of (2) consists of the two premisses of (1) linked by 'and', while the consequent of (2) is the conclusion of (1).

We might fairly say that we have reduced the problem of determining the validity of (1) to the problem of determining the validity of (2). But in order to make this reduction watertight and to find a way of solving our new problem, we must investigate the conditions under which schemata like (2) are valid.

(2) is a *hypothetical* propositional schema, so if it is valid every set of (appropriate and uniform) substitutions for the variables 'p' and 'q' will yield a true hypothetical proposition. Under what conditions, then, will we say that a hypothetical proposition is true?

Answering this question is made difficult by the fact that statements which share the form 'If p then q' play very diverse parts when they are made in ordinary English. Sometimes such statements are made to state a causal relation between two states of affairs. E.g. 'If iron is heated sufficiently it will glow red.' Sometimes they are made to inform us of an intention of the speaker. E.g. 'If it rains, I shall stay at home.' Sometimes they are made to predict the behaviour of another person. E.g. 'If it rains, Tom won't turn up.' Sometimes they are made to assert that one proposition, the consequent, logically follows from another, the antecedent. E.g. 'If 7 is a prime, then 7 is not divisible by 4.' We could spend some time enumerating other more or less finely distinguished uses. But the essential point is clear enough. Hypothetical propositions are a very mixed lot and we have no single, simple test for deciding their truth or falsity as they occur in ordinary discourse. (This should not be surprising: we also lack a single, simple test for deciding the truth or falsity of statements of the form 'x is large'.)

However there is no need to despair. In formal logic we are not interested in all the rich encrusted variety which occurs in ordinary language. Our concern is to dig beneath this variety for the more austere structural elements: and since validity springs from structure, any method for determining it must be concerned with these structural elements.

Now, despite their variety, hypothetical propositions do have certain features in common. In every case, one proposition is asserted to be *conditional on* another. The antecedent states a condition; the consequent states something which is supposed to depend on that condition. This notion of conditionality, of dependence, is not at first sight very clear, for it seems to reflect the variety of parts played by hypothetical statements, varying in nature with these parts. (E.g. if the statement is made to express a causal relationship, then one might say that the dependence is a causal dependence.) But there is a hard core to the notion of conditionality. For part of what is asserted when a hypothetical statement is made is that when the antecedent is true (i.e. the condition is fulfilled), the consequent is also true (i.e. the dependent state of affairs is the case). Notice that this is *not* to say that the truth of the consequent *follows from* the truth of the antecedent, or anything of that sort. It *is* to say that what is asserted is that *we do not have the case of the antecedent being true and the consequent being false*. That is, it is asserted that when the antecedent is true and the consequent is false (i.e. the condition is fulfilled, but the allegedly dependent state of affairs is not the case), the hypothetical proposition is false.

Now you will recall that the antecedent and consequent of a hypothetical proposition are themselves propositions, so that each is either true or false. There are consequently just four possible combinations of truth and falsity of the antecedent and consequent, viz.:

	Antecedent	Consequent
i	True	True
ii	True	False
iii	False	True
iv	False	False

Case (ii) is the outlawed combination of true antecedent and false consequent. In that case the hypothetical proposition is false. But inspection will show that in every other case we do avoid that combination. We have thus found a correspondence between the truth or falsity of a hypothetical proposition and the truth or falsity of its antecedent and consequent. (In doing this we have by-passed the non-structural features, i.e. the particular content of the propositions.) We can set out this correspondence in a table, thus:

Antecedent	Consequent	Hypothetical Proposition
True	True	True
True	False	False
False	True	True
False	False	True

Remember that we did not set out to accomplish the impossible task of finding a single way of deciding the truth or falsity of hypothetical propositions as they occur in ordinary discourse. We set out to do a job in formal logic, to investigate the underlying structure and search *there* for a way of deciding their truth or falsity. Furthermore we have succeeded. We have found, and caught in a table, one component of what is expressed by 'If . . . then . . .'. This component is known as *material implication*. It is the material implication of one proposition (the consequent) by another (the antecedent) that is true except in the case in which the antecedent is true and the consequent is false.

Now one point we must make absolutely clear, at the risk of being tedious. In what has been said, we have no intention of suggesting that 'If p then q' always means just 'p materially implies q'. In fact, in ordinary discourse, statements of the form 'If p then q' always (or almost always) mean *more* than 'p materially implies q'. But the important point is that they never mean *less*. Furthermore, material implication is the sort of notion which has a place in formal logic – it is a structurally based notion which we can deal with.

Henceforth, then, when we speak of a hypothetical proposition we shall mean a proposition expressing the material implication of the consequent by the antecedent – i.e. we shall fix our attention on the part that concerns us here and neglect the rest. So we say that *a hypothetical proposition is true except when its antecedent is true and its consequent is false – in which case it is false.*

But, you may say, 'If p then q' may never mean *less* than 'p materially implies q' – but does material implication catch *enough* of the meaning of 'If p then q'? After all, a glance at the table shows that a material implication is always true when its antecedent is false, and also when its consequent is true. That is, a false proposition materially implies any proposition; and a true proposition is materially implied by any proposition.[1] This seems quite at variance with the way we treat hypothetical statements in ordinary discourse. We do not ordinarily regard the truth of the consequent or the falsity of the antecedent as sufficient guarantee of the truth of a hypothetical proposition.

The answer here is that regarding hypothetical propositions as expressing material implications does catch enough of their meaning *for our purposes*. We *can* get the results we seek by attending to just this element and ignoring the rest – and that is sufficient justification for doing so.

So we reaffirm that hypothetical propositions, in so far as they are involved in inferences whose validity we are concerned to investigate in formal logic, are true except when they have a true antecedent and a false consequent – in which case they are false.

We recall that a hypothetical propositional schema is valid if and only if every set of substitutions for its variables yields a true (hypothetical) proposition. That is, it is valid if and only if there is no set of substitutions which yields a true antecedent and a false consequent.

Analogously, an inferential schema is valid if and only if there is no set of substitutions for its variables which yields an inference all of whose premisses are true but whose conclusion is false.

Now, corresponding to the inferential schema

$$\text{If p then q}$$
$$\frac{\text{p}}{\therefore \quad \text{q}} \tag{1}$$

we formed the propositional schema

$$\text{If (if p then q, and p), then q} \tag{2}$$

by linking the two premisses of (1) by 'and' to form the antecedent and taking the conclusion of (1) as the consequent. It is clear that the antecedent of (2) can be true only if *both* the premisses of (1) are

---

[1] These statements have been christened 'The Paradoxes of Material Implication' – an unhappy baptism since there is nothing paradoxical about them *unless* you think that material implication is what it is not. If you take the 'paradoxes' literally they are just sober truths.

true, and the consequent of (2) can be false only if the conclusion of (1) is false. But that is to say that (2) is invalid only if (1) is invalid. Equally, if (1) is invalid then (2) must also be invalid. So (2) is invalid if and only if (1) is invalid; from which it follows immediately that (1) is valid if and only if (2) is valid. Thus we have indeed reduced the problem of determining the validity of (1) to the problem of determining the validity of (2). Furthermore, it is clear that this reduction is not restricted to the special case of the schemata (1) and (2): we can always shift the problem from an inferential schema to a suitably constructed propositional schema. But, having shifted the problem, we need a method for solving it, and our next task is to find a method for determining the validity of propositional schemata.

The *truth-value* of a proposition is its truth or falsity. Since a hypothetical proposition (material implication) is true except when its antecedent is true and its consequent false, in which case it is false, the truth-value of any such proposition depends only on the truth-values of its antecedent and consequent. That is, its truth-value does not depend on the particular content of its constituent propositions. Similarly, the validity of a hypothetical propositional schema does not depend on the particular content of the propositions substituted for its variables; it is valid if and only if a true proposition results no matter what the truth-values of the propositions substituted. But that is to say that it is valid if and only if a true proposition results *independently* of the truth-values of the propositions substituted. (If my tea tastes right both when I add sugar and when I do not, then it tastes right independently of whether I add sugar or not.) We can put this shortly by saying that *a hypothetical propositional schema is valid if and only if it has the truth-value 'truth' for all uniform assignments of truth-values to its variables.*

The problem of determining the validity of a propositional schema has now reached manageable proportions. For instead of having to check (*per impossibile*) each of an infinite number of values for each propositional variable, we now have to check only two cases, the assignment of truth and falsity, for each variable. Thus, for the schema 'If p then p', we need to check only two cases:

(1) where 'p' is replaced by a true proposition – i.e. where truth is assigned to 'p' – or, for short, where p is true

(2) where 'p' is replaced by a false proposition – i.e. where falsity is assigned to 'p' – or, for short, where p is false.

If the schema is true (again a shorthand locution) in each case, then it is valid. But for the schemata 'If p then q' and 'If (if p then q, and p), then q' we need to check four cases altogether, since there are two distinct propositional variables, 'p' and 'q' in each, and when p is true, q may be either true or false, and similarly when p is false. Thus we need to consider the cases:

(1) where p is true, and q is true
(2) where p is true, and q is false
(3) where p is false, and q is true
(4) where p is false, and q is false.

If the schema is true in each case, it is valid.

The propositional schemata we are considering may be thought of as built up from propositional variables by linking them together with *connectives* or *operators*. (Material implication is an example of such an operator.) These operators are such that if they are applied to propositions, the result is a proposition, and so they are called *proposition-forming operators* (or *propositional connectives*). Material implication operates on a *pair* of propositions, and is therefore said to be a *dyadic* operator. Thus, 'If it is raining, then' is not a proposition since it is a case of a dyadic operator operating on only one proposition. The propositions on which an operator operates are called its *arguments*.

The following are *monadic operators*, (i.e. they take one argument):

(*a*) It is not the case that ('not' for short)
(*b*) Napoleon believed that

But 'Napoleon believed that' is a different sort of operator from the others. If we know that p is true, we *thereby* know that not-p is false; and if we know that p is false, we thereby know that not-p is true. And this feature of 'not' is shared by 'if . . . then . . .' – if we know whether p and q are true or false, we can from this alone determine the truth or falsity of 'If p then q'. But if you know that p is true, this does not tell you whether 'Napoleon believed that p' is true or false.

An operator is said to be *truth-functional* if the truth-value of the proposition it forms depends only on the truth-value(s) of its argument(s). And the proposition which it forms is said to be a *truth-function* of its arguments.

Another familiar truth-functional operator is 'and'. Like material implication, it is a dyadic operator. Its truth-functionality can be

seen by considering the fact that we allow a proposition of the form
'p and q' to be true if and only if both the arguments of the operator
are true.

We are now in a position to define more clearly the field of logic
in which we are working – viz. the *Propositional Calculus*. The
Propositional Calculus (PC) has as its field the class of all propositional schemata which contain no variables other than propositional
variables, and no operators other than truth-functional proposition-
forming operators.

These truth-functional operators are often known as *logical
constants*, although that term is also used to refer to some logical
operators which are not truth-functional, and with which we are not
concerned in the Propositional Calculus.

Some symbolic conventions

We now introduce a few symbolic conventions which will make for
easier working.

For 'If p then q', we shall write 'p⊃q', which we can read either
as 'If p then q' or as 'p materially implies q' (or simply as 'p implies
q', remembering though that we are not concerned with or attempting
to represent anything but *material* implication).

For 'p and q', we shall write 'p.q'. '.' is called the *conjunction* sign,
and the operator it symbolizes is called *conjunction*. 'p.q' is said to be
the *conjunction* of 'p' and 'q', which are themselves said to be its
conjuncts. We usually read '.' as 'and', but it is worth noting that in
ordinary English this role is often played by 'but' and 'although'.
[Replace 'and' by 'but' and 'although' in: 'The machine is well
designed and it won't go'. Notice how the truth-functional characteristics are preserved through the changes.]

For 'not-p', we shall write '∼p'. '∼' is the *negation* sign, and
'∼p' is called the *negation* of 'p'.

Thus the antecedent of:

$$\text{If (if p then q, and p) then q}$$

(viz., 'if p then q, and p') can be written:

$$(p⊃q).p$$

Since 'p' and 'q' are propositions, 'p⊃q' is a proposition; and therefore '(p⊃q).p' is a proposition. We introduce brackets as punctuation
since

$$p⊃q.p$$

would be ambiguous as between

$$p \supset (q \cdot p)$$

and $\qquad (p \supset q) \cdot p$

Then the whole schema we are concerned with is:

$$((p \supset q) \cdot p) \supset q$$

Since only truth-functional operators have been used in the construction of this schema, the whole schema may be regarded as a truth-function of the two variables 'p' and 'q'. It then appears that we ought to be able to compute the truth-values of the schema corresponding to each of the four possible combinations of truth-values of the variables, by using the known truth-functional characteristics of (material) implication and conjunction.

We can tabulate these truth-functional characteristics of the three operators introduced so far in the form of *basic truth-tables*. These are simply tables which set out correspondences between the truth-values of the fundamental truth-functions and the possible combinations of truth-values of the variables. The array of possible combinations of truth-values of the variables (always set out on the left) will be called the *matrix*. The matrix varies according to the number of variables considered, but for any given number of variables we adopt a standard arrangement of the matrix. The set of truth-values of the schema, correlated with the rows of the matrix and set out in the right-most column, is the *truth-table* of the schema. We can use the basic truth-tables to construct truth-tables for more complex truth-functions, since these more complex truth-functions are themselves constructed from the fundamental ones. The terminology just introduced applies throughout.

Basic truth-tables

I. Negation

p	$\sim$p
True	False
False	True

The schema '$\sim$p' contains only one variable, so there are just two possibilities to consider. These are set out in the left-hand column. When p is true its negation is false, and when p is false, its negation is true – and that is just what the table expresses.

For brevity's sake let us write '1' for 'True' and '0' for 'False'. The basic truth-table for negation then becomes:

p	$\sim$p
1	0
0	1

II. *Material Implication*

p	q	p$\supset$q
1	1	1
1	0	0
0	1	1
0	0	1

The operator here is dyadic, and as pointed out earlier there are therefore four cases to be considered. These are set out in the two-column matrix on the left. The tables expresses the fact that *a material implication is true except when the antecedent is true and the consequent is false.*

III. *Conjunction*

p	q	p·q
1	1	1
1	0	0
0	1	0
0	0	0

This table expresses the fact that *a conjunction is true if and only if both conjuncts are true.* It has four horizontal rows because conjunction is a dyadic operator.

These basic truth-tables really are basic, since they may be regarded as providing definitions of the operators, and will be used constantly in what follows. You need to have them at your finger-tips, and the few minutes required to learn them thoroughly *now* will be minutes well spent.

You now have all the materials for constructing a truth-table for any propositional schema containing one or two distinct variables and no operators other than negation, implication and conjunction. (The technique of doing so will be explained in detail in the next chapter.) Such a schema will be valid if and only if it is true (has the value 1) for each assignment of truth-values to its variables (for each of the possibilities set out in the matrix).

Thus we have found a method for determining the validity of the schema:

$$((p \supset q) \cdot p) \supset q$$

i.e. the schema:

If (if p then q, and p), then q

Thereby, in the light of the reduction effected earlier (p. 18), we have found a method for determining the validity of the inferential schema:

$$\frac{\begin{array}{l} \text{If p then q} \\ \text{p} \end{array}}{\therefore \quad q}$$

What is most important, we have a method which is not restricted in its application to this particular case. It frees us from dependence on intuition not only in this simple case where intuition works pretty well, but also in much more complicated cases where it lets us down more often than not.

CHAPTER 4

Establishing Validity (Practice)

Before proceeding to the construction of a truth-table for

$$((p⊃q)\cdot p) ⊃ q$$

we shall work through two easy examples step by step.

EXAMPLE 1.   p.~p   [Both p and not-p]

Step (i).   Only one distinct variable, 'p', is involved, so the matrix

p
1
0

suffices to give all the possible truth-values of the variables.

Step (ii).   The first conjunct is 'p', so write down the left-most column again, getting

p	p
1	1
0	0

Step (iii).   The second conjunct is '~p', so put down the truth-values for '~p' (from the basic truth-table for negation) in the next column, thus:

p	p	~p
1	1	0
0	0	1

Step (iv).   Head the next column 'p.~p'. We already have a column of truth-values for each of the conjuncts, and we know (from the basic table for conjunction) that a conjunction is true (i.e. has the value 1) *only* when both conjuncts are true. But in neither row here are both the conjuncts true. So we get the final table:

p	p	~p	p.~p
1	1	0	0
0	0	1	0

24

The fact that the final column consists only of 0's shows that, so far from being valid, 'p.∼p' is inconsistent, since *no* substitution for the variable 'p' will yield a true proposition.

EXAMPLE 2.　p ⊃ (p.q)　[If p then both p and q]

Step (i).　Since there are two distinct variables involved we need four horizontal rows to set out all possible combinations of their truth-values. Thus we get this matrix:

p	q
1	1
1	0
0	1
0	0

Step (ii).　'p ⊃ (p.q)' has the form of a material implication with a consequent which is itself a conjunction. That is, the main connective is '⊃'. So if we can get a column of truth-values for its antecedent and another for its consequent, we could use the basic truth-table for material implication to read off the values for the whole schema. The antecedent is 'p', and we already have its values on the extreme left of the matrix. Put them down again.

p	q	p
1	1	1
1	0	1
0	1	0
0	0	0

Step (iii).　The consequent of the schema is 'p.q', whose truth-values can be obtained from the basic truth-table for conjunction. Put them down in the next column.

p	q	p	p.q
1	1	1	1
1	0	1	0
0	1	0	0
0	0	0	0

Step (iv).　Since we now have values for both antecedent and consequent, we can immediately compute the values for the whole schema.

p	q	p	p·q	p ⊃ (p·q)
1	1	1	1	1
1	0	1	0	0
0	1	0	0	1
0	0	0	0	1

We now have the truth-table for 'p ⊃ (p·q)'.

The fact that there is an occurrence of '0' in the final column shows that this schema is not valid – it is not the case that every set of substitutions for the variables yields a true proposition. In fact, since this 0 corresponds to the pair 1,0 in the matrix on the left, we learn that substitution of a true proposition for 'p' and a false proposition for 'q' will always yield a false proposition.

Since the intermediate columns merely represent steps in the construction of the final column of truth-values, we do not regard them as being strictly part of the truth-table itself. In accordance with the convention adopted in the previous chapter, we reserve the term 'truth-table' for the single column of values under the schema whose truth-table it is. (These values are, of course, to be taken as corresponding to some standard matrix.)

We now construct a truth-table for

$$((p{\supset}q){\cdot}p) \supset q$$

and thereby demonstrate its validity.

The general shape of the schema is that of a material implication with a complex antecedent. The antecedent is a conjunction whose conjuncts are 'p ⊃q' and 'p'. So we begin on the left with the usual matrix for two variables, and then set down values for 'p ⊃q' and 'p'. We can then apply the rule that a conjunction is true if and only if both conjuncts are true to obtain a column of values for the whole antecedent. Next we set down the values for the consequent, 'q', and from that column and its predecessor we read off the values for the whole schema according to the truth-functional characteristics of material implication. Thus we get the following table.

p	q	p⊃q	p	(p⊃q)·p	q	((p⊃q)·p) ⊃ q
1	1	1	1	1	1	1
1	0	0	1	0	0	1
0	1	1	0	0	1	1
0	0	1	0	0	0	1

From the unbroken row of 1's in the final column we see that the schema is valid – no set of substitutions for the variables can yield a false proposition. And therefore, by the reduction effected in the last chapter, the inferential schema

$$\text{If p then q}$$
$$\underline{\text{p}}$$
$$\therefore \qquad \text{q}$$

is also valid, for no set of substitutions in it can yield true premises and a false conclusion. If there *were* a set of substitutions which did yield that, there would be some case in which the antecedent of the propositional schema (the conjunction of the premises) is true, and the consequent of the propositional schema (the conclusion) is false. But there is no such case.

We can use just the same techniques to demonstrate the invalidity of an inferential schema. Consider, for example, the schema of Denying the Antecedent. This is:

$$\text{If p then q}$$
$$\underline{\text{not-p}}$$
$$\therefore \ \text{not-q}$$

By conjoining the premises we can form the propositional schema

$$((p \supset q) \cdot {\sim}p) \supset {\sim}q$$

which is valid if and only if the inferential schema is valid. By essentially the same method as before we can construct a truth-table for this schema, the only difference being that we have to fill in values for '${\sim}p$' and '${\sim}q$' instead of for 'p' and 'q'. This presents no difficulty if you remember that negation reverses the truth-value of its argument. The table is as follows:

p	q	p⊃q	∼p	(p⊃q)·∼p	∼q	((p⊃q)·∼p) ⊃ ∼q
1	1	1	0	0	0	1
1	0	0	0	0	1	1
0	1	1	1	1	0	0
0	0	1	1	1	1	1

The 0 in the final column, in the same row as p=0 and q=1 in the matrix, shows that substitution of a false proposition for 'p' and a true proposition for 'q' in the inferential schema yields an inference with true premises and false conclusion. That is, this form of inference is invalid.

We now possess a technique which promises to be applicable to a wide variety of forms of inference, and to all the propositional forms which fall within the field of the Propositional Calculus once we have acquired knowledge of the truth-functional characteristics of other operators. But before passing to the consideration of new operators, let us examine a further form of hypothetical syllogism.

In the inferences considered so far, only one of the premisses has been an explicitly hypothetical proposition. The minor premiss may be just a simple assertion such as

> 'I am tired'
> 'Venus is a planet'
> 'All New Zealanders are British subjects'
> 'Tom is taller than Harry'

(These have varying internal structures, but none of them can be represented as built up from constituent *propositions*.) On the other hand we should note that there is nothing to stop the minor premiss being, say, a hypothetical proposition. Thus:

If it is the case that if fishes fly the moon is green, then there are fairies in the garden.

It is the case that if fishes fly the moon is green.

∴ There are fairies in the garden.

is a perfectly good case of Affirming the Antecedent.

The important point about the Mixed Hypothetical Syllogism is that the minor premiss is either the affirmation or the denial of the antecedent or consequent of the major premiss. We come now to a form of inference with two explicitly hypothetical premisses – the *Pure Hypothetical Syllogism*. Suppose we have the premisses:

If the murderer is in the room he will betray himself in some way.

If he betrays himself in some way, he will be arrested.

Now it is clear that here we can obtain only a hypothetical conclusion. We cannot, for example, conclude simply that he (the murderer) will be arrested, since the condition of his being in the room may not be fulfilled. In other words, both premisses might be true and 'He will be arrested' be false. All that we can conclude is that *if* the murderer is in the room, *then* he will be arrested. The link between the premisses is, of course, made by the fact that the consequent of the one is the antecedent of the other.

The form of the Pure Hypothetical Syllogism is:

> If p then q
> If q then r
> ∴ If p then r

This is valid if and only if the propositional schema:

$$((p \supset q).(q \supset r)) \supset (p \supset r)$$

is valid.

Now there are three distinct variables involved here, and you will find that there are just eight possible combinations of their truth-values, ranging from all three being true to all three being false. Hence the matrix must have eight horizontal rows. [There is a simple rule for finding the number of horizontal rows in any matrix. If n is the number of variables in the schema, there are just 2^n possible combinations of their truth-values. So for one variable we have 2^1 (i.e. 2) rows; for two variables, 2^2 (i.e. 4) rows; for three variables, 2^3 (i.e. 8) rows; and so on.] Thus here we have the following matrix:

p	q	r
1	1	1
1	1	0
1	0	1
1	0	0
0	1	1
0	1	0
0	0	1
0	0	0

To construct the truth-table for the schema, put down the appropriate values in each of the eight rows for the conjuncts of the antecedent, viz. '$p \supset q$' and '$q \supset r$'. From those two columns get the values for the whole antecedent. Then find the eight values for the consequent, '$p \supset r$'; from this column and the preceding one, work out the values for the whole schema. We thus get the following table. The unbroken row of 1's in the final column shows that the propositional schema, and therefore the form of inference, is valid.

p	q	r	$p \supset q$	$q \supset r$	$(p \supset q).(q \supset r)$	$p \supset r$	$((p \supset q).(q \supset r))$ $\supset (p \supset r)$
1	1	1	1	1	1	1	1
1	1	0	1	0	0	0	1
1	0	1	0	1	0	1	1
1	0	0	0	1	0	0	1
0	1	1	1	1	1	1	1
0	1	0	1	0	0	1	1
0	0	1	1	1	1	1	1
0	0	0	1	1	1	1	1

Summary of the technique

To determine the validity of an inferential schema:

(1) Construct a propositional schema which is valid if and only if the inferential schema is valid, by

    (*a*) conjoining all the premisses of the inferential schema to form the antecedent

    (*b*) replacing ' ∴ ' by ' ⊃ '

    (*c*) taking the conclusion of the inferential schema as the consequent.

(2) Construct a truth-table for the propositional schema.

(3) Read off from the truth-table the validity or invalidity of the propositional schema, and therefore of the inferential schema.

In conclusion we note that this same technique can be used to determine the formal validity of an inference (as distinct from an inferential schema). From the point of view of technique all that is needed is to set out the form of the inference, and then proceed as described above. If the inferential schema is valid, then any inference which has that form must be valid also. If the inferential schema is invalid, this shows that the inference must be regarded as logically unsound in the sense that the possibility of the premisses being true and the conclusion false has not been ruled out. Thus we can infer the validity or invalidity of an inference from the validity or invalidity of the form of which it is an instance.

EXERCISES 4

4.1 Construct truth-tables for the following and thus determine their validity.

    (*a*) $(p \cdot \sim p) \supset p$

    (*b*) $(p \supset \sim p) \supset p$

    (*c*) $p \supset (\sim p \supset p)$

    (*d*) $p \supset (q \supset p)$

    (*e*) $(p \cdot q) \supset p$

    (*f*) $((p \cdot q) \cdot r) \supset p$

    (*g*) $((p \supset q) \cdot r) \supset ((p \supset r) \cdot q)$

    (*h*) $(((p \supset q) \cdot (q \supset r)) \cdot \sim r) \supset p$

4.2 Use truth-tables to show the validity or invalidity of the remaining figures of the mixed hypothetical syllogism, viz. Affirming the Consequent and Denying the Consequent.

4.3 Show that the conclusion 'q' does not follow from premisses 'If p then q' and 'It is not the case that p'.

4.4 Determine the validity of this form of inference:

> If p is true then both q and r are true
> If r is true q is false
> r is in fact true
> _____
> ∴ p is false

4.5 Use the technique outlined at the end of Chapter 4 to determine the validity of this inference:

If I am in Armidale I am not in Wellington, and if I am in Wellington I am not in Armidale; therefore, it is not the case both that I am in Armidale and that I am in Wellington.

CHAPTER 5

Disjunction and Disjunctive Inference

If someone tells you that there is a train at either 5.10 p.m. or 5.20 p.m., he is saying, in a slightly shortened way, that *either* there is a train at 5.10 p.m. *or* there is a train at 5.20 p.m. The form of his assertion is caught by the propositional schema

Either p or q

in which two propositional variables are connected by the English expression 'Either . . . or . . .' (or simply 'or'). This operator takes two arguments, and is therefore dyadic.

Now if someone does assert that either there is a train at 5.10 p.m. or there is a train at 5.20 p.m., we would say that his assertion is false if there is a train at *neither* of those times – i.e. if both the constituent propositions are false. But if there is no train at 5.20, we would say that he had spoken truly, provided that there is a train at 5.10; and similarly he has spoken the truth if there is a train at 5.20, when there is none at 5.10. In each case, one of the constituent propositions is true. Now suppose that there is in fact a train at 5.10 and *also* one at 5.20. (That is, consider the case in which both the constituent propositions are true.) Here we could jump in either of two directions. On the one hand we could say that his assertion was true because it is certainly the case that if there are trains at both times there is a train at one of them. We would then be taking

Either p or q

in an *inclusive* way. That is, we would be taking it to mean that *at least* one of 'p' and 'q' is true, without adding the restrictive qualification that *at most* one of them is true. We shall call 'Either p or q', taken in this sense, the *disjunction* of 'p' and 'q', and symbolize it by

p ∨ q

where '∨' is the *disjunction* operator, and 'p' and 'q' are its *disjuncts*.

But we can contrast this inclusive sense with an *exclusive* sense of 'Either p or q' in which it is taken to mean that *at least and at most*

32

one of 'p' and 'q' is true. We shall call 'Either p or q', taken in this exclusive sense, the *alternation* of 'p' and 'q' and symbolize it by

$$p \vee q$$

where 'V' is the *alternation* operator, and 'p' and 'q' are its *alternatives*.

The difference between the two operators is that a disjunction is true if both disjuncts are true, while an alternation is false if both alternatives are true. Both 'pvq' and 'pVq' are true if just one of 'p' and 'q' is true; and both are false if both 'p' and 'q' are false.

We have seen that the English expression 'Either . . . or . . .' conceals *two* dyadic truth-functional operators. In fact, it is most commonly used to express disjunction, and in general alternation is made explicit in ordinary discourse by the addition of some such phrase as 'and not both'. Some philosophers are inclined to say that there are no occurrences in ordinary discourse of the pure truth-functional alternation. [It is certainly true that some examples commonly given as alternations are simply disjunctions. Consider the case 'Either he is in the dining-room or he is in the kitchen'. It is certainly true that he cannot be in both places, but this impossibility is not expressed by the proposition, but arises from the content of the constituent propositions. Therefore it ought to be regarded as a disjunction rather than as an alternation.] You should try to construct for yourself ordinary language cases of alternation, taking care to ask of each case whether the operator is purely truth-functional.

Basic truth-tables

We have seen that both disjunction and alternation are truth-functional, so we can set out their truth-functional characteristics thus:

Disjunction	p	q	pvq	*Alternation*	p	q	pVq
	1	1	1		1	1	0
	1	0	1		1	0	1
	0	1	1		0	1	1
	0	0	0		0	0	0

A disjunction is false only when both disjuncts are false. An alternation is true when exactly one alternative is true.

The disjunctive syllogism

Suppose that our friend makes his assertion that either there is a train at 5.10 or there is one at 5.20, and we know that in fact there is no train at 5.10. Then we may properly conclude that there *is* a train at 5.20. Setting the inference out more formally, we get:

Either there is a train at 5.10 or there is a train at 5.20.

It is not the case that there is a train at 5.10.
_____
∴ There is a train at 5.20.

Following our earlier usage, we shall call such an inference a *disjunctive syllogism*, since it is a deductive inference with two premisses, one of which is a disjunction (i.e. a proposition having disjunction as its main operator). The major premiss has been taken as a disjunction rather than as an alternation in accordance with a pragmatic rule that 'Either . . . or . . .' propositions are usually intended to express disjunctions unless there is an explicit 'but not both' clause. (However, we shall see that the validity of *this* inference would be unaffected if we took the major premiss as an alternation.)

The form of the inference is:

Either p or q
not-p
_____
∴ q

and it is intuitively clear that all inferences with this form are valid. However we may demonstrate the validity of the inferential schema by the methods of the previous chapter. By conjoining the premisses to form the antecedent, replacing '∴' by '⊃', and taking the conclusion as consequent, we obtain the propositional schema

$$((p \lor q) \cdot {\sim}p) \supset q$$

The inferential schema is valid if and only if this schema is valid. The truth-table for the propositional schema is:

p	q	p∨q	∼p	(p∨q)·∼p	q	((p∨q)·∼p) ⊃ q
1	1	1	0	0	1	1
1	0	1	0	0	0	1
0	1	1	1	1	1	1
0	0	0	1	0	0	1

The final column shows the validity of the propositional schema, and therefore of the inferential schema.

It is clear enough that if we had taken 'not-q' as minor premiss, we could validly obtain 'p' as conclusion. That is, *the truth of either disjunct follows from the falsity of the other*. But this does not work the other way round. We cannot derive the falsity of one disjunct from the truth of the other. To illustrate the point, consider the case which would give, as propositional schema:

$$((pvq) \cdot p) \supset \sim q$$

This is not valid, for its truth-table is:

p	q	pvq	p	(pvq)·p	$\sim$q	((pvq)·p) $\supset \sim$q
1	1	1	1	1	0	0
1	0	1	1	1	1	1
0	1	1	0	0	0	1
0	0	0	0	0	1	1

Inspection of the table shows that substitution of true propositions for both 'p' and 'q' yields a false proposition.

The forms of inference we have been considering are roughly analogous in structure to mixed hypothetical syllogisms; but it is worth noting that, by comparison with the pure hypothetical syllogism, the 'pure disjunctive syllogism' is a very feeble affair. For from two disjunctive premises we can obtain only the disjunction of all the disjuncts appearing in the premises. For example, from the premises 'Either p or q' and 'Either q or r', the best we can get is 'Either p or q, or r'. [Check for yourself that we *can* get this conclusion, by constructing a truth-table for:

$$((pvq) \cdot (qvr)) \supset ((pvq) \lor r) \quad]$$

The alternative syllogism

We have seen that we cannot derive the falsity of one disjunct from the truth of the other. Thus:

> Either p or q
>
> $\underline{\qquad p \qquad}$
>
> ∴   not-q

is not valid if the major premiss is a disjunction. But it *is* valid, if the major premiss is an alternation. This can be seen informally by considering the fact that an alternation asserts that exactly one of its alternatives is true. So if one is true, the other must be false; and if one is false, the other must be true. That is, *all four forms of the* (*mixed*) *alternative syllogism are valid*. To show that this is so for the case set out above, consider the propositional schema:

$$((pVq) \cdot p) \supset \sim q$$

This has the truth-table:

p	q	pVq	p	(pVq)·p	~q	((pVq)·p) ⊃ ~q
1	1	0	1	0	0	1
1	0	1	1	1	1	1
0	1	1	0	0	0	1
0	0	0	0	0	1	1

Terminological note

You should note that there is a certain amount of terminological variance in this area. In some books, what we have called 'alternation' and 'disjunction' are called 'strong disjunction' and 'weak disjunction' respectively. Furthermore, some other writers use 'alternation' to mean (in our language) 'disjunction'.

EXERCISES 5

5.1 Construct truth-tables for:
  (*a*) pv~p (This is a form of the *Law of Excluded Middle*, and amounts to asserting that any proposition is either true or false.)
  (*b*) (pv~p) v q
  (*c*) ((pvq) v r) ⊃ (p v (qvr))
  (*d*) (pVq) ⊃ (pvq)
  (*e*) (pvq) ⊃ (pVq)
  (*f*) (pvq) ⊃ ~(~p.~q)
  (*g*) p ⊃ (pvq)
  (*h*) (pvq) ⊃ p

5.2 Construct truth-tables for:
  (*a*) ((pVq)·~q) ⊃ p
  (*b*) (q⊃r) ⊃ ((pvq) ⊃ (pvr))
  Construct propositions with these forms.

5.3 Determine the validity of this inference:
  If either the Greeks or the Persians took the city the inhabitants were killed. In fact, the Greeks took it, so the inhabitants were killed.

CHAPTER 6

Material Equivalence: 'If and Only If'

If p then q

not-p

∴   not-q

We know that inferences of this form are invalid. But people do (fairly frequently) commit the fallacy of Denying the Antecedent. One of the commonest causes of this is a misreading of the major premiss under which it is taken to be saying more than it does say. The mistake consists in thinking that 'If p then q' means not just 'If p is true then q is true too' but 'If p is true, so is q, *and* q is not true unless p is true'. That is, the hypothetical proposition is mis-construed as:

If and only if p, then q.

If the major premiss *were* of that form, then of course we could pass from the falsity of 'p' to the falsity of 'q' – for part of the force of the premiss is that q is true *only if* p is true; i.e. that q is false *unless* p is true; i.e. that if p is false, q is false too. But the other part of the premiss is that if p is true, so is q.

Thus   If and only if p, then q

(or, as it is sometimes more conveniently put –

q, if and only if p   )

is true when and only when p and q are either both true or both false. We shall symbolize it by:

p ≡ q

The operator '≡' is called *material equivalence*, and 'p ≡ q' is read as 'p is materially equivalent to q' (or simply as 'p is equivalent to q').

Basic truth-table (*Material Equivalence*)

p	q	p ≡ q
1	1	1
1	0	0
0	1	0
0	0	1

RULE: Two propositions are equivalent when and only when they have the same truth-value.

You should note carefully that to say that two propositions are materially equivalent is not to say any *more* than that they are equivalent from the point of view of truth-values. 'p≡q' is *not* an assertion that 'p' and 'q' express the same proposition or mean the same. It is to underline this point that we call the operator *material equivalence*.

We can further underline the point by remarking that, since 1⊃1 = 1 and 0⊃0 = 1, if 'p' and 'q' have the same truth-value, they *materially* imply one another. Similarly, if 'p' and 'q' materially imply one another they have the same truth-value. That is, 'p≡q' is true just when '(p⊃q).(q⊃p)' is true; that is:

$$(p \equiv q) \equiv ((p \supset q).(q \supset p))$$

[Check this by constructing a truth-table for the schema.]

The equivalential syllogism

Our discussion of material equivalence began with considerations about forms of inference. Let us return to that point. We shall call any syllogism, at least one of whose premisses is an equivalence, an *equivalential syllogism*. The general forms are the same as for the hypothetical syllogism.

There are four forms of the *mixed equivalential syllogism*:

I. If and only if p, then q
 p
∴ q

II. If and only if p, then q
 not-p
∴ not-q

III. If and only if p, then q
 q
∴ p

IV. If and only if p, then q
 not-q
∴ not-p

All these forms are valid. It is clear enough that I and IV should be valid since their hypothetical counterparts are valid, and 'p≡q' amounts to 'p⊃q' together with 'q⊃p'.

We remarked earlier that II, whose hypothetical counterpart is invalid, is valid. We can give a formal demonstration of this fact by constructing a truth-table for

$$((p\equiv q)\cdot\sim p)\supset\sim q$$

thus:

p q	p≡q	~p	(p≡q)·~p	~q	((p≡q)·~p) ⊃ ~q
1 1	1	0	0	0	1
1 0	0	0	0	1	1
0 1	0	1	0	0	1
0 0	1	1	1	1	1

You should check the validity of III in the same fashion.

The form of the *pure equivalential syllogism* is:

> If and only if p, then q
> If and only if q, then r
> ─────────────────────────
> ∴ If and only if p, then r.

This is also valid, as we can see by constructing a truth-table for

$$((p\equiv q)\cdot(q\equiv r))\supset(p\equiv r)$$

p q r	p≡q	q≡r	(p≡q)·(q≡r)	p≡r	((p≡q)·(q≡r)) ⊃ (p≡r)
1 1 1	1	1	1	1	1
1 1 0	1	0	0	0	1
1 0 1	0	0	0	1	1
1 0 0	0	1	0	0	1
0 1 1	0	1	0	0	1
0 1 0	0	0	0	1	1
0 0 1	1	0	0	0	1
0 0 0	1	1	1	1	1

It is easy to check that 'p⊃q' and 'q⊃p' are not truth-functionally equivalent. That is:

$$(p\supset q)\equiv(q\supset p)$$

is not valid. But it is intuitively clear that

$$(p\equiv q)\equiv(q\equiv p)$$

is valid. [Check it by the truth-table method anyway.] That is, the order of the arguments of '⊃' is significant, but the order is not significant if the operator is '≡'. We express this property by saying that material equivalence is *commutative*. Conjunction, disjunction and alternation are also commutative, as you can establish by constructing truth-tables for:

$$(p.q) \equiv (q.p)$$
$$(pvq) \equiv (qvp)$$
$$(pVq) \equiv (qVp)$$

Necessary and sufficient conditions

We have seen that 'If and only if p, then q' has, as it were, two components – 'if p then q', and 'only if p then q'. The first of these asserts that the truth of p is a *sufficient condition* for the truth of q, while the second asserts that the truth of p is a *necessary condition* for the truth of q. Thus 'If and only if p, then q' asserts that the truth of p is a *sufficient and necessary condition* for the truth of q. Now suppose that p and q assert that states of affairs, A and B, are the case. Then 'If and only if p, then q' expresses the fact that the occurrence of state of affairs A is a sufficient and necessary condition for B's being the case. This means that we can use our logical apparatus to determine the validity of statements about the necessity and sufficiency of conditions. The importance of this is enhanced by the fact that the necessary and sufficient condition terminology is well adapted to talking about causal situations in the natural and social sciences.

There is one point of theoretical importance to be noted. You are familiar with the point that the truth of 'p⊃q' or 'p≡q' does not imply any connection of content between 'p' and 'q'. But we would hardly say that one event or state of affairs was either a sufficient or a necessary condition for another if they have, as we say, nothing to do with each other. For example, the statements Peru is in South America' and 'Pakistan is in Asia' are both true, but this does not incline us to say that Peru's being in South America is a necessary or sufficient, or necessary *and* sufficient, condition of Pakistan's being in Asia. That is, not every true material equivalence corresponds to a true statement of a necessary and sufficient condition type. However, just as every hypothetical proposition contains and means not less than a material implication, so every necessary and sufficient condition proposition contains a truth-functional aspect, which we pick out as material equivalence. Therefore, since in practice we consider only cases in which there is the required connection of content, we can safely determine their validity by using purely truth-functional methods.

The following tabulation of a few cases should help you in representing statements of the necessity and sufficiency of conditions. A, B and C are events whose occurrence is asserted by p, q and r respectively.

1. A is a sufficient condition for B.
   If p then q.
   p⊃q

2. A is a necessary condition for B.
   Only if p then q OR If not-p then not-q OR If q then p.
   $\sim p \supset \sim q$ OR q ⊃ p

3. A is a sufficient and necessary condition for B.
   If and only if p, then q.
   p≡q OR (p⊃q)·($\sim$p⊃$\sim$q) OR (p⊃q)·(q⊃p)

4. A and B together are sufficient and necessary for C.
   If and only if both p and q, then r.
   (p·q) ≡ r

5. A and B are jointly sufficient and A is necessary for C.
   If both p and q, then r; and if r then p.
   ((p·q) ⊃ r)·(r⊃p)

Notice that inference from the absence of a *sufficient* condition to absence of result is invalid, since it amounts to Denying the Antecedent in a mixed hypothetical syllogism. But inference from the absence of a *necessary* condition to absence of result is quite valid, since it amounts to Denying the Consequent, because we represent 'A is a necessary condition for B' by 'q⊃p'. Try this with examples.

You should also notice that simple addition of a necessary condition and a sufficient condition will not necessarily yield a necessary and sufficient condition. A single example will make this quite clear. Being a stone-fruit is a necessary condition of being a peach. Being picked from the tree in my garden (it happens to be a peach tree) is a sufficient condition for being a peach. But it is certainly not the case that being a stone-fruit picked from the tree in my garden is a necessary and sufficient condition for being a peach – it is not satisfied, for example, by the peaches my neighbour picks from *his* tree.

EXERCISES 6

6.1 Use the truth-table method to determine the validity of each
of the following:

(a) (p⊃q) ≡ (~pvq)

(b) (p≡q) ≡ (~pⱽq)

(c) (p≡q) ≡ ~(pⱽq)

(d) ((pvq) v r) ≡ (p v (qvr))

(e) ((p.q).r) ≡ (p.(q.r))

(f) ((p⊃q) ⊃ r) ≡ (p ⊃ (q⊃r))

(g) ((p≡q) ≡ r) ≡ (p ≡ (q≡r))

(h) (~p⊃~q) ≡ (q⊃p)

6.2 Discuss the validity of this inference:
'Juvenile delinquency inevitably follows on the disintegration
of home life. So the present wave of juvenile delinquency shows
that our home life has gone to pieces.'

6.3 Determine the validity of this inference:
'A state of war is sufficient to cause restrictions on internal
trade, but only if there is a strong central government. Now at
that time there were no restrictions on internal trade, so we
can conclude that either there was no war or no strong central
government.

6.4 Suppose A and B are necessary conditions for C. Determine
the validity of inference from the non-occurrence of C to the
non-occurrence of both A and B.

6.5 'The first section of the Statute of Frauds applies only where
the tenancy must of necessity last for more than three years.
So if at the time of arrangement the tenancy may last for less
than three years it is not within that section of the Statute at all.'
Discuss the validity of the inference.

CHAPTER 7

Valid Inference and Proof

So far we have been concerned to establish the validity of certain forms of inference and to explain the technique of constructing truth-tables. Let us leave this for a moment and consider the *uses* to which we can put these valid forms of inference. We can distinguish two important uses – establishing (or proving) a conclusion, and disestablishing (or disproving) a set of premisses.

Now to *prove* a proposition is not merely to show that it follows from some set of premisses – we must show that the proposition is true. But if we can show that it follows from *true premisses*, then it *must* be true. For if the conclusion follows from the premisses, the inference is valid; and the key feature of a valid inference is that if its premisses are true, the conclusion cannot be false. Or to put it another way: *Whatever follows from true premisses is itself true.* It is for this reason that we can use anything we have already proved as a premiss from which to deduce new truths – in geometry, for example.

The proof *must* proceed from true premisses, for we know that we can validly infer either a true or a false conclusion from false premisses. Thus:

> If whales are human, then they are mammals.
> Whales are human.
> ∴ They are mammals.

is a valid inference (affirming the antecedent) from premisses which are jointly false (the major is true, the minor false) to a conclusion which happens to be true.

But equally

> If whales are mammals, they are invertebrates.
> Whales are mammals.
> ∴ They are invertebrates.

is a valid inference from premisses which are jointly false (the major is false) to a conclusion which happens to be false.

Thus the combination of false premisses and a valid inference *may* yield a true conclusion, but falls short of giving us the *guarantee* of truth of the conclusion that we look for in a proof. Equally, the combination of true premisses and an invalid inference *may* yield a true conclusion, but does not guarantee its truth.

In short, a proposition is proved *if and only if* it follows from true premisses.

We frequently use the same general principles to *disprove* a proposition. Someone may contend that some proposition, p, is true; we point out that some false proposition, q, is a consequence of p. And this suffices to show that p is false also. For, *if the conclusion of a valid inference is false, at least one of the premisses must be false.* (Note that if the conclusion is true and the inference is valid it does *not* follow that the premisses are true.) We use this principle in a variety of ways, ranging from the quite informal to the quite formal. Occasionally, all the premisses required to yield the false conclusion are supplied by the person who contends that p is true. But more often we have to supply a premiss. In that case we take care that the supplied premiss will be admitted as true by both parties – for otherwise the falsity of the conclusion could be attributed to the supplied premiss.

E.g. suppose someone says 'No good player has been left out of the team', and that we seek to show that this is false by saying 'But Robinson is not in the team'. Clearly he will regard this as a disproof of his contention only if he admits that Robinson is a good player. We could set out our disproof in full, as follows:

Given that no good player has been left out of the team, and that Robinson is a good player, it follows that Robinson is in the team. But Robinson is *not* in the team, so the conclusion is false. But then at least one of the premisses must be false, since true premisses cannot validly yield a false conclusion. It is true that Robinson is a good player.

Therefore 'No good player has been left out of the team' is false.[1]

---

[1] There is a common variant of this sort of argument, which strictly does not concern us here – viz. the case in which we argue from improbability to improbability rather than from falsity to falsity, e.g.

    A. 'Flying saucers come from Venus.'

    B. 'But it is extremely unlikely that there is intelligent life on Venus.'

Notice that B's reply is often expressed in this way:

    B. 'But that presupposes that there is intelligent life on Venus (which is very unlikely).'

Now 'No good player has been left out of the team' is just another way of saying 'It is not the case that any good player has been left out of the team'; and if we have *disproved* 'It is not the case that any good player has been left out of the team', we have *proved* 'Some good player has been left out of the team'. In making this move we are relying on the validity of

$$\sim(\sim p) \supset p$$

which is one of the *Laws of Double Negation*. The other is

$$p \supset \sim(\sim p)$$

and the two can be stated together as

$$p \equiv \sim(\sim p)$$

This reliance on the Law of Double Negation provides us with a very useful method of proof. For suppose that p is the proposition to be proved. Then if we take $\sim p$ as a premiss and validly infer some known falsehood, q, from it, it follows that p is true. This sort of proof commonly appears in the form:

> Let us assume that it is *not* the case that p.
> Then it follows that so and so . . .
> Therefore it is the case that p.

An argument of this sort is known as a *Reductio ad Absurdum*. The general shape of such arguments is:

$\sim p$ (together with any other (true) premisses) (1)

∴ q (2)

But $\sim q$ (3)

∴ $\sim(\sim p)$ (4)

∴ p (5)

Notice that it is the step from (4) to (5) that rests on the validity of '$\sim(\sim p) \supset p$'. It is worth noticing too that this dependence on Double Negation is intertwined with dependence on another famous logical law – the *Law of Excluded Middle* (or Excluded Third) : 'p v $\sim p$'. For we can move from 'It is not the case that not-p' to 'It is the case that p' only if p can only be either true or false – i.e. if there is no third status for p. And what is asserted by the Law of Excluded Middle is just that every proposition is either true or false.

This draws attention to the fact that what is said to be *presupposed* by some proposition is often (despite the look of the word) something that *follows from* that proposition.

Proofs by *reductio ad absurdum* are very common in both Logic and Mathematics, as well as in less formal contexts. Although it is fair to say that the *theoretical* heart of such a proof is in the move from (3) to (5), through (4), the *practical* heart – the area in which ingenuity is required – is in the move from (1) to (2). This move commonly requires a considerable chain of argument. You should look for arguments of this type in some subject you are familiar with and see how they fit the pattern we have set out.

CHAPTER 8
The Propositional Calculus

In Chapter 3 we remarked that the Propositional Calculus ('PC' for short) has as its field the class of all propositional schemata which contain no variables other than propositional variables, and no operators other than truth-functional proposition-forming operators. In considering various common forms of inference, we have examined a few of these schemata; and we have given a fairly informal account of the conditions which a properly put together schema (whether valid or not) must satisfy. (E.g. '⊃' must have two arguments.)

It is now time to give a precise and systematic account of these conditions, and thereby to specify the field of PC in a different way. We shall do this by laying down explicit rules for the formation of schemata.

Well-formed formulae

It will be convenient to adopt a terminology widely used in the literature, and say that any properly put together schema is a *well-formed formula* ('wff' for short). Our aim is to give a set of rules which will tell us how to construct wffs, and also enable us to determine of any sequence of symbols whether it is a wff of PC. The sort of schema we want to exclude is, of course, one which fails to produce a determinate proposition when appropriate substitutions are made for all the variables.

It may help here to think of a well-formed formula as a *grammatical sentence* in the symbolic language of PC – and of the rules we shall set up as its rules of grammar. Now, to pursue this grammatical way of looking at it, in the language of PC we have three 'parts of speech':

> (1) Variables: p, q, r, . . .
> (2) Monadic operator: ∼
> (3) Dyadic operators: v, ., ⊃, ≡, V

In addition we have '(' and ')' as 'marks of punctuation'. These, of course, always go in pairs. These various symbols are often called the *Primitive Symbols* (or *Signs*) of the system.

The following set of *Rules of Formation* serves to specify completely and precisely the set of all well-formed formulae – i.e. the field of PC.

(1) A variable standing alone is a wff.

(2) If X is a wff, $\sim$X is a wff.

(3) If X and Y are wffs, then X and Y with a dyadic operator between them, and the whole enclosed in brackets, is a wff.

So, by Rule (1), 'p' is well formed. By Rules (1) and (2), '$\sim$p' is well formed. By Rules (1) and (3), '(pvq)', '(p·q)', '(p⊃q)', '(p≡q)' and '(pVq)' are all wffs. So are '(pvp)', '(p·p)' etc. By Rules (1), (2) and (3), '(p⊃$\sim$q)', '($\sim$pvp)', etc., are wffs. By successive applications of Rules (1) and (3), we obtain wffs like '((p⊃q) ≡ (pvq))'; and so on. In short, anything built up by one or more applications of one or more of these rules is a wff, and nothing else is.

There are a number of points to be made about this set of rules. Firstly, you will notice that the letters 'X' and 'Y' are used in stating the rules. These symbols are not part of the language of PC, but are used in talking about it, in stating its 'grammatical rules'. They are variables ranging over well-formed formulae – i.e. variables which take wffs as values – and are known as *meta-logical variables*. The prefix 'meta' indicates that they are not part of the logical system, PC, which forms the *object-language*, but are part of the *meta-language* used to talk about the object-language. Similarly, if I wrote a book, in English, on the grammar of German, English would be the meta-language, and German the object-language talked about in English. If I wrote a book, in English, on the grammar of English, then English would be both object-language and meta-language. This can of course only be the case when the object-language is rich enough in its means of expression to talk about itself. The symbolic language of PC is clearly not rich enough for this, so we use as meta-language English enriched by meta-logical variables. [Note that the latter are a convenience here rather than a theoretical necessity. To show that this is so, give an equally precise formulation of the Rules of Formation without using meta-logical variables.] We shall reserve the letters 'X', 'Y', 'Z', 'W', . . . for use as meta-logical variables taking wffs as values.

Secondly, notice the structure of the Rules of Formation as a specification or definition of the set or class of wffs of PC. It is essentially a set of rules for building up successive members of a class by performing certain operations on a stated basis. The first rule gives this basis, viz. the single propositional variables; the other rules specify the operations. The same kind of structure can be seen very clearly in an arithmetical example:

(1) 1 is a positive integer
(2) if n is a positive integer, n +1 is a positive integer.

Here we have a single basis, viz. 1; and a single operation. By these rules we can produce all the positive integers. For the first rule gives us the first positive integer, viz. 1. The first application of the second rule gives us $1 \cdot + 1$; the second application (to the result of the first application) gives us $(1 + 1) + 1$; and so on. Since we can reach any positive integer we like in this way, the two rules form a complete specification or definition of the set of positive integers. This type of specification is known as a *recursive specification* (or *definition*). It is essentially a description of a process for churning out or generating the members of a class.

Thirdly, notice that the Rules of Formation do not merely give a procedure for generating wffs; they also provide a *test* which we can apply to decide whether any given string of symbols is well formed or not.[1] For consider

$$(p \supset (q \cdot \sim p))$$

Starting at the innermost point (of the consequent, in this case) we can work outwards checking each part for well-formedness as we go.

'p'	is well-formed – Rule (1)
'$\sim$p'	,, ,, ,, – Rule (2)
'q'	,, ,, ,, – Rule (1)
'(q$\cdot\sim$p)'	,, ,, ,, – Rule (3)
'(p $\supset$ (q$\cdot\sim$p))'	,, ,, ,, – Rule (3)

[1] This is sometimes put by saying that the class of wffs is a *recursive class*. A class is recursive if there is some effective procedure (i.e. a procedure which is reliable and can be gone through in a finite time) for deciding of any arbitrarily given object whether or not it is a member of the class. Every finite class is recursive – for given some object, you could in principle check the class, member by member, to see if the given object is in the class. Some infinite classes are recursive, some are not. (E.g. the class of all even numbers is recursive, but the class of all true statements of arithmetic is not.)

N.B. Be careful to distinguish 'recursive class' from 'recursively specifiable class'. Every recursive class is recursively specifiable, but the reverse does not hold.

Similarly, consider '$((\sim pq) \supset r)$'. Starting at the innermost point (of the antecedent, this time)

'p'   is well-formed – Rule (1)
'$\sim$p'   „   „   „   – Rule (2)
'q'   „   „   „   – Rule (1)

'$(\sim pq)$' is not well-formed – Rule (3) is broken by the lack of a dyadic operator.

So the whole formula is not well-formed. It is, therefore, not even a candidate for being valid.

Fourthly, you will notice that the Rules of Formation, as stated, make both these expressions *ill*-formed:

(a) pvq
(b) $\sim(\sim p)$

'pvq' is ill-formed because it lacks outside brackets and so breaks Rule (3). '$\sim(\sim p)$' on the other hand is ill-formed because the rules do not provide for enclosing expressions like '$\sim p$' in brackets. However, it is practically convenient to allow both types of formulae as well-formed. So we introduce the following conventions on bracketing:

(a) We shall allow ourselves to drop the outermost pair of brackets of any wff (as we have in fact generally done).

(b) We shall allow ourselves (if we wish to) to insert a left-hand bracket between adjacent negation signs (and insert a right-hand bracket to go with it), where the rules do not demand them. E.g. to put '$\sim(\sim p)$' for '$\sim\sim p$'. [Of course, this does *not* mean that we can drop the brackets in '$\sim(\sim pvq)$'.]

Definitions

In Chapter 6 we showed that

$$(p \equiv q) \equiv ((p \supset q).(q \supset p))$$

is valid. Of course, there is nothing special about 'p' and 'q'; any equivalence is itself equivalent to the conjunction of the implication of the second equivalent by the first, and the implication of the first by the second. Thus, where X and Y are any wffs, $(X \equiv Y)$ is truth-functionally equivalent to – has the same system of truth-values as –

$$((X \supset Y).(Y \supset X)).$$

That is, we could, if we chose to, always avoid the symbol '$\equiv$', by writing every equivalence as a conjunction of two implications. Or, to put it the other way round, we can always regard a wff containing '≡' as a shorthand form of a wff containing two occurrences of '⊃' and one occurrence of '.' . Everything that can be expressed by the use of '≡' can be expressed without it. We could therefore drop '≡' from the list of symbols of PC, thus effecting a theoretical economy. However, it is convenient to have it available as shorthand. We can get the best of both worlds by *defining* material equivalence in terms of material implication and conjunction. We state the definition thus:

$$(X \equiv Y) =_{Df} ((X \supset Y).(Y \supset X))$$

where ' $=_{Df}$' is to be read 'equals by definition' or 'is definitionally equivalent to'. The effect of this is to retain '≡' among the symbols of PC, but no longer to regard it as a primitive – i.e. undefined – symbol.

We call definitions of this type *contextual definitions* to distinguish them from both recursive definitions and *explicit definitions*. An example of the latter type is:

$$\text{'father'} =_{Df} \text{'male parent'}.$$

Here only the expression to be defined occurs on the left. By contrast, in a contextual definition, the symbol to be defined occurs in the context of some well-formed sequence of symbols. In fact, it would be correct to say that a contextual definition proceeds by defining one sequence of symbols, including the special one to be defined, in terms of another in which the special symbol does not occur.

The definition

$$(X \equiv Y) =_{Df} ((X \supset Y).(Y \supset X))$$

is best thought of as a notational rule, to the effect that we may rewrite any wff containing '≡' in a certain way, thereby eliminating '≡' in favour of '⊃' and '.'. Conversely, we may rewrite any suitable wff containing '⊃' and '.', eliminating them in favour of '≡'. Thus if we have:

$$((p.q) \supset r).(r \supset (p.q))$$

we may rewrite it as:

$$(p.q) \equiv r$$

[Here the result of the rewriting is truth-functionally equivalent to the original wff because a truth-functional equivalence was the basis for constructing the definition of the familiar symbol '≡'. But notice that the same sort of definition may simply *lay it down that* two expressions are truth-functionally equivalent. This will happen when we introduce a new symbol as an abbreviation. Suppose we were to set up this definition: $(X*Y) =_{Df} \sim(X \supset Y)$. Then '$(p*q)*r$' would be equivalent to '$\sim(\sim(p \supset q) \supset r)$' just because the definition says it is. In effect, the definition provides '*' with its basic truth-table.]

In exactly the same way, in the light of considerations from Chapter 5, we may further reduce the list of primitive symbols of PC by introducing the definition:

$$(X \vee Y) =_{Df} ((X \vee Y).\sim(X.Y))^1$$

We now have 'v', '.' and '$\supset$' as the only dyadic operators which appear theoretically essential. But are all of these essential? The answer is that they are not. In fact any one of these will do as the sole dyadic operator. That is we can define conjunction and implication in terms of disjunction and negation; or we can define disjunction and conjunction in terms of implication and negation; or we can define disjunction and implication in terms of conjunction and negation.

We shall introduce definitions which allow us to take 'v' as the sole dyadic operator, thus:

$$(1) \ (X \supset Y) =_{Df} (\sim X \vee Y)$$
$$(2) \ (X.Y) =_{Df} \sim(\sim X \vee \sim Y)$$

It is easy enough to see that the first of these definitions is reasonable. We may read $\sim X \vee Y$ as 'Either X is false or Y is true'. Recalling that a disjunction is false only when both disjuncts are false, this proposition will be false only when X is true and Y is false. And that is exactly the condition under which $X \supset Y$ is false. We can establish the correctness of the second definition in the same way. For X.Y is true only when both conjuncts are true – i.e. only when neither is false – i.e. only when it is not the case that *either* is false. But that is just what is expressed by $\sim(\sim X \vee \sim Y)$.[2]

---

[1] Alternatively, we could define alternation thus:

$$(X \vee Y) =_{Df} \sim (X \equiv Y)$$

[2] Had we chosen to take '.' as the sole dyadic operator, suitable definitions would be

$$(1) \ (X \vee Y) =_{Df} \sim(\sim X.\sim Y)$$
$$(2) \ (X \supset Y) =_{Df} \sim(X.\sim Y)$$

Had we decided to take '$\supset$' as the only dyadic operator, suitable definitions would be

$$(1) \ (X \vee Y) =_{Df} (\sim X \supset Y)$$
$$(2) \ (X.Y) =_{Df} \sim(X \supset \sim Y)$$

Now it is clear that given these definitions (and those of '≡' and 'V'), we can rewrite *any* wff so that the only operators it contains are '∼' and 'v'. To take a simple example:

$$p \equiv q$$

yields   (p⊃q).(q⊃p)   [By definition of '≡']

which yields   (∼pvq).(∼qvp)   [By definition of '⊃']

which yields   ∼(∼(∼pvq) v ∼(∼qvp))   [By definition of '.']

It follows that our recursive specification of the class of well-formed formulae could have been constructed more elegantly[1] (in the sense of resting on a smaller stock of primitive (i.e. undefined) symbols), by:

    (i) listing 'v' as the only dyadic operator
    (ii) including definitions of '⊃', '.', '≡', 'V'
    (iii) making Rule (3) read:
         If X and Y are wffs, then (XvY) is a wff.

In conclusion, we may note two properties of the field (i.e. the class of wffs) of PC.

First, the class of wffs is infinite. For the first two Rules of Formation alone will generate the infinite sequence of well-formed formulae:

$$p, \sim p, \sim\sim p, \sim\sim\sim p, \ldots$$

The first member, 'p', is well-formed by Rule (1); and each successive member of the sequence is formed by applying Rule (2) to its predecessor. And since there is no upper limit to the number of negations which may precede a variable, the sequence has infinitely many members.

Second, we note that a wff may contain any number (including 0) of negation signs; but that the number of dyadic operators is determined by the number of variables. If there are n variables in a wff, it must contain exactly n–1 dyadic operators. [*N.B.* For the purposes of this rule, the number of variables is the number of occurrences of variables, *not* the number of different letters, 'p', 'q', etc., which it contains. Thus:

'pvp' and 'pvq' both contain two variables.

'(pvq) v p' and '(pvq) v r' both contain three variables.

---

[1] Elegance is not merely of aesthetic value in logic. It can also simplify the logician's tasks. For example, it is usually easier to prove that all disjunctions have a given property than to prove that every wff containing any dyadic operator has the property.

But notice that for most other purposes the number of variables *is* the number of different letters used.]

EXERCISES 8

8.1 State precisely why each of the following is well- or ill-formed:

(*a*) $\sim(p \supset (q \lor r))$

(*b*) $\sim p \lor q . \sim r$

(*c*) $(p \supset v) \sim q$

(*d*) $(q \supset r) \supset ((p \lor q) \supset (p \lor r))$

8.2 State the rules for constructing these sequences of wffs:

(*a*) p, (p∨q), ((p∨q) ∨ r), (((p∨q) ∨ r) ∨ s), . . .

(*b*) p, (∼p∨q), (∼(∼p∨q) ∨ r), (∼(∼(∼p∨q) ∨ r) ∨ s), . . .

8.3 Show that if there are n variables in a wff, it must contain exactly n–1 dyadic operators.

8.4 Although we have introduced only five dyadic truth-functional operators, there are actually sixteen in all since there are sixteen ways of selecting a sequence of four truth-values. We may tabulate them thus:

p	q	(1)	(2)	(3)	(4)	(5)	(6)	(7)	(8)	(9)	(10)	(11)	(12)	(13)	(14)	(15)	(16)
1	1	1	1	1	1	1	1	1	1	0	0	0	0	0	0	0	0
1	0	1	1	1	1	0	0	0	0	1	1	1	1	0	0	0	0
0	1	1	1	0	0	1	1	0	0	1	1	0	0	1	1	0	0
0	0	1	0	1	0	1	0	1	0	1	0	1	0	1	0	1	0

(2) is disjunction. You already possess definitions of (5), (7), (8) and (10) in terms of disjunction and negation. Construct similar definitions for the remaining eleven cases.

8.5 Consider cases (9) and (15) in the table in 8.4. We may symbolize these by 'p ⊼ q' and 'p ⊽ q' respectively. From inspection of the truth-tables it is clear that the following are valid:

(i) $(p \barwedge q) \equiv \sim(p . q)$

(ii) $(p \veebar q) \equiv \sim(p \lor q)$

which suggests the names 'non-conjunction' and 'non-disjunction' for '⊼' and '⊽' respectively. [But note that they are sometimes called 'alternative denial' and 'joint denial'.] These two operators are interesting because they are the only dyadic operators which can serve as the *sole* primitive operator of PC.

If we take ' $\uparrow$ ' as the one primitive operator we may define negation thus:

$$\sim X =_{Df} (X \uparrow X)$$

since truth-tables will show that

$$\sim p \equiv (p \uparrow p)$$

is valid.

Alternatively, with ' $\downarrow$ ' as primitive, we will have

$$\sim X =_{Df} (X \downarrow X)$$

(a) Set up Rules of Formation for PC, together with suitable definitions, with ' $\uparrow$ ' as the sole primitive operator.

(b) Do the same with ' $\downarrow$ ' as the sole primitive operator.

CHAPTER 9

Truth-Tables as a Decision Procedure

For every class of objects we may formulate questions of the form: 'Is so-and-so a member of the class?' And there is a clear sense in which any given object either is or is not a member of a particular class. I am either a member of the class of people over 6 feet tall or I am not; Queenie the elephant either is or is not a triangle; 2071 either is or is not a prime number; 'There are animals on Mars' is either a true statement or not; and so on. But, although there is, in this sense, always an answer to the question, we do not always know how to find this answer. What we need is a recipe for deciding whether or not an object, x, is a member of a class, K. We have already described such a recipe for the class of well-formed formulae of PC. The Rules of Formation provide us with a procedure for deciding of *any* arbitrarily chosen object whether it is a wff of PC. Such a recipe or procedure is called a *decision procedure* for the class. Such a procedure must be *effective* – that is, it must be precisely statable, reliable and completable in a finite time. (It must be the sort of procedure which could be carried out by a suitably constructed machine.)

The problem of finding a decision procedure for a class is called the *decision problem* of that class. The decision problem is said to be *solvable* if a decision procedure can be found, *unsolvable* if it can be shown that there is no decision procedure for the class; so the decision problem for a class is solvable if and only if the class is recursive, in the sense explained in the preceding chapter.

A particularly important type of decision problem is the decision problem for the class of *valid* wffs of some logical system. Such a problem is often called simply *the decision problem* for the system. Every logical system has such a decision problem, although not every logical system has a *solvable* decision problem. So the decision problem for PC is the problem of finding an effective method for deciding whether any arbitrarily chosen formula is a valid formula of PC. That is, solving it amounts to finding an effective procedure for sorting the wffs of PC into those which are valid and those which are not.

Truth-tables

It is intuitively clear that the decision problem for PC *is* solvable, for the method of truth-tables enables us to decide the validity of any wff. Every wff of PC has a truth-table, since every wff of PC is built up entirely from truth-functions, and every truth-function has a truth-table.

Now so far we have constructed truth-tables only for schemata containing at most 3 distinct variables. To support the remark in the last paragraph, we must now show how to construct truth-tables for wffs containing any given number of variables. The key to this lies in the construction of larger matrices. Once we have an appropriate matrix the table is constructed in just the same way as in the simpler familiar cases.

We found that the matrix for wffs containing just 1 variable has 2 horizontal rows; the matrix for wffs containing 2 variables has 4 rows; and the matrix for wffs containing 3 variables has 8 rows. Now, $2^1 = 2$, $2^2 = 4$, $2^3 = 8$; and, in general terms, if the wff contains n distinct variables, the matrix has 2^n horizontal rows.

Briefly, for every matrix:

$$\frac{\text{Columns}}{\text{Rows}} = \frac{n}{2^n}$$

In constructing a truth-table for any wff, the matrix can be written down by following these steps:

(1) Find the number, n, of distinct propositional variables, 'p' 'q', 'r', etc., in the wff.

(2) Set out n columns each headed with one of the variables in the wff.

(3) In the extreme right-hand column, fill in alternate 1's and 0's, until 2^n rows are filled.

(4) In the column second from the right, fill in alternately *pairs* of 1's and *pairs* of 0's.

(5) In the column third from the right, fill in alternately *quadruples* of 1's and *quadruples* of 0's.

(6) Continue this until the left-most column is filled – its top half with 1's, its bottom half with 0's.

Once this initial array of possible combinations is set out, construction of the truth-table proceeds in the familiar fashion, by obtaining tables for successively larger parts of the wff.

A shorter method: the Reductio Test

Although in theory a truth-table can be constructed for any wff, in practice this method for deciding validity becomes very unwieldy if the number of variables is large. For example, a wff with 6 distinct variables has a truth-table of 64 rows, while one with 10 variables has a truth-table of 1024 rows. Clearly, for practical purposes – such as determining the validity of even moderately complex inferences – we need a shorter method.

Fortunately, we can make use of argument by *reductio ad absurdum* to do the job quickly (frequently in a single line), while still using the familiar material embedded in the basic truth-tables. We shall call this method the *Reductio Test*. Before describing how to apply it, we should make two points clear:

(1) It determines only whether a wff is valid or not, and makes no distinction between inconsistency and contingency.

(2) Although any wff can be dealt with by this test, it is most convenient for dealing with a wff whose dyadic operators are mostly implications or disjunctions.

In broad outline, the method is this: We assume that the wff is *not* valid – i.e. that in some (as yet undetermined) circumstances it can have the value 0. We then trace out the consequences of this assumption. If we arrive at some contradiction as a result, we conclude that the initial assumption was false – i.e. the wff *is* valid. If we arrive at no contradiction, then the wff *can* have the value 0, so it is *not* valid.

As an example, to fill in the details of the method, consider the wff:

$$(p \supset q) \supset ((q \supset r) \supset (p \supset r))$$

We assume that it is not valid – i.e. that it does have the value 0 sometimes. We express this by writing '0' under the main operator, thus:

$$(p \supset q) \supset ((q r \supset) \supset (p \supset r))$$
$$0$$

Now we know that an implication is false only if the antecedent is true and the consequent is false. That is, our first assumption entails that $(p \supset q) = 1$ and $((q \supset r) \supset (p \supset r)) = 0$. We express this by writing in these values, thus:

$$(p \supset q) \supset ((q \supset r) \supset (p \supset r))$$
$$1 \qquad\quad 0 \qquad\qquad 0$$

Applying the same consideration to the consequent, we get two more values:

$$(p \supset q) \supset ((q \supset r) \supset (p \supset r))$$
$$1 \qquad\quad 0 \quad 1 \quad 0 \qquad 0$$

But again, if $(p \supset r)$ is false, $p = 1$ and $r = 0$:

$$(p \supset q) \supset ((q \supset r) \supset (p \supset r))$$
$$1 \qquad\quad 0 \quad 1 \quad 0 \; 100$$

Our assumption that the whole wff can have the value 0 has led us to values for 'p' and 'r'. But all the occurrences of the same variable in the wff must be true or false simultaneously. So we must assign 1 to 'p' and 0 to 'r' wherever they occur:

$$(p \supset q) \supset ((q \supset r) \supset (p \supset r))$$
$$1\,1 \qquad 0 \quad 1\,0 \quad 0 \; 100$$

Now consider the antecedent. $(p \supset q) = 1$ and has a true antecedent. It must, therefore, have a true consequent. So we must assign the value 1 to 'q' wherever it occurs:

$$(p \supset q) \supset ((q \supset r) \supset (p \supset r))$$
$$1\,1\,1 \qquad 0 \quad \underline{1\,1}\,0 \quad 0 \; 100$$

Now look at '$(q \supset r)$'. It is said to be true, but to have a true antecedent and a false consequent. This contradicts what we know to be a property of material implication – viz. that $1 \supset 0 = 0$. Therefore our original assumption must have been false. That is, this wff cannot have the value 0. It is therefore, valid.

In using this method there is no need to write down the wff several times, as we have just done. You simply write it down once and put in the values in the indicated order, in a single line underneath. If a contradiction is found, it is convenient to indicate where it occurs by underlining, as in the example above.

Again, consider '$(p \supset q) \supset p$'. We assume that this can be falsified – i.e. that there is some assignment of truth-values to the variables under which the whole wff has the value 0. Thus:

$$(p \supset q) \supset p$$
$$0$$

This necessitates

$$(p \supset q) \supset p$$
$$1 \quad\ 0\ 0$$

The assignment of 0 to 'p' as consequent leads to

$$(p \supset q) \supset p$$
$$0\ 1 \quad\ 0\ 0$$

Now the antecedent, '(p⊃q)', is said to be true and to have a false antecedent. We can therefore consistently assign 0 to 'q' (or 1, for that matter):

$$(p \supset q) \supset p$$
$$0\ 1\ 0 \quad\ 0\ 0$$

Thus the wff *can* be falsified (e.g. when 'p' and 'q' are both false); therefore, it is not valid.

Suppose that the wff were:

$$\sim(p \supset q) \supset \sim p$$

Then the first step would give us:

$$\sim(p \supset q) \supset \sim p$$
$$0$$

Now the antecedent is '∼(p⊃q)' in which the main operator is '∼'. Put the '1' under '∼'. Now if ∼(p⊃q) = 1 it follows that (p⊃q) = 0. Similarly the consequent, '∼p', has the value 0, so p = 1. Thus we get

$$\sim(p \supset q) \supset \sim p$$
$$1\ \ 10 \quad\ \ 0\ 0\ 1$$

We can consistently put q = 0, so the wff is not valid.

The advantages of this technique, in cases where it is easily applicable, are obvious enough. For example, the truth-table for '(((p⊃q) ⊃r) ⊃ s) ⊃ ((q⊃r) ⊃ (p⊃s))' has 16 rows. But by this reductio test we can determine its validity in a single line:

$$(((p \supset q) \supset r) \supset s) \supset ((q \supset r) \supset (p \supset s))$$
$$0 1 0\ \ 0\ 0\ \ 1\ 0\ \ 0\ \ 0 1 0\ \ 0\ \ 1 0 0$$

Notice that in this case we are led to an inconsistent assignment of truth-values to 'p' – this is as much a contradiction as getting the sequence '110' under 'p⊃q' (which we can get in this case by making the moves in a slightly different order).

Sometimes the Reductio Test fails to work in its simplest fashion, even for favourable-looking formulae. E.g.

$$((p \supset s) \vee (q \supset r)) \supset ((p \vee q) \supset (s \supset r))$$
$$\quad 11 \ \ 1 \quad\quad 0 \quad 0 \quad\quad 1 \quad\quad 0 \ 100$$

No further assignment of values is determined. Thus we could consistently put either 0 or 1 for 'q⊃r'.

Let us put (q⊃r) = 0. Then q = 1, so:

$$((p \supset s) \vee (q \supset r)) \supset ((p \vee q) \supset (s \supset r))$$
$$\quad 11 \ \ 1 \ 100 \quad 0 \quad\ 11 \quad 0 \ \ 100$$

At this point it is clear that we can consistently put p = 1 or p = 0; so the formula is not valid.

But note that had (q⊃r) = 0 led to a contradiction, we could *not* from that alone have concluded that the formula is valid. In such a case, we must also try (q⊃r) = 1, which might allow a consistent assignment of 0 to the whole formula.

In concluding this chapter we may note that valid schemata of PC are often called *tautologies*. By extension, a *proposition* (as distinct from a propositional schema) is said to be a tautology if it can be obtained by substitutions in a tautologous schema. But it should also be noted that the word 'tautology' is sometimes used in a wider way, to cover *all* propositions whose denial results in self-contradiction.

EXERCISES 9

9.1 Construct truth-tables for the following:

(*a*) ((p.q) ∨ (q.r)) ⊃ ((p.r) ⊃ q)

(*b*) ∼(∼p.(p.q))

(*c*) (((p⊃q) ⊃ p) ⊃ p)

(*d*) (((p∨q) ∨ r) ∨ s) ⊃ ((p.r) ∨ (q.s))

(*e*) s.((p⊃q) ⊃ ((q⊃r) ⊃ (p⊃r)))

(*f*) ((p≡q) ≡ r) ≡ (p ≡ (q≡r))

(*g*) (∼p≡∼q) ≡ (p⊃q)

(*h*) (p≡q) ≡ ((r∨q) ≡ (p∨r))

(*i*) (((((p⊃q) ⊃ (∼r⊃∼s)) ⊃ r) ⊃ t) ⊃ ((t⊃p) ⊃ (s⊃p))

9.2 Use the Reductio Test to determine whether the following are valid: (If an inconsistency is reached indicate where it lies by underlining the appropriate truth-values.)

(*a*) (p ⊃ (q⊃r)) ⊃ ((p⊃q) ⊃ (p⊃r))

(*b*) p ⊃ ((r⊃p) ⊃ p)

(c) (p⊃q) ⊃ ((p⊃r) ⊃ q)

(d) ((p⊃q) ⊃ r) ⊃ ((r⊃p) ⊃ (s⊃p))

(e) (q⊃p) ⊃ ((q⊃∼p) ⊃ (q⊃q))

(f) ((p⊃q) ⊃ r) ⊃ (s ⊃ (q ⊃ ((r⊃t) ⊃ (q⊃t))))

(g) (p⊃q) ⊃ ((pvr) ⊃ (qvr))

(h) (p ⊃ (q⊃r)) ⊃ ((r⊃s) ⊃ (p ⊃ (q⊃s)))

(i) (p⊃q) ⊃ ((p⊃r) ⊃ (p ⊃ (q∙r)))

(j) (p⊃q) ⊃ ((p⊃r) ⊃ (p ⊃ (qvr)))

(k) ((p∙q) ⊃ r) v (((r∙q) ⊃ p) v ((r∙p) ⊃ q))

(l) (p⊃q) v (((p∙r) ⊃ s)∙ ((q∙s) ⊃ p))

(m) ∼(∼(q⊃∼p) ⊃ (p⊃r)) ⊃ ∼(p∙q)

9.3 Determine the validity of these forms of inference:

(a) If p is true, then if q then r.

If r and s, then t.

If u, then s is true but t is false.

∴ If both p and q are true, u is false.

(b) If p implies q, then r is true.

If both r and s are true, then either t is false or u is false.

s is true.

∴ If q is true, p implies u.

9.4 Determine the validity of this inference:

If music is the food of love, play on. But if you do play on, then either we shall leave or Mary will get a headache. Now Mary will get a headache if and only if she gets angry; and on the other hand if we leave you won't be paid. If you are not paid, you will make a scene and Mary will get angry. So if music is the food of love, Mary will get a headache.

CHAPTER 10

Equivalence Transformations

We noted earlier that in virtue of the definition

$$(X \supset Y) =_{Df} (\sim X \lor Y)$$

we could rewrite any material implication in terms of negation and disjunction. Thus:

$$(p \cdot r) \supset (q \equiv s)$$

can be rewritten as:

$$\sim(p \cdot r) \lor (q \equiv s).$$

Of course, this works in the other direction also, so that

$$\sim(p \cdot q) \lor r$$

can be rewritten as:

$$(p.q) \supset r$$

Further we can use the definitions to rewrite any part of a wff. Thus:

$$(q \supset r) \supset ((\sim p \lor q) \supset (\sim p \lor r))$$

can be rewritten as:

$$(q \supset r) \supset ((p \supset q) \supset (p \supset r))$$

or as:

$$(q \supset r) \supset ((p \supset q) \supset (\sim p \lor r))$$

or as:

$$(\sim q \lor r) \supset (\sim(p \supset q) \lor (p \supset r))$$

and so on.

When we say that a wff 'can be rewritten' according to a definition, we mean that it can be wholly or partly rewritten without disturbing its truth-functional characteristics. Thus if a certain wff is valid (or contingent or inconsistent), so is the result of rewriting it. The reason why we can use definitions in this way is that a definition of the sort we are using is either founded on a known equivalence or amounts simply to laying it down that the *definiendum* (the expression to be defined) and the *definiens* (the expression in terms of which it is defined) are truth-functionally equivalent. So the definiens and the definiendum can hardly fail to have the same truth-functional characteristics – i.e. to be materially equivalent. And that is the crucial feature – sameness of truth-functional characteristics. As soon as we see this, we also see that *any* valid equivalence provides us with two expressions with the same truth-functional characteristics; and so if we replace any part of a wff by a truth-functionally equivalent expression, we produce a wff which is truth-functionally equivalent to the original one. The ways of rewriting wffs thus become, in theory, infinite.

We state this generalization in the form of a rule:

RULE FOR SUBSTITUTION OF EQUIVALENTS

If X is a well-formed part of a wff W, and Z is the result of replacing X by Y, then if $(X \equiv Y)$ is valid, then W is equivalent to Z.

Or, putting it less formally – we can replace any part of a formula by anything equivalent to that part, and the resulting formula will be equivalent to the original formula (assuming, of course, that both the original formula and the part in question are well-formed).

The formulation of the definitions gave us some machinery for transforming wffs. This rule now extends this machinery by allowing us to use any valid equivalence in the same way.

We shall now develop a stock of particularly useful equivalences. *They should be learnt by heart as they come up.*

A fundamental equivalence, although it cannot be used by itself to transform a wff, is the *Law of Identity*:

$$p \equiv p$$

If we read this as asserting that any wff is equivalent to itself, then we get as a special case

$$(p \supset q) \equiv (p \supset q)$$

By applying the definition of '$\supset$' to the right-hand equivalent, we get:

$$(p \supset q) \equiv (\sim p \lor q)$$

In the same way we can obtain a valid equivalence corresponding to each of the definitions.

Now let us give a more precise basis for this set of moves. What we relied on was that any schema with the general form expressed by '$p \equiv p$' is valid. And, in general terms, anything that has the general form expressed by any valid wff is valid. Suppose, then, that we are given some valid wff, containing the variable 'p'. If we generate a new wff by replacing each occurrence of 'p' by some wff (the same for each occurrence of 'p'), then the new wff will also be valid. We can formulate a rule to this effect.

RULE OF SUBSTITUTION (FOR PROPOSITIONAL VARIABLES)

If X is a valid wff, and Z is the result of substituting some wff, Y, for a propositional variable wherever it occurs in X, then Z is valid also.

It is important to notice how this rule differs from the rule for substituting equivalents. In the first place, it allows substitutions only of a wff for a propositional variable (and *not* for any more complex wff). Secondly, it is essential here that the substitution should be made uniformly – i.e. for every occurrence of the variable in the original wff. Thirdly, this rule can be applied only to *valid* wffs (see the condition of the rule), whereas the rule for substituting equivalents can be applied to any wff. [That this restriction is necessary can be seen from a simple example. Suppose that for X we choose the invalid wff 'p⊃q'. Then under some substitutions for 'q', Z will be valid but under others Z will be invalid. If we substitute 'q⊃p' for 'q', Z is the valid wff 'p ⊃ (q⊃p)'; but if we substitute 'p⊃q' for 'q', Z is 'p ⊃ (p⊃q)', which is not valid.]

It is this Rule of Substitution that we rely on to pass from

$$p \equiv p$$

to
$$(p{\supset}q) \equiv (p{\supset}q)$$

by substituting 'p⊃q' for 'p'. Indeed, we shall rely on it frequently to get the special equivalences needed to allow us to use the Rule for Substitution of Equivalents in particular cases. In practice, in equivalence transformations, it is not necessary to make this reliance explicit, but you should make sure you understand what is happening so that you could make it explicit at any stage.[1]

One of the equivalences corresponding to a definition is:

$$(p{\cdot}q) \equiv {\sim}({\sim}p{\vee}{\sim}q)$$

[1] Notice that we could avoid reliance on the Rule of Substitution by using meta-logical variables in stating the equivalences. E.g. the Law of Identity would then read 'X ≡ X'. We have taken the other course because our techniques for determining the validity of schemata have been developed in terms of propositional variables.

It has as a companion-piece:

$$(pvq) \equiv \sim (\sim p.\sim q)$$

These two are known as *De Morgan's Laws*,[1] and enable us to eliminate conjunction or disjunction in favour of the other. In addition, they are particularly useful for eliminating negations outside brackets. When using the De Morgan Laws for this purpose, it is often necessary to use as well the *Law of Double Negation*:

$$p \equiv \sim\sim p$$

For example, suppose we want to eliminate the negation sign outside the brackets in

$$\sim(p \supset q) \supset (\sim p \supset \sim q) \tag{1}$$

Using the definition of '$\supset$', we get:

$$\sim(\sim pvq) \supset (\sim p \supset \sim q) \tag{2}$$

We cannot apply the De Morgan Law, '$(p.q) \equiv \sim(\sim pv\sim q)$', directly to the antecedent of (2), since 'q' is unnegated. But substituting 'q' for 'p' in the Law of Double Negation (by the Rule of Substitution for propositional variables) gives us:

$$q \equiv \sim\sim q \tag{3}$$

By the Rule for Substitution of Equivalents, (3) allows us to transform (2) into:

$$\sim(\sim pv\sim\sim q) \supset (\sim p \supset \sim q) \tag{4}$$

By substituting '$\sim q$' for the propositional variable 'q' in the De Morgan Law, we get:

$$(p.\sim q) \equiv \sim(\sim pv\sim\sim q) \tag{5}$$

And by the Rule for Substitution of Equivalents again, (5) allows us to rewrite (4) as:

$$(p.\sim q) \supset (\sim p \supset \sim q)$$

which has the characteristic we were seeking.

In practice we could set these transformations out much more briefly, giving a brief indication of their justification which omits all mention of the two rules. Here is how it might appear:

$(\sim(p\supset q) \supset (\sim p \supset \sim q))$

$$\equiv (\sim(\sim pvq) \supset (\sim p\supset\sim q)) \qquad \text{[Def } \supset\text{]}$$
$$\equiv (\sim(\sim pv\sim\sim q) \supset (\sim p\supset\sim q)) \qquad \text{[Double Neg.]}$$
$$\equiv ((p.\sim q) \supset (\sim p\supset\sim q)) \qquad \text{[De Morgan]}$$

---

[1] After Augustus de Morgan (1806–1878). However these Laws (like many others) were known in the Middle Ages, and were probably first stated by William of Occam (*c.* 1300–1349).

Here we used the Law of Double Negation to insert a pair of negation signs. We can also use it to delete pairs of negation signs prefixed to the same wff.

And by extension, we can validly cancel any *even* number of negations; but in order to state this precisely we need to introduce the notion of two negations *having the same scope*.

Roughly, two negations have the same scope if, neglecting brackets, their arguments extend the same distance to the right. More precisely, two negations have the same scope if and only if they are

  (i) adjacent

or (ii) are separated only by left-hand brackets not required by the Rules of Formation although allowed under the conventions on bracketing.

EXAMPLES

  (a) ∼∼p   – both have the same scope.
  (b) ∼(∼pvq)   – different scopes, since the left-hand bracket *is* required by the Rules of Formation.

  (c) ∼(pv∼q)   – different scopes.
  (d) p ⊃ ∼(∼(q⊃p)) – same scope, since the separating left-hand bracket is not required by the Rules of Formation.

[Notice that the idea of *scope* is not the same as the idea of *argument*. Consider '∼∼p' (or, what is the same, '∼(∼p)'). The argument of the first negation is '∼p', that of the second is 'p', although the scopes of the two operators are the same.]

Thus: If Y results from X by cancelling any even number of negations having the same scopes, (X ≡ Y) is valid.

To see what happens if we neglect the condition about having the same scope, consider the case:

$$\sim(\sim pvq)$$

Suppose we cancel the negations. We then get

$$pvq$$

But it is easily seen that '∼(∼pvq) ≡ (pvq)' is not valid. (Verify this by a truth-table.)

You are already familiar with the fact that certain operators are *commutative* – i.e. that the order of their arguments does not affect the truth-values of the wff. In this chapter we have already made tacit use of the Commutative Law for equivalence:

$$(p \equiv q) \equiv (q \equiv p)$$

The analogous laws for alternation, disjunction and conjunction are:

$$(pVq) \equiv (qVp)$$
$$(pvq) \equiv (qvp)$$
$$(p \cdot q) \equiv (q \cdot p)$$

Since a disjunction is false only if both the disjuncts are false, it is intuitively clear that any purely disjunctive expression, of any length, is false only if all the propositional variables have the value 0. That is, the validity of a purely disjunctive wff is independent of order and grouping within the wff. This is expressed by the *Associative Law* for disjunction:

$$((pvq) \text{ v } r) \equiv (q \text{ v } (pvr))$$

Its counterpart for conjunction is:

$$((p \cdot q) \cdot r) \equiv (q \cdot (p \cdot r))$$

Given these forms of the Associative Laws we can easily derive others by equivalence transformations. Thus:

$$((pvq) \text{ v } r) \equiv (q \text{ v } (pvr))$$
$$\equiv (q \text{ v } (rvp)) \quad \text{[Commutative Law]}$$
$$\equiv ((rvp) \text{ v } q) \quad \text{[Commutative Law]}$$
$$\equiv (p \text{ v } (rvq)) \quad \text{[Associative Law – 1st form]}$$

The various forms of the Associative Laws amount, in effect, to the assertion that brackets do not count in a purely disjunctive or purely conjunctive wff. It is often convenient to dispense with brackets, even though the Rules of Formation do not allow this, so we introduce the following definitions:

$$(X \text{ v } Y \text{ v } Z) =_{Df} ((X \text{ v } Y) \text{ v } Z)$$
$$(X \cdot Y \cdot Z) =_{Df} ((X \cdot Y) \cdot Z)$$

A wff of the form $X \text{ v } Y \text{ v } Z \text{ v } \ldots \text{ v } W$ amounts to an assertion that at least one of $X, Y, Z, \ldots, W$ is true. Similarly a wff of the form $X \cdot Y \cdot Z \cdot \ldots \cdot W$ amounts to an assertion that $X, Y, Z, \ldots, W$ are all true. We shall make a considerable use of this fact in later chapters.

We now have machinery for re-ordering and regrouping disjunctions, conjunctions, equivalences and alternations. For example, by applying the definitions of '⊃' and '.' to

$$(p.(p⊃q)) ⊃ q$$

we obtain $$\sim\sim(\sim p \lor \sim(\sim p \lor q)) \lor q$$

We can delete the initial negations by the Law of Double Negation, and then rearrange the resulting wff to get:

$$(\sim p \lor q) \lor \sim(\sim p \lor q)$$

The following pair of equivalences, known as the *Distributive Laws*, are useful for transforming schemata containing both conjunction and disjunction:

$$(p.(q \lor r)) \equiv ((p.q) \lor (p.r))$$
$$(p \lor (q.r)) \equiv ((p \lor q).(p \lor r))$$

The sense of the first of these laws may be made clearer by considering this example. 'He lives in a white house, and it is in either Jackson Street or Johnson Street' is true if and only if 'Either he lives in a white house in Jackson Street or he lives in a white house in Johnson Street' is true. Construct a similar example for the second law.

Notice that when we use the Distributive Laws to transform a wff, we obtain an expanded wff in which some variable (or variables) occurs more often than in the original wff. Thus, if we take the wff '(p∨q).(r∨s)', one application of the first Distributive Law gives

$$((p \lor q). r) \lor ((p \lor q).s)$$

Two more applications of the same law give us

$$((r.p) \lor (r.q)) \lor ((s.p) \lor (s.q))$$

in which every variable now occurs twice.

[Set out these transformations in detail, making explicit all appeals to Rules, etc.]

Two other equivalences which allow us to increase the number of occurrences of a variable are:

$$p \equiv (p \lor p)$$
$$p \equiv (p.p)$$

They can also be used in the other direction – to simplify a wff by deleting 'redundant' occurrences of variables.

Now suppose we apply the Distributive Law to the antecedent of

$$(p.(\sim p \lor q)) ⊃ q$$

Then we get
$$((p.\sim p) \vee (p.q)) \supset q$$

Now the antecedent is a disjunction, one of whose disjuncts is inconsistent. But that means that the truth-table of the whole disjunction depends only on that of '(p.q)'. For it is clear that $(0 \vee X) \equiv X$. Hence we could delete '(p.$\sim$p)' without altering the truth-values of the wff. That is:
$$(((p.\sim p) \vee (p.q)) \supset q) \equiv ((p.q) \supset q)$$

It is perhaps most convenient to allow for this sort of simplification by formulating this rule:

If W is of the form X v Y, then if X is inconsistent, W is equivalent to Y. I.e. we can always drop an inconsistent disjunct.

But similarly, $(X.1) \equiv X$. So we also state the rule:

If W is of the form X.Y, then if X is valid, W is equivalent to Y. I.e. we can always drop a valid conjunct.

Some sample transformations

I. $(p \supset q) \supset ((q \supset r) \supset (p \supset r))$

   $\equiv \sim(p \supset q) \vee (\sim(q \supset r) \vee (p \supset r))$ [Def $\supset$]

   $\equiv (\sim(p \supset q) \vee \sim(q \supset r)) \vee (p \supset r)$ [Associative Law]

   $\equiv \sim\sim(\sim(p \supset q) \vee \sim(q \supset r)) \vee (p \supset r)$ [Double Negation]

   $\equiv \sim((p \supset q).(q \supset r)) \vee (p \supset r)$ [Def.]

   $\equiv ((p \supset q).(q \supset r)) \supset (p \supset r)$ [Def $\supset$]

Notice that our original formula is of the general form
$$p \supset (q \supset r)$$

and that substitution of '$p \supset q$' for 'p', '$q \supset r$' for 'q', and '$p \supset r$' for

'r' in $(p \supset (q \supset r)) \equiv ((p.q) \supset r)$

(which is a valid wff) would give us the equivalence we have obtained by transformations.

Since '$((p \supset q).(q \supset r)) \supset (p \supset r)$' is the propositional schema corresponding to the pure hypothetical syllogism, we have just shown that the form of inference

> If p then q
> $\therefore$ If it is the case that if q then r,
>   then if p then r

is valid if and only if the more usual form of the pure hypothetical syllogism is valid.

II. $(p \supset (q \supset r)) \equiv (\sim p \lor (\sim q \lor r))$ [Def $\supset$]

        $\equiv (\sim q \lor (\sim p \lor r))$ [Associative Law]

        $\equiv (q \supset (p \supset r))$ [Def $\supset$]

'$(p \supset (q \supset r)) \equiv (q \supset (p \supset r))$' is the closest we can get to an Associative Law for material implication. It is known as the *Law of Permutation*.

III. $(p \equiv q) \equiv ((p \supset q) \cdot (q \supset p))$ [Def $\equiv$]

        $\equiv (\sim p \lor q) \cdot (\sim q \lor p)$ [Def $\supset$]

        $\equiv ((\sim p \lor q) \cdot \sim q) \lor ((\sim p \lor q) \cdot p)$ [Distributive Law]

        $\equiv (\sim q \cdot (\sim p \lor q)) \lor (p \cdot (\sim p \lor q))$ [Commutative Law]

        $\equiv ((\sim q \cdot \sim p) \lor (\sim q \cdot q)) \lor ((p \cdot \sim p) \lor (p \cdot q))$

                                                 [Distributive Law]

        $\equiv (\sim q \cdot \sim p) \lor (\sim q \cdot q) \lor (p \cdot \sim p) \lor (p \cdot q)$

                                                 [Dropping brackets]

        $\equiv (\sim q \cdot \sim p) \lor (p \cdot q)$ [Dropping inconsistent disjuncts]

        $\equiv \sim \sim (\sim p \cdot \sim q) \lor (p \cdot q)$ [Double Negation]

        $\equiv \sim (p \lor q) \lor (p \cdot q)$ [De Morgan]

        $\equiv (p \lor q) \supset (p \cdot q)$ [Def $\supset$]

EXERCISES 10

10.1 Show by equivalence transformations that the following are valid:

(a) $((p \supset q) \supset \sim (q \supset p)) \equiv ((p \cdot \sim q) \lor (q \cdot \sim p))$

(b) $((p \cdot q) \cdot r) \equiv \sim (\sim p \lor \sim q \lor \sim r)$

(c) $((p \lor q) \lor r) \equiv \sim (\sim p \cdot \sim q \cdot \sim r)$

(d) $((p \supset q) \supset \sim r) \equiv (r \supset (p \cdot \sim q))$

(e) $(p \supset q) \equiv (\sim q \supset \sim p)$ [*Law of Transposition*]

10.2 Show that if and only if affirming the antecedent (mixed hypothetical syllogism) is valid, the following forms of inference are valid:

(a) p, $\therefore$ if (if p then q) then q

(b) If p then q, $\therefore$ if p then q

Construct examples of inferences with each of these forms, making the same substitutions for 'p' and 'q' in each case.

CHAPTER 11

Another Decision Procedure

We know that 'pv∼p' is valid – and, further, that any wff which has that general form (i.e. any substitution instance of it) is also valid. It requires little reflection on the properties of disjunction to see that, if X is any wff at all, any wff of the form

$$X \lor (p v \sim p)$$

must be valid. In particular, this holds if X itself is purely disjunctive – i.e. contains no dyadic operator other than 'v', and no occurrences of '∼' other than those immediately preceding a propositional variable. [Thus '(pv∼qv∼p)' is a purely disjunctive wff but '∼(pvq)' and '(p v ∼(qv∼p))' are not.] Therefore, since disjunction is associative, we can see that a purely disjunctive wff is valid if it contains some variable both negated and unnegated. Thus, we can tell by inspection that

$$(\sim pvq) \lor (pv\sim r)$$

is valid, since it can be regrouped to give

$$(qv\sim r) \lor (pv\sim p)$$

So the existence of a propositional variable both negated and unnegated is a *sufficient* condition for the validity of a purely disjunctive wff. It is, in fact, also a *necessary* condition. For unless it is satisfied it will always be possible to find an assignment of truth-values to the variables under which the whole wff turns out to be false.

Similarly, we know that 'p.∼p' is inconsistent. Therefore, any wff of the form

$$X.(p.\sim p)$$

is inconsistent. And by an argument quite analogous to the preceding one, we arrive at the conclusion that existence of a propositional variable both negated and unnegated is a necessary and sufficient condition for the inconsistency of a purely conjunctive wff.

Thus, we possess simple inspection tests for determining the validity and inconsistency of purely disjunctive and purely conjunctive wffs respectively.

We also know that a conjunction is true if and only if all the conjuncts are true, and therefore valid if and only if all the conjuncts are valid. Similarly, a disjunction is inconsistent if and only if all the disjuncts are inconsistent. Let $D_1, D_2, \ldots, D_n$ be purely disjunctive wffs; and let $C_1, C_2, \ldots, C_n$ be purely conjunctive wffs. We can determine the validity of

$$D_1 \cdot D_2 \cdot \ldots \cdot D_n \qquad (1)$$

by simple inspection. For apply the inspection test to each D. If they are all valid (i.e. each contains some variable negated and unnegated), then (1) is valid. If one or more D is invalid, then (1) is invalid.

Similarly we can determine whether

$$C_1 \vee C_2 \vee \ldots \vee C_n \qquad (2)$$

is inconsistent. If every C is, on inspection, inconsistent, then (2) is inconsistent. If one or more C is not inconsistent, then (2) is not inconsistent.

Conjunctive normal form

A wff which has the form:

$$D_1 \cdot D_2 \cdot \ldots \cdot D_n$$

is said to be in *conjunctive normal form* ('CNF' for short). It can be seen that if we can show how to find a wff in CNF which is equivalent to any given wff, we shall have a further decision procedure for PC. In fact, all the machinery for doing this has been set out in Chapter 10.

Before setting out the procedure for finding a CNF for any given wff, let us make quite precise and explicit the conditions for being in CNF.

A wff, X, is in CNF if and only if:

(i) X is an unnegated conjunction
(ii) every conjunct in X is an unnegated disjunction
(iii) every disjunct is a propositional variable or the negation of a propositional variable.

In short, X is in CNF if and only if it is a conjunction of disjunctions, and no negation sign has an argument other than a single propositional variable.

To avoid having to make special cases of certain types of wff, we introduce the notion of a *degenerate conjunction* (or disjunction). A wff is a degenerate conjunction (disjunction) if it could appear as one conjunct (disjunct) in the sense of conditions (i)–(iii). Then 'conjunction' and 'disjunction' in those conditions are taken to include the degenerate cases.

The effect of this is to allow a wff which does not contain any conjunction signs to be in CNF. E.g. '(pv~pvq)' is a degenerate conjunction and is therefore in CNF. In other words, since $D_1 \cdot D_2$ is in CNF, so is D_1 by itself. Similarly, 'p', '~p', 'q', etc., are degenerate disjunctions, so 'p.~p', 'p.q', etc., are in CNF. And similarly, 'p', '~q', etc., are themselves in CNF, as degenerate conjunctions of degenerate disjunctions, although they contain neither conjunction nor disjunction signs.

In addition we adopt these conventions:

(i) No redundant disjuncts occur in any conjunct in a CNF. That is, 'pvp' is always replaced by 'p'; '~pv~p' is always replaced by '~p'; and so on.

(ii) No redundant conjuncts occur in a CNF. E.g. '(pv~q).(pv~q)' is to be replaced by '(pv~q)'.

(iii) Within disjunctions, variables appear in the alphabetical order, p, q, r, . . . , with an unnegated occurrence of a variable preceding a negated occurrence.

According to these conventions, for example,

$$(pvrv{\sim}qvqvp) \cdot ({\sim}pvpvqvr) \cdot ({\sim}pvpvqvr)$$

is to be rewritten as

$$(pvqv{\sim}qvr) \cdot (pv{\sim}pvqvr)$$

Any wff can be put into CNF (i.e. a wff in CNF equivalent to the original wff can be found) by following these rules:[1]

(1) Use the definitions to remove all occurrences of '⊃', '≡' and 'v' (i.e. obtain a wff containing only the operators '~', 'v', '.').

(2) Use De Morgan's Laws and the Law of Double Negation to remove all negations outside brackets.

(3) Use the Law of Double Negation to ensure that no variable is preceded by more than one negation sign.

(4) Use the Distributive Law

$$(p \text{ v } (q.r)) \equiv ((pvq) \cdot (pvr))$$

as many times as is necessary to produce a conjunction of disjunctions.

[1] A proof that every wff of PC can be put into CNF is given in Appendix 1.

We can then use '(pvp) ≡ p', '(p•p) ≡ p' and Associative and Commutative Laws to put the CNF into the conventional form.

EXAMPLE I

$$p \supset (q{\supset}p)$$
$$\equiv \sim p \vee (\sim qvp) \quad [\text{Def} \supset]$$
$$\equiv p \vee \sim p \vee \sim q \quad [\text{Dropping brackets and Assoc}]$$

The last line is in CNF, being a degenerate conjunction. Inspection shows that 'p' occurs both negated and unnegated. Therefore the CNF is valid. Therefore the wff, 'p ⊃ (q⊃p)' to which the CNF is equivalent, is valid.

EXAMPLE II

$$(p{\bullet}(p{\supset}q)) \supset q$$
$$\equiv \sim(p{\bullet}(\sim pvq)) \vee q \quad [\text{Def} \supset]$$
$$\equiv (\sim p \vee \sim(\sim pvq)) \vee q \quad [\text{De Morgan, Double Neg}]$$
$$\equiv (\sim p \vee (p{\bullet}\sim q)) \vee q \quad [\text{De Morgan, Double Neg}]$$
$$\equiv ((\sim pvp){\bullet}(\sim pv\sim q)) \vee q \quad [\text{Distrib}]$$
$$\equiv (q \vee (\sim pvp)){\bullet}(q \vee (\sim pv\sim q)) \quad [\text{Distrib}]$$
$$\equiv (q \vee \sim p \vee p){\bullet}(q \vee \sim p \vee \sim q) \quad [\text{Dropping brackets}]$$
$$\equiv (p \vee \sim p \vee q){\bullet}(\sim p \vee q \vee \sim q) \quad [\text{Reordering}]$$

Inspection shows that each conjunct is valid; therefore the CNF is valid, and so is the original wff. You will notice that the applications of De Morgan's Laws and the Law of Double Negation have been run together. You will find it convenient to work out and commit to memory such special forms of the De Morgan Laws as:

$$\sim(p{\bullet}q) \equiv (\sim pv\sim q)$$
$$\sim(pv\sim q) \equiv (\sim p{\bullet}q)$$

as well as extended forms like:

$$\sim(p{\bullet}q{\bullet}r) \equiv (\sim p \vee \sim q \vee \sim r)$$

Knowing these will enable you to work out CNF's much more quickly and easily.

Another short cut could have been used in this example. We could have regrouped the line

$$(\sim p \vee (p{\bullet}\sim q)) \vee q$$

to obtain

$$(\sim pvq) \vee (p{\bullet}\sim q)$$

Then a single application of the Distributive Law would give

$$((\sim pvq) \ v \ p) \cdot ((\sim pvq) \ v \sim q)$$

which requires only dropping brackets and reordering within the disjunctions to give the CNF.

EXAMPLE III

$$(pvq) \supset (p \cdot q)$$

$\equiv \sim (pvq) \ v \ (p \cdot q)$	[Def $\supset$]
$\equiv (\sim p \cdot \sim q) \ v \ (p \cdot q)$	[De Morgan]
$\equiv ((\sim p \cdot \sim q) \ v \ p) \cdot ((\sim p \cdot \sim q) \ v \ q)$	[Distrib]
$\equiv (pv \sim p) \cdot (pv \sim q) \cdot (qv \sim p) \cdot (qv \sim q)$	[Distrib]
$\equiv (pv \sim p) \cdot (pv \sim q) \cdot (\sim pvq) \cdot (qv \sim q)$	[Reordering]

The CNF is invalid since the second and third conjuncts are invalid. Therefore the original wff is invalid.

EXAMPLE IV

$$(p \equiv q) \supset \sim (p \cdot \sim q)$$

$\equiv ((p \supset q) \cdot (q \supset p)) \supset \sim (p \cdot \sim q)$	[Def $\equiv$]
$\equiv \sim ((\sim pvq) \cdot (\sim qvp)) v \sim (p \cdot \sim q)$	[Def $\supset$]
$\equiv (\sim (\sim pvq) \ v \sim (\sim qvp)) \ v \ (\sim pvq)$	[De Morgan]

[At this point we can in fact read off the validity of the wff, since '$(\sim pvq)$' appears both negated and unnegated. But let us obtain the CNF as we set out to do.]

$\equiv ((p \cdot \sim q) \ v \ (q \cdot \sim p)) \ v \ (\sim pvq)$	[De Morgan]
$\equiv (((p \cdot \sim q) \ v \ q) \cdot ((p \cdot \sim q) \ v \sim p)) \ v \ (\sim pvq)$	[Distrib]
$\equiv ((qvp) \cdot (qv \sim q) \cdot (\sim pvp) \cdot (\sim pv \sim q)) \ v \ (\sim pvq)$	[Distrib]
$\equiv ((\sim pvq) \ v \ (qvp)) \cdot ((\sim pvq) \ v \ (qv \sim q)) \cdot$	
$\quad ((\sim pvq) \ v \ (\sim pvp)) \cdot ((\sim pvq) \ v \ (\sim pv \sim q))$	[Distrib]
$\equiv (pv \sim pvqvq) \cdot (\sim pvqvqv \sim q) \cdot (pv \sim pv \sim pvq) \cdot (\sim pv \sim pvqv \sim q)$	
	[Dropping brackets, reordering]
$\equiv (pv \sim pvq) \cdot (\sim pvqv \sim q) \cdot (pv \sim pvq) \cdot (\sim pvqv \sim q)$	
	[Dropping redundant variables]

Inspection shows that every conjunct is valid. Therefore the original wff is valid.

Disjunctive normal form

A wff is in CNF if it has the form

$$D_1 \cdot D_2 \cdot \ldots \cdot D_n \qquad\qquad (n \geq 1)$$

A wff is said to be in *disjunctive normal form* ('DNF' for short) if it has the form

$$C_1 \vee C_2 \vee \ldots \vee C_n \qquad (n \geqq 1)$$

where $C_1, C_2, \ldots, C_n$ are purely conjunctive wffs. That is, a wff is in DNF if it is an unnegated disjunction of unnegated conjunctions of propositional variables, either negated or unnegated. As before, 'disjunction' and 'conjunction' are taken to include the degenerate cases, and the same conventions on ordering and redundancy are followed. The procedure for finding the DNF for any wff is exactly the same as for finding its CNF, except that we use the other Distributive Law, viz.

$$(p \cdot (q \vee r)) \equiv ((p \cdot q) \vee (p \cdot r))$$

We can then determine by inspection whether the wff is inconsistent, by seeing whether every conjunction contains some variable both negated and unnegated.

Perfect normal forms

A CNF is said to be *perfect* if every conjunct contains as a disjunct every propositional variable (negated or unnegated) that occurs in the whole wff. Thus the wff

$$(p \vee r) \cdot (p \vee \sim q)$$

while in CNF is not in *perfect* CNF, since 'q' does not occur in the first conjunct, and 'r' does not occur in the second. However, we can easily find a perfect CNF equivalent to any given non-perfect CNF. To illustrate the method, consider the first conjunct of the example above. By substitution we obtain a special form of the Distributive Law, viz.

$$(p \vee (q \cdot \sim q)) \equiv ((p \vee q) \cdot (p \vee \sim q))$$

From this, the rule for dropping an inconsistent disjunct gives us

$$p \equiv ((p \vee q) \cdot (p \vee \sim q))$$

Using this equivalence, we transform the first conjunct, '(p∨r)', into

$$(((p \vee q) \cdot (p \vee \sim q)) \vee r)$$

By the Distributive Law this gives us

$$(p \vee q \vee r) \cdot (p \vee \sim q \vee r)$$

Similarly, we obtain and use

$$p \equiv ((p \vee r) \cdot (p \vee \sim r))$$

to transform the second conjunct into

$$(pv{\sim}qvr){\cdot}(pv{\sim}qv{\sim}r)$$

Thus from the non-perfect CNF

$$(pvr)(p{\cdot}v{\sim}q)$$

we obtain the perfect CNF

$$(pvqvr){\cdot}(pv{\sim}qvr){\cdot}(pv{\sim}qvr){\cdot}(pv{\sim}qv{\sim}r)$$

and, dropping the redundant conjunct, we get

$$(pvqvr){\cdot}(pv{\sim}qvr){\cdot}(pv{\sim}qv{\sim}r)$$

We can freeze this procedure in the following rule:

If, in any CNF, D is a conjunct which does not contain some propositional variable, p_k, then $D \equiv ((D \vee p_k){\cdot}(D \vee {\sim}p_k))$

Similarly, a DNF is said to be perfect if every disjunct contains as a conjunct every propositional variable (negated or unnegated) that occurs in the whole wff. And every DNF can be put into the perfect form. In this case we use the other Distributive Law, forming the special case:

$$(p{\cdot}(qv{\sim}q)) \equiv ((p{\cdot}q) \vee (p{\cdot}{\sim}q))$$

which gives us

$$p \equiv ((p{\cdot}q) \vee (p{\cdot}{\sim}q))$$

The Rule in this case is:

If, in any DNF, C is a disjunct which does not contain some propositional variable, p_k, then $C \equiv ((C{\cdot}p_k) \vee (C{\cdot}{\sim}p_k))$

We may note in passing that, although we can tell by inspection of a DNF only whether it is inconsistent or not, we can tell by inspection of a *perfect* DNF whether or not it is *valid*. For a perfect DNF is valid if and only if every consistent conjunction of all its variables is found among its disjuncts.

This result will be of some importance later on, so let us explain and justify it now. By a consistent conjunction we mean one in which no variable occurs both negated and unnegated. Thus, if the DNF contains only the variables 'p' and 'q', the full list of consistent conjunctions is:

$$p{\cdot}q$$
$$p{\cdot}{\sim}q$$
$${\sim}p{\cdot}q$$
$${\sim}p{\cdot}{\sim}q$$

It takes but little reflection to see that, no matter how truth-values are assigned to the variables, it will always be the case that one of these conjunctions is true. Therefore the disjunction of them all must be valid. Therefore any disjunction which contains them all *among* its disjuncts must be valid. Conversely, if they do not *all* appear as disjuncts then it will be possible to assign truth-values to the variables in such a way that the disjunction is sometimes false – i.e. it will be invalid.

We have argued the case of two variables, but it is clear that the same argument will work for any number. In each case, the set of consistent conjunctions mirrors the structure of a truth-table matrix of the appropriate number of variables.

Notice that it does not matter if an inconsistent conjunction appears in a perfect DNF. Provided that *all* the consistent ones occur, the wff is valid; and if they are not all there, mere absence of inconsistent conjunctions does not mean that the wff is valid.

Extended perfect normal forms

Let $p_1, \ldots, p_n$ be the variables which occur in a wff X, and let q_1 be some variable distinct from any of $p_1, \ldots, p_n$. Then it is always possible to find a perfect CNF for X, each conjunct of which contains not only each of $p_1, \ldots, p_n$, but q_1 as well. To do so, we first find for X an ordinary perfect CNF, X′, in the way just explained. Let D be any conjunct in X′. Then, by the rule given above, we can replace D by

$$(D \vee q_1) \cdot (D \vee \sim q_1)$$

By applying this procedure to each conjunct in X′, we obtain a new perfect CNF, X″, of the required type. We shall call X″ *the perfect CNF of X in terms of* $p_1, \ldots, p_n$ *and* q_1.

It is clear that by repeating this procedure we can find a perfect CNF for X in terms of any set of variables which includes all those that occur in X.

The same principles apply, *mutatis mutandis*, to perfect DNF.

These new perfect normal forms are not mere curiosities. When we are comparing two wffs which do not have all their variables in common, it is often useful to construct the perfect CNF or the perfect DNF of each in terms of all the variables that occur in either.

EXERCISES 11

11.1 Determine the validity of the following wffs by putting each into CNF:

(a) q ⊃ (p ⊃ (q⊃p))

(b) ((p⊃q) ⊃ p) ⊃ p

(c) ((p⊃q) ⊃ p) ⊃ q

(d) (p⊃q) ⊃ ((p•r) ⊃ (q•r))

(e) ((p∨q) ⊃ ∼r) ⊃ ((r⊃p) ∨ (r⊃q))

(f) ∼((p•q) ⊃ ((p⊃r) ⊃ q))

(g) (p≡q) ⊃ ((p⊃r) ⊃ (q⊃r))

11.2 Put each of the wffs in 11. 1 into DNF.

11.3 Obtain a perfect CNF and a perfect DNF for each of the following:

(a) (p∨q) ⊃ ((q⊃r) ⊃ (p∨r))

(b) s ⊃ (s•(p ⊃ (∼p⊃q)))

(c) ((p⊃q) ⊃ r) ⊃ ((r⊃p) ⊃ (s⊃p))

(d) (p ⊃ (q≡r)) ⊃ (∼(p⊃q) ≡ ∼(p⊃r))

PART II

The Propositional Calculus: Axiomatic Systems

CHAPTER 12

Operations of Inference

In the chapter on Equivalence Transformations, we met the operation of uniform substitution of wffs for propositional variables. This operation preserves validity in the sense that if the substitutions are made in a *valid* wff, the resulting wff is also valid. That this is so follows from the fact that a wff is valid if it has the value 1 for all possible assignments of truth-values to the variables, provided that each assignment is uniform in the sense that the same value is given to each occurrence of a given variable in the wff. Now every wff has the value 1 or the value 0 for each assignment of truth-values to its variables; and so provided that substitution of wffs for propositional variables is uniform, validity is preserved.

Thus we possess an operation which enables us to obtain new valid formulae from given ones. In fact, from any given valid wff we may generate, by successive substitutions, an infinite sequence of new valid wffs. As a very simple case of such a sequence, consider

$$p \supset p \tag{1}$$
$$(p{\cdot}q) \supset (p{\cdot}q) \tag{2}$$
$$(p{\cdot}(q{\cdot}r)) \supset (p{\cdot}(q{\cdot}r)) \tag{3}$$
$$(p{\cdot}(q{\cdot}(r{\cdot}s))) \supset (p{\cdot}(q{\cdot}(r{\cdot}s))) \tag{4}$$

This sequence can in fact be generated in a variety of ways. The two simplest ways are:

(*a*) by substitution each time in (1) itself
(*b*) by substitution in (n–1) to obtain (n).

[Or expressing it diagrammatically:

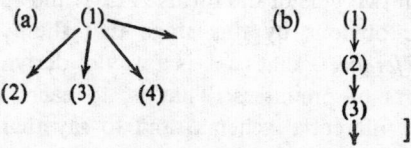

An even simpler case of such a sequence is:

$$p \supset p \qquad (1)$$
$$q \supset q \qquad (2)$$
$$r \supset r \qquad (3)$$
$$\cdot \ \cdot \ \cdot \qquad \cdot \ \cdot$$

Another operation which preserves validity is that of *adjunction* – i.e. conjoining two wffs to obtain a third. It is an immediate consequence of the truth-functional characteristics of conjunction that if X and Y are valid wffs then X.Y is also valid.

The familiar operation of *substitution of equivalents* clearly preserves validity. Moreover, by replacing a given wff by its various equivalents we can generate many new wffs; and by this operation we can obtain a wff whose shape is quite different from the original one, as, for example, when 'pvq' is replaced by '$\sim(\sim p.\sim q)$'.

Another important validity-preserving operation is that of *detachment*. Like adjunction this is an operation on two formulae, viz. an implication and its antecedent, to obtain a third, viz. the consequent of the implication, which is thus 'detached' from its antecedent. Detachment obviously preserves validity; for if an implication, X $\supset$ Y, and its antecedent, X, are both valid, a little reflection on the truth-table for '$\supset$' shows that the consequent, Y, must also be valid.

To illustrate the operation of detachment, consider the two wffs:

$$(p \supset (q \supset p)) \supset (q \supset (p \supset p)) \qquad (1)$$
$$p \supset (q \supset p) \qquad (2)$$

Both of these are valid formulae, and given that fact, detachment enables us to establish the validity of the consequent of (1), viz. '$q \supset (p \supset p)$'.

These are just a few of the operations which enable us to generate new valid formulae from given ones. There are, in fact, infinitely many such operations of all grades of complexity. As an example of one somewhat more complex than, say, detachment, we may mention *composition* – that is, the operation of obtaining a wff of the form X $\supset$ (Y.Z) from two wffs of the forms X $\supset$ Y and X $\supset$ Z.

It should be obvious by this stage that these operations are operations of *inference* – that each is a way of deriving a conclusion from given sorts of premisses. That is, to each operation there corresponds an inferential schema, and to say that the operation preserves validity is to say that this inferential schema is valid in an appropriate sense.

Let us have a closer look at these inferential schemata. The schema corresponding to the operation of detachment has the familiar form of affirming the antecedent in the Mixed Hypothetical Syllogism, and may be written down as:

$$\frac{\begin{array}{l} X \supset Y \\ X \end{array}}{\therefore Y}$$

You will notice that this differs from the familiar sort of inferential schema by containing variables 'X' and 'Y' which take as values not propositions (which are true or false) but propositional schemata (which are valid or invalid). We shall therefore call it a *second order* inferential schema. Now a first order inferential schema is valid if and only if no set of uniform and appropriate substitutions for its variables yields an inference with true premises and a false conclusion. Analogously, a second order inferential schema is valid if and only if no set of uniform and appropriate substitutions for its variables yields a first order inferential schema with valid premises and an invalid conclusion.

It is easy to set down the second order schemata corresponding to adjunction and composition, but in order to set out the schema for substitution we need some way of writing the wff which results from the operation on a wff, X. Since this wff is what we get when some propositional variable, say 'p', in X is uniformly replaced by a wff, say Y, let us write it as:

$$X (Y/p)$$

Then the inferential schema is:

$$\frac{X}{\therefore X (Y/p)}$$

Now here we have considered a very limited type of substitution, since we have envisaged only substitution for one variable at a time. We shall call such substitutions *simple substitutions*. But if this limited operation preserves validity, so does a more extended one in which several variables are simultaneously replaced by several wffs – not necessarily different wffs – although, of course, the substitution must be uniform over all instances of each variable. That simultaneous substitution does preserve validity can be shown by demonstrating that it can always be replaced by a succession of simple substitutions. In fact, we shall show that, if n is the number of variables for which simultaneous substitutions are made, the same resulting formula can always be obtained in not more than 2n simple substitutions. For suppose that $p_1, \ldots, p_n$ are distinct variables in a wff, X, for which we wish to substitute wffs $Y_1, \ldots, Y_n$ respectively. Then choose variables $q_1, \ldots, q_n$ which do not occur in X or in any of the wffs $Y_1, \ldots, Y_n$, and successively substitute q_1 for p_1, q_2 for p_2, and so on to q_n for p_n, to obtain a wff, X'. Then in X' successively substitute Y_1 for q_1, Y_2 for q_2, and so on to Y_n for q_n. We thus obtain the result of the simultaneous substitution in X by two sequences of n substitutions – i.e. in 2n simple substitutions.

To illustrate the point, we consider a case where n = 2. Suppose X is

$$(p \cdot q) \supset (q \cdot p) \tag{1}$$

Then the simultaneous substitution of 'pvq' for 'p', and 'qvr' for 'q' in (1) gives us

$$((pvq) \cdot (qvr)) \supset ((qvr) \cdot (pvq))$$

But we can reach the same result in 2n (i.e. 4) successive simple substitutions, viz.:

$$(1) \ (s/p) \text{ which gives } (s \cdot q) \supset (q \cdot s) \tag{2}$$
$$(2) \ (t/q) \text{ which gives } (s \cdot t) \supset (t \cdot s) \tag{3}$$
$$(3) \ (pvq/s) \text{ which gives}$$
$$((pvq) \cdot t) \supset (t \cdot (pvq)) \tag{4}$$
$$(4) \ (qvr/t) \text{ which gives}$$
$$((pvq) \cdot (qvr)) \supset ((qvr) \cdot (pvq))$$

In fact, in this case, as in many others, the desired result can be obtained in fewer than 2n simple substitutions. The important point is that we never need to take *more than* 2n steps to get the same result as by simultaneous substitution. (As an exercise, you should find a shorter chain of simple substitutions equivalent to the simultaneous substitution just considered, and set down clearly the features of the case which make such a shorter chain possible.)

Letting $Y_1, Y_2, \ldots, Y_n$ be n not necessarily distinct wffs, and $p_1, p_2, \ldots, p_n$ be n distinct propositional variables in a wff X, we can write the most general inferential schema for substitution thus:

$$X$$
$$\therefore X(Y_1/p_1, Y_2/p_2, \ldots, Y_n/p_n)$$

The simpler schema set out earlier is a special case of this one – viz. the case of n = 1.

It will be recalled from Part I that to *prove* a proposition is to obtain it as the conclusion of a valid inference whose premisses are known truths. Here we are dealing not with propositions but with propositional *schemata*, where validity is the analogue of truth. Whereas a proof of a *proposition* is a guarantee of its truth, a proof of a propositional *schema* is a guarantee of its validity. To prove a schema is to obtain it as the conclusion of a valid inferential schema whose premisses are known to be valid. And it is just this that our operations of substitution, detachment, etc., enable us to do – to construct proofs of wffs.

A proof has two faces. On the one hand it can be regarded as establishing the validity of the conclusion sought (and obtained). (From this point of view, it is tempting to describe a proof as a test – but it must be remembered that it is not an *effective* test in the way that a truth-table is, for we have no *guarantee* that a given wff can be proved from given premisses in a finite number of moves.) On the other hand, a proof can be regarded as the *construction* of a new wff whose validity is guaranteed in advance, even though its shape may not be foreseen. It is under this second view that we can most clearly distinguish the interests and emphases of Part I and the present Part. In Part I we concentrated our attention on determining validity of schemata already given; in Part II we shall concentrate it on means of generating valid schemata from very limited bases. Another way of marking the difference would be to say that whereas in Part I we were exploring part of the theory of validity, here we are concerned with part of the theory of deducibility.

CHAPTER 13

Axiomatic Systems

An inferential schema may be thought of as a *claim* that given as premises certain valid propositional schemata, a further propositional schema is also valid. If the inferential schema is valid, then the claim is a good one – the schema is a guarantee of the validity of the conclusion, given the validity of the premises. We might therefore formulate a *rule of inference* corresponding to each valid inferential schema. Each such rule of inference is a rule for the employment of some inferential operation, and licenses us to assert as valid a new wff of the prescribed form. It is in this sense that we may say that the rules of inference generate new formulae.

But the generation must begin somewhere, proceed from some basis. That is to say, we must have some premises.

An *axiomatic system* or *axiomatization* of the propositional calculus consists essentially of:

(i) a set of wffs of PC, called the *axioms* of the system
(ii) a set of *rules of inference* which license operations on wffs of PC
(iii) the set of all wffs of PC which can be obtained from the axioms by use of the rules of inference; these new wffs are called *theorems* of the system, or *consequences* of the axioms under the stated rules of inference.

Sometimes it is convenient to have one word to denote a formula which is either an axiom or a theorem of a particular system. In that case we say that the formula is a *thesis* (plural: *theses*) of the system.

Thus an axiomatization of PC can be regarded as a set of wffs of PC, generated in a specified way. And, in general, an axiomatization of any field can be regarded as a set of wffs of that field, generated in a specified way. It is always required that the method of generation be *effective*, in the sense that any particular application of a rule must yield a definite result, the same on each occasion, in a finite number of operations. This is sometimes expressed by saying that the rules must be *mechanical* in nature. It is also required that axiomhood be effective, in the sense that we possess some effective method for deciding whether or not any given wff is an axiom. In all the systems we shall be concerned with, the number of axioms is finite, so that effectiveness of axiomhood is guaranteed provided the axioms are listed. [We can state these points briefly by saying that the set of theses must be recursively specifiable, and the set of axioms must be a recursive subset of the set of theses. For an explanation of 'recursively specifiable' and 'recursive', see p. 49.]

It can be seen that although the system may *consist* of its theses, it can be *specified* completely by giving a list of the axioms and rules of inference. In order to make it quite clear what field is being axiomatized, we should also set out the primitive signs and rules of formation, together with any definitions we wish to introduce. When all this is given, we have set out an *axiomatic basis* for the system. [There may of course be more than one axiomatic basis for a given system – i.e. more than one set of axioms and rules of inference which will serve to generate the same set of theses.]

Now suppose we have before us some field or theory which we wish to axiomatize. We suppose that the field is well defined in that a definite 'language' has been set up, in the sense that we have a list of the primitive signs, together with adequate Formation Rules and such definitions as are convenient. In short, we suppose we have a recursive set of wffs. Then in general we want any axiomatic system we set up in that field to satisfy two conditions:

(1) every thesis is a valid wff of the field
(2) every valid wff of the field is a thesis of the system.

In other words, we want the set of all theses of the system to coincide exactly with the set of all valid wffs of the axiomatized field.

Condition (1) is closely related to the condition of *consistency*, in the sense of freedom from contradiction. A system is said to be free from contradiction if it has no pair of theses of the forms X and $\sim X$. (Although the type of inconsistency which springs most readily to mind is that in which two *axioms* contradict one another, this is just a special case. A system is no less inconsistent if two theorems contradict one another than if two axioms do.) How condition (1) is related to consistency can be seen by reflecting on the notion of validity. It is clear that X and $\sim X$ cannot both be valid; so if every thesis is valid, X and ∼X cannot both be theses. (The relation will be set out in detail in Chapter 19.) It is relatively easy to ensure that an axiomatic system satisfies condition (1): all that is required is that each axiom should be valid, and that the rules of inference preserve validity. [Of course, we are assuming here that we have an adequate theory of validity for the field being axiomatized, which will enable us to decide whether or not the axioms are valid, and the rules validity-preserving. In fields such as PC, where we possess a decision procedure, there is no trouble about this and the assumption is quite justified.]

A system which satisfies condition (2) is said to be *complete*. Completeness is an important characteristic, but one which is not attainable in every field; and even in those relatively simple fields, such as PC, where it is attainable, it is not easy to ensure it in advance. That is to say, it is not easy, in setting up an axiomatization of PC, to select a sufficiently powerful set of axioms and rules of inference to generate every valid wff of PC.

However, a considerable number of consistent and complete axiomatic systems of PC have been devised, and we shall examine some of these in what follows. One general remark is possible at this stage. In most of these axiomatizations of PC, it is necessary to take as primitive (i.e. as given at the outset, as part of the axiomatic basis) only *two* inferential operations – viz.: substitution for propositional variables, and detachment. That is, most of the systems have only two primitive rules of inference, which we state as follows:

RULE OF SUBSTITUTION: If X is a thesis containing propositional variables, $p_1, \ldots, p_n$, and $Y_1, \ldots, Y_n$ are (not necessarily distinct) wffs, then $X(Y_1/p_1, \ldots, Y_n/p_n)$ is a thesis.

RULE OF DETACHMENT (or MODUS PONENS): If X and X⊃Y are theses, then Y is a thesis.

Similarly the number of axioms employed is usually small. For example, in the first system we shall examine there are just five axioms:

(1) (pvp) ⊃ p
(2) q ⊃ (pvq)
(3) (pvq) ⊃ (qvp)

(4) $(p \vee (q \vee r)) \supset (q \vee (p \vee r))$

(5) $(q \supset r) \supset ((p \vee q) \supset (p \vee r))$

From these five axioms (and, indeed, as it will turn out later, from only four of them) we can obtain, as consequences under the two rules of inference just stated, all the valid wffs of PC.

CHAPTER 14

Formal Axiomatic Systems

So far we have considered axiomatic systems as systematizations of some field or another, in particular of PC. In doing this, we are continuing the point of view adopted in Part I, under which we are concerned with formulae as *propositional* formulae, with variables as propositional variables, with operators as proposition-forming operators; and similarly the rules are regarded as rules for generating propositional formulae. That is, we have not been concerned with axiomatic systems as purely formal structures, but as structures interpreted in a certain way.

Now we might have begun in quite a different way, presenting axiomatic systems as systems with a certain sort of structure but not intended as systematizations of anything. In that case, the signs (or marks or symbols or objects) used to present the system (i.e. to represent the structure) would not mean anything or stand for or denote anything. So, given a suitable choice of marks (signs, symbols) and of rules, we would obtain a structure formally similar to an axiomatic system constructed, say, by systematization of PC. To make this point quite clear, let us reflect for a moment on the Rules of Formation for PC, set out in Chapter 8. It will be recalled that we first gave a classified list of the primitive symbols, labelling them as propositional variables, monadic and dyadic operators, and brackets. This list was followed by a set of rules for forming sequences (i.e. wffs) of the primitive symbols. Inspection of these rules will show that they do not depend at all on the particular nature of the symbols nor on their intended interpretation. The Rules of Formation are quite *mechanical* rules for forming combinations of listed symbols, and it is quite irrelevant that, e.g., 'p' is a propositional variable. '∼p v (qvp)' will be a wff according to these rules whether or not 'p' and 'q' are propositional variables, whether or not 'v' and '∼' are truth-functional proposition-forming operators, and whether or not '(' and ')' are merely marks of punctuation. Under our intended interpretation of these symbols, the wffs generated by the rules are *propositional* schemata. Under a different interpretation the wffs will consist of the same strings of symbols, but they will be schemata in a different field. E.g. if 'p', 'q', 'r', . . . denote the real numbers 1, 2, 3, . . . respectively, 'v' is interpreted as addition, and '~X' as $+ \sqrt{X}$ then the wffs generated by the rules will be arithmetical expressions. Under the propositional interpretation, '~p v (qvp)' is interpreted as 'Either it is not the case that a proposition is true or either another proposition or the first is true'; under the arithmetical interpretation '~p v (qvp)' expresses nothing propositional, but rather the numerical expression $+ \sqrt{1} + (2 + 1)$, which designates the number 4.

The important thing to notice is that the Rules of Formation work equally well and in just the same way under each of these interpretations of the primitive symbols. And since the Rules are independent of such interpretations, they will work in just the same way under no interpretation at all. In that case the wffs will just be strings of symbols neither asserting nor designating anything, but exactly the same strings of symbols will appear as wffs.

Now if we continue this, by selecting some set of these meaningless strings of symbols and calling them axioms (or initial formulae or angels or whatever you like), and formulate further rules for generating other wffs from those selected, the result is a *formal axiomatic system* – or, for short, a *formal system*. A formal system, then, is a certain sort of structure (of symbols or any other sorts of objects you care to choose); while an axiomatic system in the sense of Chapter 13 is such a structure with an intended interpretation. We shall use 'formal system' and 'axiomatic system' in this way throughout – to mark the uninterpreted/interpreted contrast.

Now, just because an axiomatic system is an interpreted system, so that the symbols mean something to us, our intuition can work more readily than it can in the context of a formal system. For example, we can frequently just see that a certain combination of symbols is well-formed (or not) because we know what it means. But in the case of a formal system there are no meanings to guide us. As a consequence it is often possible when setting up or working within an axiomatic system to lean on our intuitions, in a way that is not possible with respect to a formal system. In the latter case, we have no more than the symbols to deal with, and no other tools than the rules as stated. A particular formulation of a rule may be quite adequate for working purposes in a certain axiomatic system, and yet be useless, through lack of preciseness, in a structurally similar formal system. To illustrate this point, let AS be a certain axiomatization of PC, and let FS be a formal system structurally similar to AS. Suppose AS contains as one of its Rules of Inference:

If a wff, X, is implied by a thesis, then X is itself a thesis.

Now, this is a quite adequate formulation of the Rule of Detachment, *provided it is seen against the background of the intended interpretation of AS.* For it is that interpretation which makes the essential step of connecting, say, the symbol '⊃' and the notion of implication. And it is our awareness of this connection which enables us to see both how to use the rule in constructing proofs in AS and also that the rule is a 'reasonable' one. But if the same rule occurs in FS it will be useless. For there, although we are supposing that the symbol '⊃' occurs in just the same way in just the same wffs as in AS, it is not connected with any notion at all. Consequently the rules of FS must deal explicitly and only with the symbols as bare marks on paper. It should also be clear that there can be no question of the 'reasonableness' of the rules of FS – for that notion can enter only with some intended interpretation.

Now it may seem that a formal system is a trivial thing as compared with an axiomatic system, that it is merely a sort of game to be played with pencil and paper. And so it is. One can derive no startling truths as theorems of any formal system – at best one could obtain startling patterns of marks. Yet one must beware of taking 'It's only a game' so seriously as to obscure the importance of *these* games. Their importance derives from just those internal features which make them game-like: that their symbols are bare symbols, without 'meaning'; that in formulating their rules we must be entirely explicit and precise, making reference to nothing but the symbol-shapes themselves. And it derives also from an external feature which will have become evident to you by now. We may obtain an axiomatic system from a formal system, by giving the latter an interpretation; and, conversely, we may obtain a formal system from an axiomatic system by neglecting all interpretations, and, if necessary, rewriting it so that no covert interpretation persists. [E.g. it is clear that not only must the primitive objects be free of labels such as 'propositional variables', but also none of the rules can contain such terms, otherwise the interpretation will persist, although somewhat concealed.] We could state this relation between the two sorts of systems by saying that *a formal system exhibits the formal structure of some axiomatic system* (or, more strictly, of some class of axiomatic systems).

If a formal system, FS, is obtained by 'disinterpreting' an axiomatic system, AS, we shall call FS a *formalization* of AS – and, conversely, AS an *interpretation* of FS. From the considerations of the last paragraph it should be clear that formalization (as the process of producing a formalization) of an axiomatic system can be an important tool in the study of axiomatic systems. Formalization lays bare the structure, and, in particular, exposes areas of structural complexity and simplicity.

At this point, it is convenient to set out in full the *basis* (i.e. primitives, rules, etc.) of a rather simple formal system. This will serve to illustrate some points already made, as well as some to be made subsequently. In particular, consideration of this example should make clear:

(*a*) the general structure of a formal system
(*b*) the nature of interpretation and formalization
(*c*) the relation between a formal system and an axiomatic system.

In order to make it absolutely clear that this is a formal system, to be considered simply as a system of symbols, we shall call it the C-system.

The C-system

Primitive objects   *Class I*: p, q, r, . . .
              Class II: C

[To facilitate statement of rules, etc., we introduce into the meta-language[1] the term 'letter' to mean any object of Class I; we use the meta-linguistic name 'C' to denote the one object of Class II.]

RULES OF FORMATION

   F1. Any symbol-sequence consisting of a single letter is a wff.
   F2. If X and Y are wffs, then the symbol-sequence C X Y is a wff.

AXIOMS

   A1. CCpqCCqrCpr
   A2. CCCpqpp
   A3. CpCqp

---

[1] See Part I, Chapter 8. The meta-language here is a slightly enriched fragment of English; the object-language contains only the primitive objects of the C-system and sequences of those objects.

RULES OF TRANSFORMATION

R1. If X is a thesis containing distinct letters, $p_1, \ldots, p_n$, and $Y_1, \ldots,$ Y_n are (not necessarily distinct) wffs, then $X(Y_1/p_1, \ldots,$ $Y_n/p_n)$ is a thesis.

R2. If X and CXY are theses, then Y is a thesis.

It will be observed that we have used a number of familiar terms in the meta-language, such as 'wff', 'axiom', 'thesis' as well as the notational convention '$X(Y_1/p_1, \ldots, Y_n/p_n)$'. All these could have been replaced – e.g. the first three could have been replaced by 'string', 'initial preferred string' and 'preferred string'. They have been retained simply to save the reader from having to learn a battery of new meta-linguistic terms, and because they seem to have little or no tendency to impose an interpretation on the system; certainly much less than the phrase, 'Rule of Inference' which has been dropped in favour of 'Rule of Transformation'. This change has been made because 'inference' has its primary use in propositional contexts, and carries that flavour so strongly that to label R1 and R2 as Rules of Inference would suggest (or even entail) that the wffs of the C-system are propositional in nature. I.e. the meta-language would tend to impose an interpretation on the object-language: there would, so to speak, be a seepage of intuitive content from one to the other. Accordingly, we have avoided that term, and chosen 'Rule of Transformation' as being neutral in the desired way, and yet being a correctly suggestive label. For R1 and R2 are just that – rules for transforming one symbol-sequence (or pair of symbol-sequences) into another.

Let FS be any formal system. Then FS has some number, n, of Rules of Transformation, R1, ..., Rn. (In the case of the C-system, n = 2). In what follows we shall use 'Ri', 'Rj' and 'Rk' to refer to arbitrarily chosen members of the set R1, ..., Rn. If, in a formal system FS, a wff X is obtained from wffs $(Y_1, \ldots, Y_m)$, by use of some Rule of Transformation, Rk, we shall say that X is an *Rk-transform* of $(Y_1, \ldots, Y_m)$ in FS. It can be seen that obtaining X as an Rk-transform of $(Y_1, \ldots, Y_m)$ in FS is the formal analogue of deducing one proposition from others as premisses. Now suppose that, in some given system, X is an Rk-transform of Y_1 and Y_2, while Y_1 is an Rj-transform of Z_1 and Z_2, and Y_2 is an Ri-transform of Z_3 and Z_4. Then we could say that X is an *Ri, Rj, Rk-transform* of (Z_1, Z_2, Z_3, Z_4). Or if it is not necessary to specify the rules under which the transformations take place (beyond the general requirement that they are rules of the given system), we could just say that X is a transform of $(Z_1, \ldots, Z_4)$. We can now see what a proof in a formal system is. It is a guarantee neither of truth nor of validity. In fact, it is not a guarantee at all. It is merely a chain of transformations; to prove a wff is just to obtain it as a transform of the axioms. That is, the theses of a formal system are just the transforms of the axioms, together with the axioms themselves.[1]

All this can be illustrated in the C-system. Consider the wff CCCqprCpr. This is in fact a transform of the axioms, in particular an R1, R2-transform, in the following way:

$$CCpCqpCCCqprCpr \tag{1}$$

is an R1-transform of A1, for (1) = A1(Cqp/q). The required wff, CCCqprCpr, is an R2-transform of the two wffs, (1) and A3 – for (1) has the form CA3CCCqprCpr. Thus CCCqprCpr is a transform of the axioms. We could set out this proof of the wff more formally, thus:

A1(Cqp/q)	: CCpCqpCCCqprCpr	(1)
A3	: CpCqp	(2)
(1), (2) by R2	: CCCqprCpr	(3)

Here it is quite clear that no 'premisses' other than the axioms and no rules other than R1 and R2 are employed. Hence we see that (3) is a transform of the axioms. In the formal setting-out, each line of the proof is numbered on the right for reference purposes, while on the left appears the justification for each transformation – that is, we are told in each case what is being transformed by what rule to give the wff immediately to the right. It will be noted that in line (1) we do not explicitly mention R1, this being implicit in the convention '(Cqp/q)'.

Although the C-system is quite uninterpreted, so that there is nothing to be said about the *meanings* of the primitive objects or wffs, we can say something about the formal *status* of the objects in each class of the primitive objects. It will be observed that the rule, R1, provides for uniform substitution of wffs for letters, while there is no rule providing for substitution for any occurrence of C. It is just this fact that enables us to distinguish letters from C other than by their shapes. We may catch the distinction by saying that the letters are *formal variables*, while C is a *formal constant*. It must be

---

[1] We could of course regard the axioms as trivial transforms of themselves, and thus simplify the account of thesishood.

emphasized however that this is a purely structural distinction – it does not carry with it any suggestion that a letter is a variable in the ordinary sense of something which takes as values objects which lie outside the system (e.g. numbers, propositions, points in space). Similarly, C is not a constant in the sense of something which denotes a particular object (individual, class, relation, operation). [We may remark that variables and constants are often conceived as two species of name; that is, as *linguistic* entities. This account will not apply to formal variables and constants since the primitive objects of a formal system are not linguistic entities.]

To make absolutely certain that there is no confusion between the two sorts of variable, let us continue to call one sort *formal variables* and call the others *value-bearing variables*; and similarly for constants. (In other contexts, when we use 'variable' without qualification, we shall mean 'value-bearing variable', as we have up to this point.) Now if 'x' is a value-bearing variable, there is associated with it some set of objects such that 'x' indifferently denotes those objects (or takes those objects as values, or ranges over that set). We say that this set is the *range of variation*, or simply the *range*, of 'x'. (If we say that 'x' is a *numerical* variable, we are really saying that its range contains objects of a certain sort, viz. numbers.) The members of the range of 'x' are the *values* of 'x'. A value-bearing constant denotes just one object (using 'object' in a broad sense to include classes, relations, operations, etc.); and if we wish to assimilate value-bearing constants and variables to one another, we could say that a value-bearing constant is a value-bearing variable whose range contains exactly one member. If we wish to keep the distinction sharp, it is perhaps better to speak of the *denotation* rather than the range of a value-bearing constant.

It is clear that if 'x' is a formal variable, then if we supply it with a range, we shall thereby transform it into a value-bearing variable. And similarly, if it is a formal constant, giving it a denotation will transform it into a value-bearing constant. Further, if we thus transform all the primitive objects of a formal system into value-bearing signs, the result will be an *interpretation* of the formal system – i.e. an axiomatic system, in a rather wide sense of that term. The sense is wide in this way: the ranges and denotations assigned to the various classes of primitive objects may not 'go together', so that the wffs of the resulting axiomatic system do not 'make sense'. Thus an axiomatic system may not be an axiomatization of any field.

We shall call an interpretation under which the wffs do not 'make sense' an *incongruous interpretation*, and one in which the various assignments do 'go together' a *congruous interpretation*. A precise explanation of the notion of congruity lies outside the scope of this work, but a few informal remarks should make it sufficiently clear for our purposes.

A little reflection on the Formation Rules of the C-system shows that the formal constant, C, is a dyadic connective, in the sense that two wffs can be put together to make a single wff by writing one after the other and prefixing C to the resulting symbol-sequence. In particular, any two letters can be connected by a prefixed C in this way. It is then clear that in any interpretation of the C-system, C must be a dyadic operator of some sort. For the interpretation to be congruous, this operator must take as arguments the objects in the range of variation assigned to the letters. Further, since C can connect wffs which themselves begin with C (e.g. from 'Cpq' and 'Cqr' we obtain 'CCpqCqr'), every wff must, in some way, take as values objects in the range assigned to the letters if the interpretation is to be congruous.

The simplest way of ensuring congruity in this case is to:

(1) specify some range of values, M, for the letters
(2) interpret C in such a way that for any particular assignment of values, v_i and v_j in M, to any two letters, 'p' and 'q', the wff 'Cpq' has a definite value in M.

We can then be certain that the resulting interpretation of the C-system is an axiomatization of some field or another. Roughly speaking, the field will be determined by the choice of the range, M, while the amount of the field axiomatized will depend on the interpretation of C.

If, for example, we assign as range for the letters the set of propositions – i.e. interpret the letters as propositional variables – and interpret C as some dyadic proposition-forming operator taking propositions as arguments, the resulting interpretation is an axiomatization of the logic of propositions. If C is interpreted as some truth-functional operator, then the axiomatic system is an axiomatization of part of PC. The standard interpretation of the C-system is, in fact, that in which the letters are interpreted as propositional variables and C as material implication (i.e. 'Cpq' is read as 'p materially implies q'). The axiomatic system thus obtained is an axiomatization of that part of PC which has material implication as the only operator.[1] Now in view of the truth-functional character of material implication, the only aspect of the propositions in the range, M, which concerns us is their truth-values. So we could simplify the business of interpretation by letting M have only two members – i.e. putting

$$M = \{True, False\}$$

or, for short

$$M = \{1, 0\}$$

We can then give the interpretation of C in the form of a truth-table:

p	q	Cpq
1	1	1
1	0	0
0	1	1
0	0	1

It should be noticed however that the standard interpretation is not the only congruous one. To take just one example:

Consider $M = \{0, 1\}$, where 0 and 1 are natural numbers. Then interpret C as natural number subtraction, in which $0 - 1 = 0$, as in the following table:

$$C11 = C01 = C00 = 0$$
$$C10 = 1$$

The resulting axiomatic system is an algebraic one – we may note in passing that in the field axiomatized, the analogue of a valid wff is a 'polynomial' which is identically zero.

Each of the axiomatic systems produced by interpreting the C-system has the same formal structure – viz. the C-system itself. Thus it can be seen that in moving to the study of a formalization of an axiomatic system, we reach a new level of abstractness, and, by consequence, of structural clarity. What we lose sight of are the distinctively propositional or arithmetical or geometrical or biological features of the axiomatic system. Yet in a sense we do not lose sight of these features at all – we see them more clearly by seeing just how they fit on to and clothe the underlying structure. It is for this reason that, in the sequel, although we always have an intended interpretation before us, we shall set out each axiomatization of PC with a degree of completeness and precision which would be appropriate to a fully formal system.

[1] This system is complete in the sense that every valid purely implicational wff is a thesis. The axioms used here (and written in the Polish notation – see Appendix 2) were devised by A. Tarski and P. Bernays (1930).

CHAPTER 15

The System PM (I)

In 1910, in the first volume of *Principia Mathematica*, Whitehead and Russell presented an axiomatization of PC, with disjunction and negation as primitive operators. It is this axiomatic system, to which we give the name 'PM', which will engage our attention for the next few chapters. It is worth remarking that in *Principia Mathematica* the system appears only as the first stage of a much larger design, and that it is isolated here as being the classical systematization of PC.[1]

Although '$\sim$' and '$\vee$' are the only primitive operators in PM, '$\supset$' is introduced by definition and used in stating the axioms. This use of a defined operator in the axioms is purely a matter of convenience; each axiom could be set out in terms of '$\sim$' and '$\vee$' only, and the definition of '$\supset$' used to obtain as theorems the five wffs listed below as axioms. The convenience comes from the fact that under the intended propositional interpretation it is easier to see the sense of a wff written as an implication. Thus it is somewhat easier to see the sense of

$$(p \vee p) \supset p$$

than $\qquad \sim(p \vee p) \vee p$

and it is certainly easier to understand

$$(q \supset r) \supset ((p \vee q) \supset (p \vee r))$$

than $\qquad \sim(\sim q \vee r) \vee (\sim(p \vee q) \vee (p \vee r))$

We set out the basis for PM in full, indicating the intended interpretation in listing the primitive symbols.

The System PM

Primitive Symbols

         1. p, q, r, . . . [Propositional variables]

[1] Note that some authors use 'PM' to refer to the whole system of *Principia Mathematica*, and not just to the PC fragment of it as we do here.

2. $\sim$ [Monadic operator, negation]
3. v   [Dyadic operator, disjunction]
4. (,)   [Brackets]

Formation Rules

F1. A propositional variable standing alone is a wff.
F2. If X is a wff then $\sim$X is a wff.
F3. If X and Y are wffs, then (XvY) is a wff.

Axioms

A1. $((pvp) \supset p)$
A2. $(q \supset (pvq))$
A3. $((pvq) \supset (qvp))$
A4. $((p v (qvr)) \supset (q v (pvr)))$
A5. $((q \supset r) \supset ((pvq) \supset (pvr)))$

Transformation Rules

R1. [*Substitution*] If X is a thesis containing propositional variables, $p_1, \ldots, p_n$, and $Y_1, \ldots, Y_n$ are (not necessarily distinct) wffs, then $X(Y_1/p_1, \ldots, Y_n/p_n)$ is a thesis.

R2. [*Detachment*] If X and $(X \supset Y)$ are theses, then Y is a thesis.

Definitions

1. $[\supset]$ $(X \supset Y) =_{Df} (\sim X v Y)$
2. $[\cdot]$ $(X \cdot Y) =_{Df} \sim(\sim X v \sim Y)$
3. $[\equiv]$ $(X \equiv Y) =_{Df} ((X \supset Y) \cdot (Y \supset X))$

In order to avoid unnecessary bracketing we adopt at once with respect to PM the conventions used hitherto, allowing us to drop outside brackets and introduce or drop those pairs of which the left-hand member lies between negations with the same scope. Thus we shall henceforth write A1 as

$$(pvp) \supset p$$

instead of $((pvp) \supset p)$

and similarly for the other axioms.

Now at this point one might raise a theoretical question about the definitions. For how is one to use them? Do we not need a further Transformation Rule licensing us to rewrite wffs according to the definitions, since neither R1 nor R2 makes any provision for this? In fact, in some textbooks you will find a third Transformation Rule doing just this job. But the view taken here is that such a rule is unnecessary because the meta-linguistic sign '$=_{Df}$' means simply 'is a notational variant of' (or 'is shorthand for'). That is, definitional rewriting is *just* rewriting – it is purely a notational change. (However, in framing definitions we do not proceed arbitrarily. We take care that the definiens and definiendum are truth-functionally equivalent, since we want every thesis of the axiomatic system to be a valid propositional schema.) Thus to frame a special Transformation Rule is to suggest that when we obtain 'p⊃q' by definitionally rewriting '∼pvq' we are getting a new wff as conclusion of an inference; and this obscures the fact that 'p⊃q' *is just another way of writing* '∼pvq'. If we must associate definitional change with a rule, then the best course seems to be to regard the definition itself as a Transformation Rule – but a *pure* rule of symbolic transformation, in a way that R1 and R2 are not, since under the intended interpretation R1 and R2 are rules of *inference*, while the definitions do not have their character changed in this way by interpretation.

We are now in a position to begin the construction of proofs of theorems in PM. You are urged to work through these proofs carefully, making sure that you see just what is being done at each step, and why it is a sensible move to make, given that the aim is to reach the theorem in question. By this careful cultivation of hindsight you will develop foresight which you can employ in the exercises at the end of the chapter, thus gaining greater and greater facility in following and constructing proofs in the system.

It should be clear from considerations brought forward in earlier chapters that, although the axioms are the ultimate premisses in every proof, it is both sound in theory and convenient in practice to use as a premiss any established thesis, whether it be an axiom or a previously proved theorem. Theorems will be numbered T1, T2, . . . , and referred to as such. In addition, some frequently used theorems will be given names. In each case the name is suggestive of the sense of the theorem, or is that of some logician who is specially associated with it. (An example of the latter has already been met in *De Morgan's Laws*.)

As foreshadowed in the last chapter, each line of a proof will contain three items, viz.: in the centre, *a wff*; on the left, the *justification* for writing that wff at this point in the proof; and on the right, a *reference-number* for the wff. The justification in each case takes the form of reference to the axioms, theorems or earlier lines in the proof, followed by an indication of the operation on them which produces the wff. We adopt certain conventions in writing the justifications, and these should be clear from the following examples. (The examples are not supposed to be connected; each one is simply an example of a line in a proof.)

EXAMPLE 1.   A3 : (p∨q) ⊃ (q∨p)   (4)

The justification for putting down this wff as line (4) of the (supposed) proof is that it is Axiom 3. No operation has been performed on it, so 'A3' is sufficient justification. The case is entirely similar in:

EXAMPLE 2.   T1 : (p ⊃ (q⊃r)) ⊃ (q ⊃ (p⊃r))   (1)

EXAMPLE 3.   A2(∼p/p, ∼p/q) :   ∼p ⊃ (∼p∨∼p)   (5)

Here line (5) is obtained by substitutions in A2, under the rule R1, but by the convention adopted on p. 97, no explicit mention of R1 is required.

EXAMPLE 4.   (1), A1 × D : (p ⊃ (p∨p)) ⊃ (p⊃p)   (2)

Here line (2) is obtained by an operation of *detachment*, under R2, on line (1) of the proof and A1, and this is indicated by '(1), A1 × D'.

EXAMPLE 5.   (1) × Def ⊃ : q ⊃ (p⊃q)   (2)

Line (2) is obtained by rewriting line (1) according to the definition of '⊃'.

Proofs of theorems

T1.   (p ⊃ (q⊃r)) ⊃ (q ⊃ (p⊃r))   [Perm]

PROOF:

A4	:	(p ∨ (q∨r)) ⊃ (q ∨ (p∨r))	(1)
(1)(∼p/p,∼q/q)	:	(∼p ∨ (∼q∨r)) ⊃ (∼q ∨ (∼p∨r))	(2)
(2) × Def ⊃	:	(p ⊃ (q⊃r)) ⊃ (q ⊃ (p⊃r))	(3)

We call T1 the Law of Permutation,[1] or *Perm* for short. Perm is an extremely useful thesis, allowing us to change the order of terms in any implication associated to the right. It thus plays the part of a rather restricted associative law for '⊃'. [Notice that an implication

---

[1] Some authors call T1 the Law of Commutation.

associated to the left – e.g. '(p⊃q) ⊃ r' – cannot be reordered in an analogous way, since the requisite wff,

$$((p⊃q) ⊃ r) ⊃ ((p⊃r) ⊃ q)$$

is neither valid nor a thesis of PM.]

The use of Perm will be explained after proving:

T2.   (q⊃r) ⊃ ((p⊃q) ⊃ (p⊃r))   [Syll]

PROOF:

A5	: (q⊃r) ⊃ ((pvq) ⊃ (pvr))	(1)
(1)(∼p/p)	: (q⊃r) ⊃ ((∼pvq) ⊃ (∼pvr))	(2)
(2) × Def ⊃	: (q⊃r) ⊃ ((p⊃q) ⊃ (p⊃r))	(3)

Now T2 is an implication associated to the right – i.e. it has the form X ⊃ (Y ⊃ Z) – and by using Perm we can obtain from it a new theorem with the form Y ⊃ (X ⊃ Z). There are two quite equivalent ways in which we might do this:

(a) We can make substitutions in Perm, so that the antecedent of the resulting wff is T2, and then use R2 to detach the consequent.

(b) we could make use of Perm to prove a new Transformation Rule in PM, to the effect that whenever a wff of the form

$$X ⊃ (Y ⊃ Z)$$

is a thesis, so is the wff of the form

$$Y ⊃ (X ⊃ Z),$$

and then use this Derived Transformation Rule to obtain the new theorem from T2.

That these two procedures are equivalent will be seen quite clearly from the following proof of the Derived Rule of Permutation.

DR1.   If X ⊃ (Y ⊃ Z) is a thesis, so is Y ⊃ (X ⊃ Z).

PROOF:

Let X, Y and Z be any wffs, such that X ⊃ (Y ⊃ Z) is a thesis.

Perm(X/p,Y/q,Z/r)	: (X ⊃ (Y ⊃ Z)) ⊃ (Y ⊃ (X ⊃ Z))	(1)
By hypothesis	: X ⊃ (Y ⊃ Z)	(2)
(1), (2) × D	: Y ⊃ (X ⊃ Z)	(3)

Thus we have shown that whenever X ⊃ (Y ⊃ Z) is a thesis, so is Y ⊃ (X ⊃ Z).

We can now very easily obtain:

T3. $(p \supset q) \supset ((q \supset r) \supset (p \supset r))$ [Syll]

PROOF:

T2 × DR1 : $(p \supset q) \supset ((q \supset r) \supset (p \supset r))$

However, we could have proceeded in the other way, thus:

T1($q \supset r/p$, $p \supset q/q$, $p \supset r/r$):

$$((q \supset r) \supset ((p \supset q) \supset (p \supset r))) \supset ((p \supset q) \supset ((q \supset r) \supset (p \supset r))) \qquad (1)$$

T2   : $(q \supset r) \supset ((p \supset q) \supset (p \supset r))$ (2)

(1),(2) × D   : $(p \supset q) \supset ((q \supset r) \supset (p \supset r))$ (3)

These moves are precisely those incapsulated in a generalized form in the proof of DR1.

Now it should be clear that, given any thesis, T, whose main operator is '$\supset$', we can obtain a derived rule to the effect that to any thesis of the form of the antecedent of T there corresponds a thesis with the form of the consequent of T; and equally that any results obtainable by use of such a rule can be obtained directly by substitution in T together with detachment. Accordingly, we shall not, in general, prove such Derived Rules, but simply use the form '$\times T_j$' to indicate that the step is taken by use of the Derived Rule corresponding to the thesis T_j. In addition, we shall abbreviate proofs by simply giving the number of the theorem proved in the last line. Thus we could write the proof of T3:

$$\text{T2} \times \text{Perm} \quad : \quad \text{T3}$$

The theses T2 and T3 bear an obvious relation to the Pure Hypothetical Syllogism, and consequently each of them is known as the Law of Syllogism, or simply *Syll*. From either we can easily obtain the Derived Rule, DR2, that if X $\supset$ Y and Y $\supset$ Z are theses, so is X $\supset$ Z. The proof proceeds exactly as that of DR1, except that two successive detachments[1] are used.

T4. $p \supset (q \supset p)$ [Simp]

PROOF:

A2   : $q \supset (p \vee q)$ (1)

(1)($\sim q/p$, p/q) : $p \supset (\sim q \vee p)$ (2)

(2) × Def $\supset$:   T4

---

[1] A convenient name for this operation is 'double detachment'.

T4 is known as the Law of Simplification, or *Simp* for short. That the name is apt may be seen more clearly by considering the closely related thesis (to be obtained later), '(p.q) ⊃ p'.

T5. p ⊃ (pvp)

PROOF:

| A2 | : | q ⊃ (pvq) | (1) |
| (1)(p/q) | : | T5 | |

T6. p ⊃ p   [Id]

PROOF:

T5	:	p ⊃ (pvp)	(1)
A1	:	(pvp) ⊃ p	(2)
(1),(2) × Syll	:	T6	

T6 is the Law of Identity, or *Id* for short.

T7. ∼p ∨ p

PROOF:

| T6 | : | p⊃p | (1) |
| (1) × Def ⊃ | : | T7 | |

T8. p ∨ ∼p

PROOF:

A3	:	(pvq) ⊃ (qvp)	(1)
(1)(∼p/p,p/q)	:	(∼pvp) ⊃ (pv∼p)	(2)
T7	:	∼pvp	(3)
(2),(3) × D	:	T8	

T7 and T8 will be recognized as two forms of the familiar Law of Excluded Middle.

Two other familiar implications are 'p⊃∼∼p' and '∼∼p⊃p' which together constitute the Law of Double Negation. Let us use these as cases in reflecting a little on the strategy of proof. When constructing a proof of some theorem, you will find it worth while to keep the definitions in the corner of the mind's eye, so to speak – that is, you will find it profitable to acquire the habit of seeing implications as disjunctions with one argument negated, equivalences as pairs of implications, and conjunctions as fully negated disjunctions. More central, perhaps, is to remember what the axioms (and previously proved theorems too) enable one to do – in other words, it is worth while seeing the axioms as embodying certain operations. Thus, for example, A3 enables you to change the order of the arguments of a disjunction, while A4 enables you to make a more extensive change of order and of grouping as well. Suppose we want to prove

$$p\supset\sim\sim p$$

By the definition of ' $\supset$ ' this is another way of writing

$$\sim pv\sim\sim p$$

But this is just a variant of T8 – in fact it can be obtained from T8 by putting ' $\sim p$ ' for 'p'. At this point all the work of the proof is done, and all that remains is to write it out in our standard form.

T9. $p \supset \sim\sim p$

PROOF:

T8	:	$pv\sim p$	(1)
$(1)(\sim p/p)$	:	$\sim pv\sim\sim p$	(2)
$(2) \times \text{Def} \supset$	:	T9	

Let us try the same technique on ' $\sim\sim p\supset p$ '. By the definition of ' $\supset$ ' this becomes.

$$\sim\sim\sim pvp$$

A glance over the axioms and T1–T9 is enough to show that we cannot obtain this directly by substitution. However, A3 could be used to get it, *if* we could obtain

$$pv\sim\sim\sim p$$

(That is the sort of point worth noting and remembering.) Once again, we cannot get 'pv$\sim\sim\sim$p' by substitution alone. Can we find some thesis such that substitutions in it will yield a wff of the form

$$X \supset (pv\sim\sim\sim p)$$

where X is a thesis? (We could then use R2.) Again the answer is 'No'. This is the place to introduce a further strategic rule of thumb – *When in doubt, try Syll* (or the closely related A5). Syll and A5 have the general shape

$$X \supset (Y \supset Z)$$

and so will any wff resulting from them by substitution. In applying the rule of thumb we look for substitutions in Syll which will give us the desired wff as Z (or in some cases as Y ⊃ Z), and such that each of X and Y (or just X) is a thesis. The desired wff here is

$$pv{\sim}{\sim}{\sim}p$$

and A5 is $\qquad$ (q⊃r) ⊃ ((pvq) ⊃ (pvr))

Now A5(${\sim}{\sim}{\sim}p/r$) is $\quad$ (q⊃${\sim}{\sim}{\sim}p$) ⊃ ((pvq) ⊃ (pv${\sim}{\sim}{\sim}p$))
in which 'pv${\sim}{\sim}{\sim}p$' is in the right place, but neither 'q⊃${\sim}{\sim}{\sim}p$' nor 'pvq' is a thesis. But suppose we also put ${\sim}p/q$ in A5. Then we have '(${\sim}p⊃{\sim}{\sim}{\sim}p$) ⊃ ((pv${\sim}p$) ⊃ (pv${\sim}{\sim}{\sim}p$))' which looks more hopeful, since 'pv${\sim}p$' is T8. What about '${\sim}p⊃{\sim}{\sim}{\sim}p$'? This is easily obtained from T9 by making the substitution ${\sim}p/p$. So now we know how to prove 'pv${\sim}{\sim}{\sim}p$', and, as noted earlier, given this we can obtain the desired '${\sim}{\sim}{\sim}pvp$' by use of A3. Writing it out formally we get:

T10. $\quad {\sim}{\sim}p⊃p$

PROOF:

A5	: (q⊃r) ⊃ ((pvq) ⊃ (pvr))	(1)
(1)(${\sim}p/q,{\sim}{\sim}{\sim}p/r$) :		
	(${\sim}p⊃{\sim}{\sim}{\sim}p$) ⊃ ((pv${\sim}p$) ⊃ (pv${\sim}{\sim}{\sim}p$))	(2)
T9	: p⊃${\sim}{\sim}p$	(3)
(3)(${\sim}p/p$)	: ${\sim}p ⊃ {\sim}{\sim}{\sim}p$	(4)
(2),(4) × D	: (pv${\sim}p$) ⊃ (pv${\sim}{\sim}{\sim}p$)	(5)
T8	: pv${\sim}p$	(6)
(5),(6) × D	: pv${\sim}{\sim}{\sim}p$	(7)
A3	: (pvq) ⊃ (qvp)	(8)
(8)(${\sim}{\sim}{\sim}p/q$)	: (pv${\sim}{\sim}{\sim}p$) ⊃ (${\sim}{\sim}{\sim}pvp$)	(9)
(7),(9) × D	: ${\sim}{\sim}{\sim}pvp$	(10)
(10) × Def ⊃	: T10	

At this point it is convenient to introduce a further convention which will abbreviate proofs considerably. So far, whenever a premiss, whether an axiom or a theorem, has been introduced in a proof, we have written it out in full. Thus, in the proof of T10, we have:

T9	: p⊃${\sim}{\sim}p$	(3)
(3)(${\sim}p/p$)	: ${\sim}p⊃{\sim}{\sim}{\sim}p$	(4)

In future we shall generally run two lines of this sort together, thus:

T9(${\sim}p/p$)	: ${\sim}p⊃{\sim}{\sim}{\sim}p$	(3)

We shall always do this when the premiss is an axiom, and generally when it is a theorem. However, if the theorem is rarely used and has been proved some time earlier, we shall write the steps in the longer form.

T11. $(p \supset q) \supset (\sim q \supset \sim p)$ [Transp]

PROOF:

Syll[T2]($\sim\sim q/r$)	: $(q \supset \sim\sim q) \supset ((p \supset q) \supset (p \supset \sim\sim q))$	(1)
T9(q/p)	: $q \supset \sim\sim q$	(2)
(1),(2) × D	: $(p \supset q) \supset (p \supset \sim\sim q)$	(3)
A3($\sim p/p, \sim\sim q/q$)	: $(\sim p v \sim\sim q) \supset (\sim\sim q v \sim p)$	(4)
(4) × Def ⊃	: $(p \supset \sim\sim q) \supset (\sim q \supset \sim p)$	(5)
(3),(5) × Syll	: T11	

T11 is known as the Law of Transposition,[1] or *Transp* for short, as is its converse, which we shall obtain as T12. Both are extremely useful in proving other theorems. Before setting out the proof of T12, a few further remarks on strategy are in order. We want to prove

$$(\sim q \supset \sim p) \supset (p \supset q)$$

Now it is quite plain that T11 ($\sim q/p$, $\sim p/q$) will give us a thesis with the correct antecedent, viz.

$$(\sim q \supset \sim p) \supset (\sim\sim p \supset \sim\sim q) \tag{1}$$

and intuition tells us that the consequent of this thesis is equivalent to the consequent of T12. So we ought to be able to prove

$$(\sim\sim p \supset \sim\sim q) \supset (p \supset q) \tag{2}$$

Then we could use Syll to get T12 from (1) and (2). Using this strategy we get the following proof.

T12. $(\sim q \supset \sim p) \supset (p \supset q)$ [Transp]

PROOF:

T11($\sim q/p, \sim p/q$)	: $(\sim q \supset \sim p) \supset (\sim\sim p \supset \sim\sim q)$	(1)
Syll[T3]($\sim\sim p/q, \sim\sim q/r$)	:	
	$(p \supset \sim\sim p) \supset ((\sim\sim p \supset \sim\sim q) \supset (p \supset \sim\sim q))$	(2)
(2),T9 × D	: $(\sim\sim p \supset \sim\sim q) \supset (p \supset \sim\sim q)$	(3)
Syll[T2]($\sim\sim q/q, q/r$)	:	
	$(\sim\sim q \supset q) \supset ((p \supset \sim\sim q) \supset (p \supset q))$	(4)

---

[1] It is sometimes called the Law of Contraposition.

T10(q/p)	:	$\sim\sim q \supset q$	(5)
(4),(5) × D	:	$(p \supset \sim\sim q) \supset (p \supset q)$	(6)
(3),(6) × Syll	:	$(\sim\sim p \supset \sim\sim q) \supset (p \supset q)$	(7)
(1),(7) × Syll	:	T12	

In each of the last two proofs occur lines like line (7) of T12, in which the justification reads '(3),(6) × Syll'. This sort of thing will occur frequently, so let us make sure that it is quite clear what is going on here. In this case, it means that if we carry out the operation

$$\text{Syll[T3]}(\sim\sim p \supset \sim\sim q/p,\ p \supset \sim\sim q/q,\ p \supset q/r)$$

we get the thesis

$$((\sim\sim p \supset \sim\sim q) \supset (p \supset \sim\sim q)) \supset (((p \supset \sim\sim q) \supset (p \supset q)) \supset$$
$$((\sim\sim p \supset \sim\sim q) \supset (p \supset q)))$$

which is of course,

$$(3) \supset ((6) \supset (7)) \quad \text{[call this (X)]}$$

Then (X),(3) × D yields

$$(6) \supset (7) \quad \text{[call this (Y)]}$$

and (Y),(6) × D yields

$$(7)$$

All this is expressed very concisely in the formula

(3),(6) × Syll	:	$(\sim\sim p \supset \sim\sim q) \supset (p \supset q)$	(7)

which may be read, for working purposes, as: If (3) and (6) are the premisses of a Pure Hypothetical Syllogism, then (7) is the conclusion.

T13. $(q \supset r) \supset ((q v p) \supset (r v p))$

[This theorem differs from A5 only in having the order of the arguments in the disjunction reversed. We should therefore expect that A3 – as well as A5 itself – would be used in the proof.]

PROOF:

Syll[T3](qvp/p, pvq/q, pvr/r):

$((q v p) \supset (p v q)) \supset (((p v q) \supset (p v r)) \supset ((q v p) \supset (p v r)))$		(1)
A3(p/q,q/p) : $(q v p) \supset (p v q)$		(2)
(1),(2) × D : $((p v q) \supset (p v r)) \supset ((q v p) \supset (p v r))$		(3)

Syll[T2](qvp/p, pvr/q, rvp/r):

$((p v r) \supset (r v p)) \supset (((q v p) \supset (p v r)) \supset ((q v p) \supset (r v p)))$		(4)
A3(r/q) : $(p v r) \supset (r v p)$		(5)

(4),(5) × D   :   ((qvp) ⊃ (pvr)) ⊃ ((qvp) ⊃ (rvp))   (6)

(3),(6) × Syll :   ((pvq) ⊃ (pvr)) ⊃ ((qvp) ⊃(rvp))   (7)

A5,(7) × Syll   :   T13

T14.   (p v (qvr)) ⊃ ((pvq) v r)   [Assoc]

PROOF:

A3(q/p,r/q)   :   (qvr) ⊃ (rvq)   (1)

A5(qvr/q, rvq/r)   :   ((qvr) ⊃ (rvq)) ⊃

                         ((p v (qvr)) ⊃ (p v (rvq)))   (2)

(1),(2) × D   :   (p v (qvr)) ⊃ (p v (rvq))   (3)

A4(r/q,q/r)   :   (p v (rvq)) ⊃ (r v (pvq))   (4)

(3),(4) × Syll   :   (p v (qvr)) ⊃ (r v (pvq))   (5)

A3(r/p, pvq/q)   :   (r v (pvq)) ⊃ ((pvq) v r)   (6)

(5),(6) × Syll   :   T14

T14 is clearly a companion-piece to A4, and is one of a group of Associative Laws (*Assoc* for short). The proof exemplifies the strategy used in proving such theses, and consequently the proofs of the next three theorems are given only in sketch form.

T15.   ((pvq) v r) ⊃ (p v (rvq))

PROOF:

A3(pvq/p, r/q), A4(r/p,p/q,q/r) × Syll   :   T15

T16.   (p v (qvr)) ⊃ (p v (rvq))

PROOF:

A3(q/p,r/q), A5(qvr/q, rvq/r) × D   :   T16

T17.   ((pvq) v r) ⊃ (p v (qvr))

PROOF:

T16(r/q,q/r), T15 × Syll   :   T17

Given Id, i.e. T6, as a thesis, we can easily obtain the thesis

(p⊃q) ⊃ (p⊃q)

and thence the theses

(p⊃q) ⊃ (~pvq)

and   (~pvq) ⊃ (p⊃q)

by use of the definition of '⊃'. A closely related (and certainly valid) pair of wffs is

(pvq) ⊃ (~p⊃q)

and   (~p⊃q) ⊃ (pvq)

T18.   (pvq) ⊃ (∼p⊃q)

PROOF:

T13(q/p,p/q,∼∼p/r)	:	(p⊃∼∼p) ⊃ ((pvq) ⊃ (∼∼pvq))	(1)
(1),T9 × D	:	(pvq) ⊃ (∼∼pvq)	(2)
(2) × Def ⊃	:	T18	

T19.   (∼p⊃q) ⊃ (pvq)

PROOF:

[The proof is entirely similar to that of T18, so we give only the following sketch.]

T13(q/p,∼∼p/q,p/r), T10 × D × Def ⊃ : T19

T20.   (p ⊃ (q⊃r)) ⊃ ((p∙q) ⊃ r)   [Imp]

PROOF:

Id (p⊃(q⊃r)/p)	:	(p ⊃ (q⊃r)) ⊃ (p ⊃ (q⊃r))	(1)
(1) × Def ⊃	:	(p ⊃ (q⊃r)) ⊃ (∼p v (∼qvr))	(2)
T14(∼p/p,∼q/q)	:	(∼p v (∼qvr)) ⊃ ((∼pv∼q) v r)	(3)
(2),(3) × Syll	:	(p ⊃ (q⊃r)) ⊃ ((∼pv∼q) v r)	(4)
T18(∼pv∼q/p, r/q)	:	((∼pv∼q) v r) ⊃ (∼(∼pv∼q) ⊃ r)	(5)
(4),(5) × Syll	:	(p ⊃ (q⊃r)) ⊃ (∼(∼pv∼q) ⊃ r)	(6)
(6) × Def ∙	:	T20	

T20 is known as the Law of Importation (or *Imp* for short), since its effect is to 'import' the antecedent of the consequent into the antecedent of the whole wff. If the proof of Imp is examined, it will be seen that it proceeds by successive transformations of the consequent of line (1), Syll being used to connect each transformation of the consequent to the antecedent. In future, proofs of this sort will be written more briefly, with explicit reference to Syll omitted. The following rewritten proof of Imp will serve to illustrate this abbreviation.

Id(p⊃(q⊃r)/p)	:	(p ⊃ (q⊃r)) ⊃ (p ⊃ (q⊃r))	(1)
(1) × Def ⊃	:	⊃ (∼p v (∼qvr))	(2)
(2) × Assoc	:	⊃ ((∼pv∼q) v r)	(3)
(3) × T18	:	⊃ (∼(∼pv∼q) ⊃ r)	(4)
(4) × Def ∙	: T20		

T21. $(p \cdot q) \supset p$

PROOF:

Simp[T4] × Imp   :   T21

T22. $(p \cdot q) \supset q$

PROOF:

Simp × Perm	:	$q \supset (p \supset p)$	(1)
(1)(p/q,q/p)	:	$p \supset (q \supset q)$	(2)
(2) × Imp	:	T22	

T21 and T22 are really alternative forms of Simp. But they are used in a slightly different way. If X is some given thesis, and Y is any wff, Simp enables us to obtain the thesis, $Y \supset X$. [Simp(X/p,Y/q), $X \times D : Y \supset X$] On the other hand, if we have a thesis, $X \supset W$, and Y is any wff, T21 enables us to obtain $(X \cdot Y) \supset W$.
[T21(X/p,Y/q), $X \supset W$ × Syll   : $(X \cdot Y) \supset W$]
Similarly, T22 enables us to obtain $(Y \cdot X) \supset W$. In addition, of course, T21 and T22 enable us to obtain as a thesis either conjunct of a given conjunctive thesis.

T23. $p \supset (q \supset (p \cdot q))$ [Adj]

PROOF:

T8	:	$p \vee \sim p$	(1)
(1)($\sim p \vee \sim q/p$)	:	$(\sim p \vee \sim q) \vee \sim(\sim p \vee \sim q)$	(2)
(2) × Assoc	:	$\sim p \vee (\sim q \vee \sim(\sim p \vee \sim q))$	(3)
(3) × Def .	:	$\sim p \vee (\sim q \vee (p \cdot q))$	(4)
(4) × Def $\supset$	:	T23	

T23 is the Law of Adjunction (*Adj* for short), and gives rise to the Derived Rule of Adjunction, to the effect that if X and Y are theses, X.Y is also a thesis. This law is especially useful in proving equivalences, as it provides the necessary link between the proofs of an implication and its converse and the use of the definition of '$\equiv$'. Thus, given the theses T9 and T10, viz. '$p \supset \sim \sim p$' and '$\sim \sim p \supset p$', we can use Adj to obtain

$$(p \supset \sim \sim p) \cdot (\sim \sim p \supset p)$$

and thence $p \equiv \sim \sim p$

by the definition of '$\equiv$'.

T24. $(p \supset q) \supset ((p \lor q) \supset q)$

PROOF:

$T13(q/p, p/q, q/r)$: $(p \supset q) \supset ((p \lor q) \supset (q \lor q))$ (1)

$Syll[T2](p \lor q/p, q \lor q/q, q/r)$:

      $((q \lor q) \supset q) \supset (((p \lor q) \supset (q \lor q)) \supset ((p \lor q) \supset q))$ (2)

$(2), A1(q/p) \times D$: $((p \lor q) \supset (q \lor q)) \supset ((p \lor q) \supset q)$ (3)

$(1),(3) \times Syll$: T24

T25. $(p \supset (q \supset r)) \supset ((p \supset q) \supset (p \supset r))$

PROOF:

$T13(r/p, p \lor q/q, q/r)$: $((p \lor q) \supset q) \supset (((p \lor q) \lor r) \supset (q \lor r))$ (1)

$T24, (1) \times Syll$: $(p \supset q) \supset (((p \lor q) \lor r) \supset (q \lor r))$ (2)

$(2)(\sim q/p, \sim p/q)$: $(\sim q \supset \sim p) \supset (((\sim q \lor \sim p) \lor r) \supset (\sim p \lor r))$ (3)

$(3), Transp \times Syll$: $(p \supset q) \supset (((\sim q \lor \sim p) \lor r) \supset (\sim p \lor r))$ (4)

$(4) \times Perm$: $((\sim q \lor \sim p) \lor r) \supset ((p \supset q) \supset (\sim p \lor r))$ (5)

$(5), Assoc \times Syll$: $(\sim q \lor (\sim p \lor r)) \supset ((p \supset q) \supset (\sim p \lor r))$ (6)

$(6) \times Def \supset$: $(q \supset (p \supset r)) \supset ((p \supset q) \supset (p \supset r))$ (7)

$(7), Perm \times Syll$: T25

T26. $(p \supset q) \supset ((p \supset r) \supset (p \supset (q \cdot r)))$ [Comp].

PROOF:

$Adj(q/p, r/q)$: $q \supset (r \supset (q \cdot r))$ (1)

$Syll[T2](r \supset (q \cdot r)/r)$:

      $(q \supset (r \supset (q \cdot r))) \supset ((p \supset q) \supset (p \supset (r \supset (q \cdot r))))$ (2)

$(2),(1) \times D$: $(p \supset q) \supset (p \supset (r \supset (q \cdot r)))$ (3)

$T25(r/q, q \cdot r/r)$: $(p \supset (r \supset (q \cdot r))) \supset ((p \supset r) \supset (p \supset (q \cdot r)))$ (4)

$(3),(4) \times Syll$: T26

This thesis is the Law of Composition, or *Comp* for short. It is worth noting that this name is also given in some works to its 'imported' form – i.e. to

$Comp \times Imp$: $((p \supset q) \cdot (p \supset r)) \supset (p \supset (q \cdot r))$

just as the name 'Syll' is also given to the imported form:

$Syll \times Imp$: $((p \supset q) \cdot (q \supset r)) \supset (p \supset r)$.

EXERCISES 15

Prove the following in PM. (You may, of course, use as premisses any thesis already obtained.)

15.1 $(p \supset \sim p) \supset \sim p$

15.2 $(p \supset \sim q) \supset (q \supset \sim p)$

15.3 $(q \supset \sim p) \supset (p \supset \sim q)$

15.4 $p \supset (p \lor q)$

15.5 $\sim p \supset (p \supset q)$

15.6 $p \supset (\sim p \supset q)$

15.7 $(\sim p \supset p) \supset p$

15.8 $\sim (p \lor q) \supset \sim p$

15.9 $\sim (p \lor q) \supset \sim q$

15.10 $\sim (p \lor q) \supset (\sim p \lor \sim q)$

15.11 $\sim (p \supset q) \supset (\sim p \supset \sim q)$

15.12 $\sim (p.q) \supset (\sim p \lor \sim q)$

CHAPTER 16

PM II - *Substitution of Equivalents*

You are already familiar with the fact that Substitution of Equivalents is a validity-preserving operation. That is to say, if we replace a well-formed part of some valid wff by a wff equivalent to the part, the resulting wff is also valid. You will recall that this replacement need not be carried out uniformly: that is, if a wff X occurs more than once as a part of a wff Y, we may replace any of the occurrences of X by some equivalent wff without replacing the others.

Since the operation is validity-preserving, we can frame the corresponding rule of inference:

Rule for substitution of equivalents

If X, Y, Z, W are wffs, such that Z is a part of X, and Y is the result of replacing an occurrence of Z in X by its proved equivalent[1] W, then if X is a thesis, so is Y.

We can rewrite this rule in a more perspicuous schematic form if we adopt certain notational conventions. For 'X is a thesis' we write '⊢X'; and for 'Y is the result of replacing an occurrence of Z in X by W', we write 'Y = X[W/Z]'. The use of square brackets in the latter serves to distinguish this sort of replacement from uniform replacement of propositional variables. We can state the rule thus:

If X, Y, Z, W are wffs such that:

$$\left.\begin{array}{l} \text{1. Z is a part of X} \\ \text{2. } \vdash (Z \equiv W) \\ \text{3. } Y = X[W/Z] \\ \text{4. } \vdash X \end{array}\right\} \text{ then } \vdash Y$$

It should be clear that this rule would be a very useful one to have in PM, now that we have proved Adj so that theses in '≡' are within our reach. But since it is not one of the primitive rules of the system, we must prove that it holds in PM – i.e. we must obtain it

[1] To say that W is a proved equivalent of Z is just to say that W ≡ Z is a thesis.

as a derived rule. It follows that the rule would not enable us to prove anything which could not be proved without it – but it would enable us to shorten many proofs. To take one simple example, suppose we have proved

$$p \equiv \sim\sim p \tag{1}$$

and

$$(p \supset \sim p) \supset \sim p \tag{2}$$

and that we wish to prove

$$(\sim p \supset p) \supset p$$

Now $(2)(\sim p/p)$: $(\sim p \supset \sim \sim p) \supset \sim \sim p \tag{3}$

By (1) and Rule of Substitution of Equivalents, we obtain the desired theorem from (3) in a single operation.

But without this rule, we must proceed in some such fashion as this:

$(3),T10 \times Syll$: $(\sim p \supset \sim \sim p) \supset p \tag{4}$

$Syll[T2](\sim p/p, p/q, \sim\sim p/r)$:

$$\qquad\qquad (p \supset \sim\sim p) \supset ((\sim p \supset p) \supset (\sim p \supset \sim\sim p)) \tag{5}$$

$(5),T9 \times D$: $(\sim p \supset p) \supset (\sim p \supset \sim\sim p) \tag{6}$

$(6),(4) \times Syll$: $(\sim p \supset p) \supset p$

In order to derive this Rule in PM, we shall proceed as follows:

1. We shall state and prove a Lemma – i.e. a subsidiary result. This proof will proceed by exhaustive consideration of cases.
2. We shall prove that if the Lemma holds, so does the Rule.

Lemma: If X, Y, Z, W are wffs such that:

$$\left.\begin{array}{l} \text{1. Z is a part of X} \\ \text{2. } \vdash (Z \equiv W) \\ \text{3. } Y = X[W/Z] \end{array}\right\} \text{ then } \vdash (X \equiv Y)$$

[*Informal statement of lemma*: If we replace some part of a wff (a thesis or not) by some proved equivalent of the part, the result is equivalent to the original wff.]

Bearing in mind that disjunction and negation are the only primitive operators of PM, we can see that to prove that the Lemma holds generally it suffices to prove that it holds in certain cases. For the definitions enable us to transform any wff into one containing no operators other than negation and disjunction. The main operator of the wff will be either '$\sim$' or 'v', and the same will be true of any well-formed part of the wff. So we need to consider the case in which the whole of X is to be replaced by its equivalent, W – i.e. X *is* the wff Z; and the case in which X is the negation of Z – i.e. Z is the negated part of X; and the case in which X is a disjunction, one of the disjuncts being Z. Since Z may be either the first or the second disjunct, this third case splits into two subcases. We tabulate the cases thus:

Case 1. X is Z
Case 2. X is $\sim$Z
Case 3. (*a*) X is UvZ
(*b*) X is ZvU where U is some wff.

Proof of Lemma

Case 1. The Lemma obviously holds, for we have $\vdash (Z \equiv W)$ by hypothesis, and so immediately obtain $\vdash (X \equiv Y)$; for X is Z, and Y, being X[W/Z], is W.

Case 2. We have to show that if Z and W are equivalent, so are their negations – i.e. that if $\vdash (Z \equiv W)$ then $\vdash (\sim Z \equiv \sim W)$. Accordingly we prove:

T27. $(p \equiv q) \supset (\sim p \equiv \sim q)$

PROOF:

T21(p⊃q/p, q⊃p/q)	: $((p \supset q) \cdot (q \supset p)) \supset (p \supset q)$	(1)
(1), Transp × Syll	: $((p \supset q) \cdot (q \supset p)) \supset (\sim q \supset \sim p)$	(2)
T22(p⊃q/p, q⊃p/q)	: $((p \supset q) \cdot (q \supset p)) \supset (q \supset p)$	(3)
(3), Transp × Syll	: $((p \supset q) \cdot (q \supset p)) \supset (\sim p \supset \sim q)$	(4)
(2),(4) × Comp	: $((p \supset q) \cdot (q \supset p)) \supset ((\sim p \supset \sim q) \cdot (\sim q \supset \sim p))$	(5)
(5) × Def $\equiv$	: T27	

We now set up the hypothesis, $Z \equiv W$ (1)
Then T27(Z/p, W/q),(1) × D: $\sim Z \equiv \sim W$
Now, X is $\sim$Z, and Y, being X[W/Z], is $\sim$W. Hence under the conditions of the Lemma, $\vdash (X \equiv Y)$. Thus the Lemma holds in Case 2.

Case 3. For the subcase 3a we have to show that if $\vdash (Z \equiv W)$ then $\vdash ((UvZ) \equiv (UvW))$. Accordingly we prove:

T28. $(p \equiv q) \supset ((rvp) \equiv (rvq))$

PROOF:

T21(p⊃q/p, q⊃p/q) × Def $\equiv$	: $(p \equiv q) \supset (p \supset q)$	(1)
A5(r/p,p/q,q/r)	: $(p \supset q) \supset ((rvp) \supset (rvq))$	(2)

(1),(2) × Syll	: $(p \equiv q) \supset ((rvp) \supset (rvq))$	(3)
T22($p \supset q/p$, $q \supset p/q$) × Def $\equiv$	: $(p \equiv q) \supset (q \supset p)$	(4)
A5($r/p, p/r$)	: $(q \supset p) \supset ((rvq) \supset (rvp))$	(5)
(4),(5) × Syll	: $(p \equiv q) \supset ((rvq) \supset (rvp))$	(6)
(3),(6) × Comp	: $(p \equiv q) \supset (((rvp) \supset (rvq))$.	
	$((rvq) \supset (rvp)))$	(7)
(7) × Def $\equiv$	: T28	

We set up the hypothesis, $Z \equiv W$ (1)
Then T28(Z/p, W/q, U/r), (1) × D   : $(UvZ) \equiv (UvW)$ (2)
In this case X is UvZ, so Y, being X[W/Z], is UvW. Hence under the conditions of the Lemma, $\vdash (X \equiv Y)$. So the Lemma holds in Case 3a.

For the subcase 3b, we have to show that if $\vdash (Z \equiv W)$ then $\vdash ((ZvU) \equiv (WvU))$. Accordingly we prove:

T29. $(p \equiv q) \supset ((pvr) \equiv (qvr))$

The actual proof of this thesis is omitted here since it is exactly the same as that of T28, except that T13 is used in place of A5. Similarly we omit the argument to show that the Lemma holds in Case 3b, since it is exactly analogous to the argument for Case 3a.

The considerations presented in drawing up the list of cases are sufficient to show that if the Lemma holds in these cases it holds in every case. For every case reduces to one or more of Cases 1–3. [For example, suppose that X has the form S v (UvZ), and $\vdash (Z \equiv W)$. Then Y has the form S v (UvW). The equivalence of X and Y follows from the fact that, under Case 3a, UvZ is equivalent to UvW; so that the replacement of Z by W amounts to the replacement of UvZ by UvW – again, Case 3a.] Hence, the Lemma holds in every case.

THEOREM: *If the Lemma holds, so does the Rule.*

We observe that the conditions of the Rule are those of the Lemma, with the additional condition that X is a thesis. Therefore, we need to show that if the conditions of the Lemma hold, and X is a thesis. then Y is also a thesis.

We have already proved (in the proof of T28) that:

$$(p \equiv q) \supset (p \supset q)$$

whence, by substitution,

$$\vdash ((X \equiv Y) \supset (X \supset Y)) \tag{1}$$

Now if the conditions of the Lemma hold, its conclusion holds, i.e.

$$\vdash (X \equiv Y) \tag{2}$$

$(1),(2) \times D \quad : \qquad \vdash (X \supset Y) \tag{3}$

The additional condition of the Rule is

$$\vdash X \tag{4}$$

$(3),(4) \times D \quad : \qquad \vdash Y$

We have shown that if the conditions of the Rule for Substitution of Equivalents hold, Y is a thesis. Thus the Rule holds in PM.

We now have the Rule for Substitution of Equivalents at our disposal, but in order to use it we need some theses of the form $Z \equiv W$. Obtaining some of these is easy, since we have all the relevant materials already – viz. pairs of implications, adjunction and the definition of '$\equiv$'. For example, $p \equiv \sim\sim p$ can be obtained directly from T9 and T10 in this way.

T30. $p \equiv \sim\sim p$

PROOF:

T9, T10 $\times$ Adj $\times$ Def $\equiv$: T30

In the following list of equivalential theses, all those that are derived in this simple way will be stated without proof. You can easily fill in the proofs by checking over T1–T29 and A1–A5.

T31. $(p \supset q) \equiv (\sim q \supset \sim p)$ [Transp]

T32. $(p \vee q) \equiv (q \vee p)$ [Commutative Law for Disjunction]

PROOF:

A3, A3(q/p,p/q) $\times$ Adj $\times$ Def $\equiv$: T32

T33. $p \equiv (p \vee p)$

T34. $(p \cdot q) \equiv (q \cdot p)$ [Commutative Law for Conjunction]

PROOF:

T22, T21 $\times$ Comp : $(p \cdot q) \supset (q \cdot p)$ (1)

$(1)(q/p,p/q)$: $(q \cdot p) \supset (p \cdot q)$ (2)

$(1),(2) \times$ Adj $\times$ Def $\equiv$: T34

Where we wish to justify a move by appeal to the Rule for Substitution of Equivalents, we shall use the notation '(n), $T_j \times$ Eq' where '(n)' is the reference to the wff to be transformed, T_j is the equivalential thesis appealed to, and '$\times$ Eq' indicates that the operation is substitution of equivalents. An example of this will be found in the proof of the next theorem.

T35. $p \equiv (p.p)$

PROOF:

A1($\sim$p/p)	:	$(\sim p v \sim p) \supset \sim p$	(1)
(1) $\times$ Transp	:	$\sim \sim p \supset \sim (\sim p v \sim p)$	(2)
(2),T30 $\times$ Eq	:	$p \supset \sim (\sim p v \sim p)$	(3)
(3) $\times$ Def .	:	$p \supset (p.p)$	(4)
T21(p/q)	:	$(p.p) \supset p$	(5)
(4),(5) $\times$ Adj $\times$ Def $\equiv$	:	T35	

T36. $p \equiv p$ [Id]

T37. $(p \equiv q) \equiv (q \equiv p)$

PROOF:

T36($p \equiv q$/p)	:	$(p \equiv q) \equiv (p \equiv q)$	(1)
(1) $\times$ Def $\equiv$	:	$\equiv ((p \supset q).(q \supset p))$	(2)
(2),T34 $\times$ Eq	:	$\equiv ((q \supset p).(p \supset q))$	(3)
(3) $\times$ Def $\equiv$	:	T37	

Since the proof of T37 proceeds only by successive transformations of the right-hand side of line (1), we have omitted the constant left-hand side in the intermediate lines.

T38. $(p \equiv q) \equiv (\sim p \equiv \sim q)$

PROOF:

T27($\sim$p/p,$\sim$q/q)	:	$(\sim p \equiv \sim q) \supset (\sim \sim p \equiv \sim \sim q)$	(1)
(1),T30 $\times$ Eq	:	$(\sim p \equiv \sim q) \supset (p \equiv q)$	(2)
(2),T27 $\times$ Adj $\times$ Def $\equiv$	:	T38	

T39. $(p v q) \equiv (\sim p \supset q)$

T40. $(p v q) \equiv \sim (\sim p . \sim q)$

PROOF:

T36(p.q/p)	:	$(p.q) \equiv (p.q)$	(1)

(1) × Def .	: $\sim(\sim pv\sim q) \equiv (p\cdot q)$	(2)
(2),T38 × Eq	: $\sim\sim(\sim pv\sim q) \equiv \sim(p\cdot q)$	(3)
(3)($\sim p/p,\sim q/q$)	: $\sim\sim(\sim\sim pv\sim\sim q) \equiv \sim(\sim p\cdot\sim q)$	(4)
(4),T30 × Eq	: T40	

You should notice that the justification for line (3), viz. '(2),T38 × Eq' is a highly abbreviated expression for a rather complex operation. For concealed in it is the fact that strictly speaking we need to substitute $\sim(\sim pv\sim q)/p$ and $p\cdot q/q$ in T38, thus obtaining the equivalence

$$(\sim(\sim pv\sim q) \equiv (p\cdot q)) \equiv (\sim\sim(\sim pv\sim q) \equiv \sim(p\cdot q))$$

which then is the '$Z \equiv W$' of the Rule, (2) being X and (3) being Y. That is, T38 is being appealed to as that thesis which will yield the appropriate '$Z \equiv W$' by substitution. Similar remarks apply to line (3) of the proof of T37, where T34 is used.

T41. $(p \vee (qvr)) \equiv ((pvq) \vee r)$ [Assoc]

T42. $(p \vee (qvr)) \equiv (q \vee (pvr))$ [Assoc]
PROOF:
A4, A4(q/p,p/q) × Adj × Def $\equiv$: T42

T43. $((pvq) \vee r) \equiv (p \vee (rvq))$ [Assoc]
PROOF:

T41,T37 × Eq	: $((pvq) \vee r) \equiv (p \vee (qvr))$	(1)
(1),T32 × Eq	: T43	

You should formulate for yourself, and prove, the remaining variants of the Associative Law for Disjunction.

T44. $(p\cdot(q\cdot r)) \equiv (q\cdot(p\cdot r))$ [Assoc]
PROOF:

T42($\sim p/p,\sim q/q,\sim r/r$)	: $(\sim p \vee (\sim qv\sim r)) \equiv$ $(\sim q \vee (\sim pv\sim r))$	(1)
(1),T38 × Eq	: $\sim(\sim p \vee (\sim qv\sim r)) \equiv$ $\sim(\sim q \vee (\sim pv\sim r))$	(2)
(2),T30 × Eq	: $\sim(\sim pv\sim\sim(\sim qv\sim r)) \equiv$ $\sim(\sim qv\sim\sim(\sim pv\sim r))$	(3)

(3) × Def .   : (p.∼(∼qv∼r)) ≡ (q.∼(∼pv∼r)) (4)
(4) × Def .   : T44

T45. ((p.q).r) ≡ (p.(q.r))   [Assoc]

PROOF:

T36((p.q).r/p)	:	((p.q).r) ≡ ((p.q).r)	(1)
(1) × Def .	:	≡ ∼(∼∼(∼pv∼q) v∼r)	(2)
(2),T30 × Eq	:	≡ ∼((∼pv∼q) v ∼r)	(3)
(3),T41 × Eq	:	≡ ∼(∼p v (∼qv∼r))	(4)
(4),T30 × Eq	:	≡ ∼(∼p v ∼∼(∼qv∼r))	(5)
(5) × Def .	:	≡ ∼(∼p v ∼(q.r))	(6)
(6) × Def .	: T45		

You should formulate for yourself, and prove, the remaining variants of the Associative Law for Conjunction.

EXERCISES 16

Prove the following in PM:

16.1 (∼p⊃q) ⊃ (∼q⊃p)

16.2 (∼q⊃p) ⊃ (∼p⊃q)

16.3 (p v (q v (rvs))) ⊃ (q v (p v (svr)))

16.4 (p ⊃ (q⊃r)) ≡ ((q.p) ⊃ r)

16.5 (p v (q.r)) ≡ ((r.q) v p)

16.6 (p⊃q) ⊃ ((p⊃r) ⊃ (p ⊃ (q⊃r)))

16.7 (p.q) ⊃ (p⊃q)

16.8 (pvq) ⊃ ((q⊃r) ⊃ ((q⊃r) ⊃ (pvr)))

16.9 ∼(pvq) ⊃ ((p⊃q).(q⊃p))

CHAPTER 17

PM (III) – Some Further Theorems

The purpose of this chapter is simply to set out proofs of a few more of the important theorems of PM. On the whole, these proofs are a little more difficult than most of the ones set out in earlier chapters; but you should have no trouble in following them if you have already worked through the earlier ones. In fact, once you have worked your way carefully through this batch, you should be in a very good position to prove for yourself any theorem of PM you may want to.

Some of the theorems in this chapter have been included because they will be needed later on; others have been included primarily for their intrinsic interest as logical laws.

If you reflect on the sense of the Law of Importation,

$$(p \supset (q \supset r)) \supset ((p \cdot q) \supset r)$$

it will be evident that its converse ought to be a thesis also. For Imp asserts that if one proposition implies that a second proposition implies a third, then the first and second propositions *jointly* imply the third. But this consequent amounts to saying that if the first and second propositions are both true, then the third is true. And in that case, if the first is true, then provided the second is also true, the third is true.

i.e. $((p \cdot q) \supset r) \supset (p \supset (q \supset r))$

This is known as the Law of Exportation (*Exp* for short) since its effect is to 'export' one proposition from the antecedent to the consequent.

T46. $((p \cdot q) \supset r) \supset (p \supset (q \supset r))$ [Exp]

PROOF:

Id((p.q)⊃r/p)	:	$((p \cdot q) \supset r) \supset ((p \cdot q) \supset r)$	(1)
(1) × Def .	:	$\supset (\sim(\sim p \vee \sim q) \supset r)$	(2)
(2) × Transp	:	$\supset (\sim r \supset \sim\sim(\sim p \vee \sim q))$	(3)
(3),T30 × Eq	:	$\supset (\sim r \supset (\sim p \vee \sim q))$	(4)

125

(4) × Def ⊃	:	⊃ (~r ⊃ (p⊃~q))	(5)
(5) × Perm	:	⊃ (p ⊃ (~r⊃~q))	(6)
(6),Transp × Eq	:	T46	

T47.　((p⊃r)•(q⊃s)) ⊃ ((pvq) ⊃ (rvs))

[This thesis may look rather odd at first sight, but this oddity will disappear as soon as you notice that it is just an elaboration of a fundamental property of material implication. For T47 asserts that if we have two true material implications, then if either has a true antecedent, at least one of the consequents must be true.]

PROOF:

T21(p⊃r/p, q⊃s/q)	:	((p⊃r)•(q⊃s)) ⊃ (p⊃r)	(1)
A5(p/q,q/p)	:	(p⊃r) ⊃ ((qvp) ⊃ (qvr))	(2)
(1),(2) × Syll	:	((p⊃r)•(q⊃s)) ⊃ ((qvp) ⊃ (qvr))	(3)
(3),T32 × Eq	:	((p⊃r)•(q⊃s)) ⊃ ((pvq) ⊃ (qvr))	(4)
T22(p⊃r/p, q⊃s/q)	:	((p⊃r)•(q⊃s)) ⊃ (q⊃s)	(5)
T13(r/p,s/r)	:	(q⊃s) ⊃ ((qvr) ⊃ (svr))	(6)
(5), (6) × Syll	:	((p⊃r)•(q⊃s)) ⊃ ((qvr) ⊃ (svr))	(7)
(7),T32 × Eq	:	((p⊃r)•(q⊃s)) ⊃ ((qvr) ⊃ (rvs))	(8)
(4),(8) × Comp	:	((p⊃r)•(q⊃s)) ⊃	
		(((pvq) ⊃ (qvr))•((qvr) ⊃ (rvs)))	(9)
Syll[T3] × Imp	:	((p⊃q)•(q⊃r)) ⊃ (p⊃r)	(10)
(10)(pvq/p, qvr/q, rvs/r)	:		
		(((pvq) ⊃ (qvr))•((qvr) ⊃ (rvs))) ⊃ ((pvq) ⊃ (rvs))	(11)
(9),(11) × Syll	:	T47	

T48.　((p⊃q)•(r⊃q)) ⊃ ((pvr) ⊃ q)

PROOF:

| T47(r/q,q/r,q/s) | : | ((p⊃q)•(r⊃q)) ⊃ ((pvr) ⊃ (qvq)) | (1) |
| (1),T33 × Eq | : | T48 | |

T48 may also be proved without making use of T47, in much the same way as T47.

T49.　(p⊃q) ⊃ ((p•r) ⊃ (q•r))

PROOF:

Syll[T3](~r/r)	:	(p⊃q) ⊃ ((q⊃~r) ⊃ (p⊃~r))	(1)
(1) × Transp	:	⊃ (~(p⊃~r) ⊃ ~(q⊃~r))	(2)
(2) × Def ⊃	:	⊃ (~(~pv~r) ⊃ ~(~qv~r))	(3)
(3) × Def •	:	T49	

T49 is a conjunctive analogue of T13. Prove for yourself the analogue of A5.

T50. $((p \supset r) \cdot (q \supset s)) \supset ((p \cdot q) \supset (r \cdot s))$

Now, T50 is a conjunctive analogue of T47, so it would be reasonable to try to derive it from that theorem, bearing in mind the relation between conjunction and disjunction provided by the definition of the former. And all the more so, since we have Transp at hand to insert and delete negations as required. Then the crucial part of the proof becomes the correct choice of substitutions in T47 – for if we just put $\sim p/p$, $\sim q/q$ and so on in T47, everything will come out the wrong way round. The simplest method is:

PROOF:

T47($\sim r/p, \sim s/q, \sim p/r, \sim q/s$) :

$$((\sim r \supset \sim p) \cdot (\sim s \supset \sim q)) \supset ((\sim r \lor \sim s) \supset (\sim p \lor \sim q)) \quad (1)$$

(1) $\times$ Transp : $((\sim r \supset \sim p) \cdot (\sim s \supset \sim q)) \supset (\sim(\sim p \lor \sim q) \supset$
$$\sim(\sim r \lor \sim s)) \quad (2)$$

(2) $\times$ Def . : $((\sim r \supset \sim p) \cdot (\sim s \supset \sim q)) \supset ((p \cdot q) \supset (r \cdot s)) \quad (3)$

(3),Transp $\times$ Eq(twice) : T50

A glance over the equivalence theorems set out in the preceding chapter will reveal that we have at our disposal almost all the apparatus for standard equivalence transformations. The only major tools still lacking are the *Distributive Laws* – and this deficiency will be made good in the next two theorems. With these proved, we shall have in PM all the apparatus required for transformations into conjunctive and disjunctive normal forms – a fact of some importance later on.

T51. $(p \cdot (q \lor r)) \equiv ((p \cdot q) \lor (p \cdot r))$ [Distrib]

PROOF:

Adj	: $p \supset (q \supset (p \cdot q))$	(1)
Adj(r/q)	: $p \supset (r \supset (p \cdot r))$	(2)
(1),(2) $\times$ Comp	: $p \supset ((q \supset (p \cdot q)) \cdot (r \supset (p \cdot r)))$	(3)

T47(q/p,r/q, p.q/r, p.r/s) :

$$((q \supset (p \cdot q)) \cdot (r \supset (p \cdot r))) \supset ((q \lor r) \supset ((p \cdot q) \lor (p \cdot r))) \quad (4)$$

(3),(4) $\times$ Syll	: $p \supset ((q \lor r) \supset ((p \cdot q) \lor (p \cdot r)))$	(5)
(5) $\times$ Imp	: $(p \cdot (q \lor r)) \supset ((p \cdot q) \lor (p \cdot r))$	(6)
T21	: $(p \cdot q) \supset p$	(7)

T21(r/q)	: (p•r) ⊃ p	(8)
(7),(8) × Adj	: ((p•q) ⊃ p)•((p•r) ⊃ p)	(9)
T48(p•q/p, p/q, p•r/r)	:	
	(((p•q) ⊃ p)•((p•r) ⊃ p)) ⊃ (((p•q) v (p•r)) ⊃ p)	(10)
(9),(10) × D	: ((p•q) v (p•r)) ⊃ p	(11)
T22, T22(r/q) × Adj	: ((p•q) ⊃ q)•((p•r) ⊃ r)	(12)
(12) × T47	: ((p•q) v (p•r)) ⊃ (qvr)	(13)
(11),(13) × Comp	: ((p•q) v (p•r)) ⊃ (p•(qvr))	(14)
(6),(14) × Adj × Def ≡	: T51	

Note that the later part of this proof has been compressed a little. Line (12) embodies moves strictly analogous to lines (7)–(9), while line (13) bears the same relation to lines (10)–(11).

T52. (p v (q•r)) ≡ ((pvq)•(pvr))   [Distrib]

PROOF:

A5(q•r/q, q/r)	: ((q•r) ⊃ q) ⊃ ((p v (q•r)) ⊃ (pvq))	(1)
T21(q/p,r/q)	: (q•r) ⊃ q	(2)
(1),(2) × D	: (p v (q•r)) ⊃ (pvq)	(3)
A5(q•r/q), T22(q/p,r/q) × D	: (p v (q•r)) ⊃ (pvr)	(4)
(3),(4) × Comp	: (p v (q•r)) ⊃ ((pvq)•(pvr))	(5)
Id((pvq)•(pvr)/p)	: ((pvq)•(pvr)) ⊃ ((pvq)•(pvr))	(6)
(6),T39 × Eq(twice)	: ((pvq)•(pvr)) ⊃ ((∼p⊃q)•(∼p⊃r))	(7)
Comp(∼p/p) × Imp	: ((∼p⊃q)•(∼p⊃r)) ⊃ (∼p ⊃ (q•r))	(8)
(7),(8) × Syll	: ((pvq)•(pvr)) ⊃ (∼p ⊃ (q•r))	(9)
(9),T39 × Eq	: ((pvq)•(pvr)) ⊃ (p v (q•r))	(10)
(5),(10) × Adj × Def ≡	: T52	

Two further theses which will be useful in later developments are

$$(p•(p⊃q)) ≡ (p•q)   (T53)$$

and $$p ≡ ((p•q) v (p•∼q))   (T54)$$

Both are really special cases of the Distributive Laws; T53 being the T51 form when the left-hand side is

$$p•(∼pvq)$$

and T54 being the T52 form when the left-hand side is

$$p v (q•∼q)$$

However, despite these relationships, it is more convenient not to base the proofs of T53 and T54 directly on the Distributive Laws.

T53. $(p.(p \supset q)) \equiv (p.q)$

PROOF:

T21(p⊃q/q)	: $(p.(p \supset q)) \supset p$	(1)
Id(p⊃q/p)	: $(p \supset q) \supset (p \supset q)$	(2)
(2) × Perm	: $p \supset ((p \supset q) \supset q)$	(3)
(3) × Imp	: $(p.(p \supset q)) \supset q$	(4)
(1),(4) × Comp	: $(p.(p \supset q)) \supset (p.q)$	(5)
Simp(p/q,q/p)	: $q \supset (p \supset q)$	(6)
(6),T22 × Syll	: $(p.q) \supset (p \supset q)$	(7)
T21	: $(p.q) \supset p$	(8)
(7),(8) × Comp	: $(p.q) \supset (p.(p \supset q))$	(9)
(5),(9) × Adj × Def ≡	: T53	

T54. $p \equiv ((p.q) \vee (p.\sim q))$

PROOF:

Simp(q/p,p/q) × Perm	: $p \supset (q \supset q)$	(1)
(1) × Def ⊃	: $p \supset (\sim q \vee q)$	(2)
(2),T32 × Eq	: $p \supset (q \vee \sim q)$	(3)
Id	: $p \supset p$	(4)
(3),(4) × Comp	: $p \supset (p.(q \vee \sim q))$	(5)
(5),T51 × Eq	: $p \supset ((p.q) \vee (p.\sim q))$	(6)
T48(p.q/p,p/q,p.∼q/r)	: $(((p.q) \supset p).((p.\sim q) \supset p)) \supset$ $(((p.q) \vee (p.\sim q)) \supset p)$	(7)
T21, T21(∼q/q) × Adj	: $((p.q) \supset p).((p.\sim q) \supset p)$	(8)
(7),(8) × D	: $((p.q) \vee (p.\sim q)) \supset p$	(9)
(6),(9) × Adj × Def ≡	: T54	

Another theorem which will be useful later on, and whose sense is obvious, is:

T55. $((p \supset q).(\sim p \supset q)) \supset q$

PROOF:

T24	: $(p \supset q) \supset ((p \vee q) \supset q)$	(1)
(1),T39 × Eq	: $(p \supset q) \supset ((\sim p \supset q) \supset q)$	(2)
(2) × Imp	: T55	

EXERCISES 17

Prove the following in PM:

17.1 $(p \supset (q.r)) \supset ((p \supset q).(p \supset r))$

17.2 $((p \supset q) \supset p) \supset p$

17.3 $(p \supset q) \supset ((q \supset r) \supset ((r \supset s) \supset (p \supset s)))$

17.4 $(p \supset (q \supset (r \supset s))) \supset (p \supset (r \supset (q \supset s)))$

17.5 $(p \supset (q \supset (r \supset s))) \supset (r \supset (q \supset (p \supset s)))$

17.6 $(p \supset (q \supset r)) \supset ((r \supset s) \supset (p \supset (q \supset s)))$

17.7 $(p.q) \supset ((p.r) \supset (q.r))$

17.8 $((p \equiv q).(q \equiv r)) \supset (p \equiv r)$

17.9 $(p \equiv q) \supset ((p \equiv r) \supset (q \equiv r))$

CHAPTER 18

PM IV – Independence and Non-Independence

T56. $(p \lor (qvr)) \supset (q \lor (pvr))$

PROOF:

A2(r/q)	: $r \supset (pvr)$	(1)
A5(q/p,r/q,pvr/r)	: $(r \supset (pvr)) \supset ((qvr) \supset (q \lor (pvr)))$	(2)
(1),(2) $\times$ D	: $(qvr) \supset (q \lor (pvr))$	(3)
A5(qvr/q,qv(pvr)/r)	: $((qvr) \supset (q \lor (pvr))) \supset$	
	$\quad ((p \lor (qvr)) \supset (p \lor (q \lor (pvr))))$	(4)
(4),(3) $\times$ D	: $(p \lor (qvr)) \supset (p \lor (q \lor (pvr)))$	(5)
A3(r/p,p/q)	: $(rvp) \supset (pvr)$	(6)
A2(r/p,p/q)	: $p \supset (rvp)$	(7)
(6),(7) $\times$ Syll	: $p \supset (pvr)$	(8)
A2(q/p,pvr/q)	: $(pvr) \supset (q \lor (pvr))$	(9)
(8),(9) $\times$ Syll	: $p \supset (q \lor (pvr))$	(10)
A5(qv(pvr)/p,p/q,qv(pvr)/r)	: $(p \supset (q \lor (pvr))) \supset$	
	$\quad (((q \lor (pvr)) \lor p) \supset ((q \lor (pvr)) \lor (q \lor (pvr))))$	(11)
(11),(10) $\times$ D	: $((q \lor (pvr)) \lor p) \supset$	
	$\quad ((q \lor (pvr)) \lor (q \lor (pvr)))$	(12)
A1(qv(pvr)/p)	: $((q \lor (pvr)) \lor (q \lor (pvr))) \supset (q \lor (pvr))$	(13)
(12),(13) $\times$ Syll	: $((q \lor (pvr)) \lor p) \supset (q \lor (pvr))$	(14)
A3(qv(pvr)/q)	: $(p \lor (q \lor (pvr))) \supset ((q \lor (pvr)) \lor p)$	(15)
(14),(15) $\times$ Syll	: $(p \lor (q \lor (pvr))) \supset (q \lor (pvr))$	(16)
(5),(16) $\times$ Syll	: T56	

T56 is of course the same wff as the axiom A4; and the proof we have set out shows that it is unnecessary to put it down as an axiom, since it can be proved from the other axioms and therefore everything that can be proved by use of A4 can be proved by use of T56. We express this fact by saying that A4 is a *non-independent axiom*. This does not mean that it is in any way impaired as an axiom, but merely that we can do without it. In fact it is sometimes very convenient, even if theoretically untidy, to have one or more non-independent axioms in a system. For example, in the present case, having A4 as an axiom allowed us to obtain the very useful Perm easily at an early stage. However, inspection of the proof of T56 will show that the only thesis used, apart from A1, A2, A3 and A5, is Syll in the form '$(q \supset r) \supset ((p \supset q) \supset (p \supset r))$', so that T56 could, in principle, be proved at a very early stage.

In showing that an axiom is non-independent, it is clearly essential that one should not make use of the axiom itself or of any thesis obtained from it, since either course would make the proof circular. Inspection of the proof of T56 will show that these conditions are satisfied.

Since A4 is non-independent, the axiom-set for PM could be reduced by one. But no further reduction of this sort is possible; neither A1 nor A2 nor A3 nor A5 is a consequence of the other three under Substitution and Detachment, and these four are therefore said to be *independent axioms*.

Proving independence

Now it is clear that mere failure to find a proof is not enough to demonstrate independence. We need some method for showing that the axiom cannot be a transform of the other axioms under the Rules of Transformation of the system. As soon as we put it this way, it becomes quite clear that the independence or non-independence of an axiom is a formal, structural feature of a system, and has nothing to do with its intended interpretation – say as an axiomatization of PC. That is to say, in investigating the independence of an axiom in a system, we are concerned with the system simply as an uninterpreted, formal axiomatic system. (You may therefore find it helpful to refresh your memory of Chapter 14 at this stage.)

It will be recalled that Substitution and Detachment are validity-preserving operations, in the sense that if the operations are carried out on valid wffs, the resulting wff is also valid. That is, if a wff, X, is a transform of valid wffs, under Substitution and Detachment, then X is also valid. And, in general, in any system with Rules of Transformation, R1, R2, . . . , Rn, then for any property preserved by those rules, if X is a transform of wffs possessing that property, then X must possess it also. It follows that if S is a formal system with axioms A1, A2, . . . , Ak, and X is some wff of S, then if there is some property possessed by the axioms and preserved by the

Rules of Transformation of S, but not possessed by X, then X is not a transform of the axioms – i.e. X is not a theorem of S. In particular, in order to show the independence of a particular axiom, Aj, of S, it will suffice to find some property possessed by the remaining axioms and preserved by the rules, but not possessed by Aj. Hence, to demonstrate the independence of A1 in PM, it will suffice to find a property possessed by A2, A3 and A5, preserved by Substitution and Detachment, but not possessed by A1. This will show that A1 is not a theorem of the truncated system formed from PM by using as axioms only A2, A3 and A5, and hence that A1 is independent in PM.

Now you will recall that our original definition of validity of a propositional schema, in terms of yielding a true proposition under every set of appropriate and uniform substitutions, turned out to be equivalent, as far as PC is concerned, to a definition in terms of having a truth-table consisting entirely of 1's. But in the light of our discussion of formal axiomatic systems, it can be seen that this second account of validity involves three things:

(i) choosing a range of values, M (viz. $\{1,0\}$), for the formal variables, p, q, r, . . .

(ii) giving an interpretation to each formal constant – i.e. whatever operator-symbols are taken as primitive – by drawing up the appropriate basic truth-tables.

(iii) choosing a member of M, viz. '1', and defining validity in terms of always having that value.

In fact we have typically gone further than this by specifying the nature of the objects in M – by identifying them as truth-values – and this is necessary if we are to complete the work of interpretation. But it should be clear that holding back from this last step still allows us to define a notion of validity which is exactly co-extensive with our original one, although it lacks those connections with the notion of necessary truth which pointed the way in the first place.

We can now generalize this rather skeletal notion of validity of a wff of PC. For we could have chosen a different range of values, M' (e.g. M' might contain more members than M), and a different interpretation of the operator-symbols; or we could have chosen a different member of M for the definition of 'validity'. Of course, the resulting notion of 'validity' would probably have no connection with necessary truth at all, and hence be quite unlike our usual notion of validity. But, like validity in the usual sense, it would be a special case of what we might call Φ-*validity*. We explain this notion as follows. Let S be a formal system, and I_j a particular interpretation of S in which the range of values is M. (The nature of the members of M may or may not be specified.) Then we shall say that a wff of S is Φ_j-*valid* if, under the interpretation I_j, the wff always has a particular value chosen from M. This chosen value is called the *designated value*. (Note that there is no reason why there should not be more than one designated value. If two values are designated, then the wff is Φ_j-valid if it always has one or the other of those values.)

In proving the independence of the remaining axioms of PM, we shall always choose as the crucial property preserved by the rules some special case of Φ-validity. That is, the independence proof for each axiom rests on the construction of a new interpretation for PM.

Any bewilderment at the strangeness of these interpretations will be diminished if you bear in mind that, owing to the generality of the notion of Φ-validity, the interpretations are in a certain sense arbitrary. For the nature of the objects in each range of values, M, is completely irrelevant, and the number of them is dictated only by convenience. The only reason for choosing *these* interpretations (i.e. these choices of M and the associated pseudo-truth-tables) is that they give rise to suitable properties – i.e. suitable cases of Φ-validity. For simplicity, we have chosen numbers as the members of each M, but we *could* have chosen colours or any other objects instead.

Independence of A1

We choose $M = \{1, 2, 3\}$.

The interpretation for '$\sim$' and 'v' is given by the tables:

p	$\sim$p
1	3
2	2
3	1

p	q	pvq
1	1	1
1	2	1
1	3	1
2	1	1
2	2	1
2	3	2
3	1	1
3	2	2
3	3	3

which may be more conveniently set out:

Table I

		~
	1	3
p	2	2
	3	1

Table II

		q		
	v	1	2	3
	1	1	1	1
p	2	1	1	2
	3	1	2	3

From Tables I and II, we can obtain Table III below by the definition of '⊃' in PM.

For example, we can find the rightmost value in the top line of Table III – i.e. the value of 'p⊃q' when p = 1 and q = 3 – i.e. the value of 1⊃3 – thus: By the definition of '⊃', we can find the value of 1⊃3 by finding that of ∼1 v 3. But by Table I, ∼1 = 3; so we need to find the value of 3 v 3. By Table II, 3 v 3 = 3; so 1⊃3 = 3.

Table III

		q		
	⊃	1	2	3
	1	1	2	3
p	2	1	1	2
	3	1	1	1

In this interpretation, '1' is the designated value.

We define Φ_1-validity by saying that a wff is Φ_1-valid if and only if it has the designated value for all assignments of values to its variables from the set M, under Tables I–III.

Now Φ_1-validity is preserved by Substitution in just the way that validity is. It is also preserved by Detachment, for when X and X ⊃ Y take the designated value, so, according to Table III, does Y.

You should now test A1, A2, A3 and A5 for Φ_1-validity in the familiar truth-table fashion. (Note that the table for a wff containing n distinct variables will have 3^n rows.) You will find that each of A2, A3 and A5 is Φ_1-valid, but A1 is not since it has the table:

p	pvp	(pvp) ⊃ p
1	1	1
2	1	2
3	3	1

The occurrence of the undesignated '2' in the final column shows that A1 is not Φ_1-valid. Thus we have found a property possessed by

A2, A3 and A5, and preserved by the Rules of Transformation of PM, but not possessed by A1. Hence A1 is an independent axiom in PM.

Independence of A2, A3, A5

In a similar fashion we can establish the independence of A2, A3 and A5. The interpretations giving rise to the notions of Φ_2-, Φ_3- and Φ_5-validity are set out in skeleton form below.

For A2

Defined property is Φ_2-validity.

$M = \{1, 2, 3, 4\}$.   Designated value = 1.

	$\sim$	v	1	2	3	4
1	4	1	1	1	1	1
2	3	2	1	4	1	4
3	2	3	1	1	4	4
4	1	4	1	4	4	4

For A3

Defined property is Φ_3-validity.

$M = \{1, 2, 3, 4\}$.   Designated value = 1.

	$\sim$	v	1	2	3	4
1	4	1	1	1	1	1
2	3	2	1	2	1	2
3	2	3	1	1	3	4
4	1	4	1	2	3	4

For A5

Defined property is Φ_5-validity.

$M = \{1, 2, 3, 4\}$.   Designated value = 1.

	$\sim$	v	1	2	3	4
1	2	1	1	1	1	1
2	1	2	1	2	3	4
3	4	3	1	3	3	1
4	1	4	1	4	1	4

EXERCISES 18

18.1 Use the methods of this chapter to construct a detailed argument to show that no inconsistent wff is provable in PM.

CHAPTER 19

Consistency and Completeness of PM

When we are confronted with an axiomatic system, the two great questions are: Is it consistent? Is it complete? As we saw in the discussion of axiomatic systems in Chapter 13, consistency and completeness each involve a relation between the notions of provability and validity; and it is because of this that consistency gives us a guarantee against triviality (at least against triviality of the most extreme sort), and completeness is a guarantee of adequacy. Several senses of consistency and completeness can be distinguished, so the main questions give rise to more special questions whether the system is consistent (complete) in this or that sense.

Consistency

Although the notion of consistency is firmly rooted in and springs from that of freedom from contradiction, and it is this feature that we are primarily concerned to establish by a consistency-proof, we take as logically fundamental here the notion of every thesis being valid. Not only is this notion clearer and more precise than that of freedom from contradiction, but it also the case that if we can show of a certain system that every thesis is valid, it is a relatively easy step to show that the system is free from contradiction in any applicable sense. (We shall see later that there are axiomatic systems for which it is not at all clear that it is significant to say that they are free from contradiction.)

We distinguish the following senses of consistency:

(i) *consistency with respect to negation.* A system will be said to be consistent in this sense if there is no thesis, X, such that ∼X is also a thesis. A system which is consistent with respect to negation is free from contradiction, in at least the most straightforward, and perhaps the only, sense.

(ii) *absolute consistency.* A system will be said to be absolutely consistent if not every wff of the system is a thesis.

137

(iii) *consistency in the sense of Post.*[1] A system will be said to be consistent in this sense if there is no thesis of the system which consists of a single propositional variable.

It can be seen that both the first and the third senses depend for their applicability on particular features of the system. Consistency with respect to negation is inapplicable unless the system contains an identifiable negation-operator; and consistency in the sense of Post is applicable only if the system contains some class of variables identifiable as propositional variables. But a system which is consistent in any of these three senses is at least not a system in which 'anything goes', and is thus not trivial in that extreme sense.

THEOREM I. If X is a thesis of PM, X is valid.

Theorem I follows directly from the familiar facts that the axioms of PM are valid, and its Rules of Transformation preserve validity.

THEOREM II. PM is consistent with respect to negation.

PROOF: Let X be any wff. Then X and $\sim$X cannot both be valid. Therefore, by Theorem I, they cannot both be theses of PM. Therefore, PM is consistent with respect to negation.

THEOREM III. PM is absolutely consistent.

PROOF: Select any axiom, say A1. Then $\sim$(A1) is a wff of PM which, by Theorem II, is not a thesis of PM. Therefore PM is absolutely consistent.

THEOREM IV. PM is consistent in the sense of Post.

PROOF: Let X be any wff consisting of a single propositional variable. Then X is not valid, and is, by Theorem I, not a thesis of PM. Therefore PM is consistent in the sense of Post.

Completeness

The root of the notion of completeness is to be found in that of the adequacy of an axiomatic system as an axiomatization of some field, in the sense that the axiomatic basis is sufficiently powerful to generate all the truths of that field. Thus the fundamental notion is that an axiomatic system, with an intended interpretation giving

[1] This sense of consistency was introduced by the American logician E. L. Post in 1921.

rise to an appropriate definition of validity, is complete if every valid wff is a thesis of the system. In treating of the completeness of PM, we take it in its usual interpretation as an axiomatization of PC with the usual definition of validity.

If a system is complete in the sense just explained, this means that the axiomatic basis is *sufficient* for the generation of the set of all its valid wffs. This suggests that we might distinguish a further sense of completeness in which a system would be said to be complete if the axiomatic basis cannot be made more powerful without inconsistency resulting. A system which is complete in the first sense will be said to be *weakly complete*, or simply *complete*, while a system complete in the second sense will be said to be *strongly complete*.

Before proceeding to investigate the completeness of PM, we need to give a more precise account of strong completeness. Suppose we have an axiomatic system, S, which is weakly complete. We might attempt to make its set of theses even more inclusive by adding a new independent axiom, Ax, thus forming a new system which we shall call S + Ax. Now S + Ax may be either consistent or inconsistent. If it is inconsistent for every choice of Ax, then we say that S is strongly complete. Notice that since S + Ax may be inconsistent with respect to negation, absolutely or in the sense of Post, there are three corresponding senses of strong completeness.

We shall now show that PM is weakly complete and also strongly complete in each of the three senses. In doing this we shall make use of the *conjunctive normal form* (CNF) treated in Chapter 11.

THEOREM I. If X is a valid wff of PM, then X is a thesis of PM. (I.e. PM is weakly complete.)

PROOF:

Lemma A. Every wff, X, of PM has a CNF, X', such that $\vdash (X \equiv X')$.

Proof of Lemma A: We have shown for PC in general that every wff has an equivalent CNF.[1] It will be recalled that that result was obtained by showing that by equivalence transformations the following are eliminable:

   (i) all operators other than negation, disjunction and conjunction
   (ii) negations of negations
   (iii) negations of conjunctions and disjunctions
   (iv) disjunctions of conjunctions

[1] See Chapter 11 and Appendix 1.

and that order and grouping within disjunctions and conjunctions can be arranged in any way. In order to show that Lemma A holds, all that is required is to show that all the required machinery is available in PM. It is so available in the shape of the definitions, the Law of Double Negation, De Morgan's Law (T40 form), the Distributive Laws, the Commutative and Associative Laws for conjunction and disjunction, and the Lemma for Substitution of Equivalents (p. 118). Therefore, Lemma A holds.

Lemma B. Every valid wff in CNF is a thesis of PM.

First, recall the structure of an expression in CNF. It has the general form of a conjunction of disjunctions. It follows that for a CNF to be valid each of its constituent disjunctions must be valid. Now a constituent disjunction in a CNF, in which only propositional variables can appear negated, can be valid only if it contains among its disjuncts some propositional variable both negated and unnegated. We therefore introduce the following definition:

A valid constituent disjunction (in a CNF) is a wff with disjunction as its only dyadic operator, which, by the use of the commutative and associative laws, can take the form

$$Y \lor (p_k \lor \sim p_k)$$

where p_k is some propositional variable.

Proof of Lemma B: Every valid constituent disjunction is a thesis of PM, since:

A2(Y/p, $p_k \lor \sim p_k/q$) : $(p_k \lor \sim p_k) \supset (Y \lor (p_k \lor \sim p_k))$ (1)

(1),T8(p_k/p) × D : $Y \lor (p_k \lor \sim p_k)$

and the Commutative and Associative Laws, together with the Rule for Substitution of Equivalents, hold in PM. But, since Adj is also a thesis of PM, every conjunction of such disjunctions is a thesis of PM, and hence every valid CNF is a thesis of PM. Thus, Lemma B holds.

Now let X be any valid wff of PM, and X' its CNF. By Lemma A,

$$\vdash (X \equiv X')$$ (1)

and since we have shown that every thesis of PM is valid, it follows that $X \equiv X'$ is valid. Since X is valid by hypothesis, it follows that X' is valid also. Hence, by Lemma B,

$$\vdash X'$$ (2)

But $$(p \equiv q) \supset (q \supset p)$$

is a thesis of PM, so by substitution and detachment, using (1), we obtain

$$\vdash (X' \supset X) \tag{3}$$

Then, (2),(3) $\times$ D gives us

$$\vdash X$$

That is, if X is a valid wff of PM, then X is a thesis of PM. Thus Theorem I holds, and PM is weakly complete.

THEOREM II. PM is strongly complete with respect to negation, absolutely, and in the sense of Post.

PROOF:

Let X be any wff of PM which is not a thesis. Let PM + X be the system resulting when X is added to the axioms of PM (everything else remaining the same). And let X' be the CNF of X. Now if X is not a thesis of PM, it follows from the weak completeness of PM that X is not valid. Therefore, X' is not valid, and hence must contain at least one conjunct, Y, which is not a valid constituent disjunction. Now since '(p.q) $\supset$ p' is a thesis of PM, and hence of PM + X, X' $\supset$ Y is a thesis of PM + X; but so is X' (since Lemma A holds for PM + X if it holds for PM). Therefore, Y is also a thesis of PM + X. Now in Y substitute 'p' for each unnegated variable, and '$\sim$p' for each negated variable. By applying the Law of Double Negation as often as necessary, we thus obtain from Y a thesis of the form:

$$p \vee p \vee \ldots \vee p$$

Using A1, we obtain from this, as a thesis of PM + X, the wff, 'p'.

Thus PM + X is inconsistent in the sense of Post. But if 'p' is a thesis, then, by substitution, every wff is a thesis, so PM + X is also absolutely inconsistent. And if every wff is a thesis, then, in particular, $\sim$X is a thesis, so the system is inconsistent with respect to negation. Therefore, by the definition of strong completeness, PM is strongly complete with respect to negation, absolutely, and in the sense of Post.

EXERCISES 19

19.1 Let PM* be a system with '$\supset$' and '$\vee$' as the only primitive

operators, and whose Axioms and Rules of Transformation
are those of PM.

Show that every thesis of PM* is valid, and discuss the
question: In what sense does it follow that PM* is consistent?

19.2 Show that

$$(p \supset (p \supset q)) \supset (p \supset q) \tag{1}$$

is a thesis of PM by the following method:

(a) Put (1) into CNF.

(b) Prove each conjunct and then use Adj to get the CNF as
a thesis.

(c) 'Reverse' the reduction to CNF to obtain (1).

19.3 Meredith has shown (1953) that the system which results from
replacing the axioms of PM by the single axiom

$$((p \supset q) \supset (r \lor (svt))) \supset ((s \supset p) \supset (r \lor (tvp))) \tag{1}$$

is complete. Use the method of 19.2 to show that (1) is a
thesis of PM.

CHAPTER 20

The System TB

We have seen that PM is a complete axiomatization of the full Propositional Calculus. Now there are two ways in which a system could fail to be complete in this way. On the one hand, the system could be like PM in having as its set of wffs all the wffs of PC, but unlike PM in having a set of axioms and Rules of Transformation which are not powerful enough to generate every valid wff. (An example of such a system would be PM with, say, A2 deleted.) On the other hand, the system could be unlike PM in having as its wffs only some selection from the wffs of PC, but like PM in having a set of axioms and Rules of Transformation which are powerful enough to generate every one of its wffs which is valid. Although such a system would not be a complete axiomatization of the whole of PC, it would be a complete axiomatization of a certain part of PC. We shall call such a part of PC a *fragment of PC*, and an axiomatization of a fragment might be called a *fragmentary axiomatization of PC*.

One fragment of PC which is of special interest is the *implicational* fragment, which contains just those wffs which have '⊃' as their only operator. Familiar examples of valid wffs of this type are Syll, Perm, Simp and Id. It is not hard to think of others, like

$$p ⊃ (q ⊃ (p⊃q))$$

which we could regard as an implicational analogue of Adj; or

$$(p ⊃ (q⊃r)) ⊃ ((r⊃s) ⊃ (p ⊃ (q⊃s)))$$

which we could regard as a sort of extension of Syll, since it allows us to telescope two applications of it.

A complete axiomatization of the implicational fragment of PC was devised by A. Tarski and P. Bernays (1930) and is set out below as the system TB.

The System TB

Primitive Symbols

1. p, q, r, . . . [Propositional variables]

2. ⊃   [Dyadic operator, material implication]
3. (,)   [Brackets]

Formation Rules

F1. A propositional variable standing alone is a wff.
F2. If X and Y are wffs, then (X ⊃ Y) is a wff.

Axioms

A1. (p⊃q) ⊃ ((q⊃r) ⊃ (p⊃r))   [Syll]
A2. ((p⊃q) ⊃ p) ⊃ p   [Peirce]
A3. p ⊃ (q⊃p)   [Simp]

Transformation Rules

R1. [*Substitution*]. As for PM.
R2. [*Detachment*]. As for PM.

We adopt our usual convention about bracketing, which allows us to drop outside brackets, and have already followed this in the statement of the axioms. We shall also occasionally use square brackets to make the structure of a long wff clearer to the eye. The axiom A2, named *Peirce*, is so named after the famous American logician, C. S. Peirce (1839–1914).

The methods of proof available in TB, viz. substitution and detachment, are exactly as in PM, and we shall use the same conventions in setting out proofs. There is one respect in which the *technique* of proof in TB tends to differ from that in PM – proofs in TB have rather more of the character of a frontal attack, since the lack of definitions forces us to rely more on initial substitutions which will give the desired theorem after one or more detachments. Sometimes the initial substitutions are rather extensive, but careful study of the proofs that follow will soon develop facility in selecting them.

Some theorems of TB

To distinguish the theorems of TB from those of PM, we shall employ the Greek letter 'Θ' instead of 'T', numbering the theorems Θ1, Θ2, . . .

Θ1.   ((q⊃p) ⊃ r) ⊃ (p⊃r)

PROOF:

A1(q⊃p/q) : (p ⊃(q⊃p)) ⊃ (((q⊃p) ⊃ r) ⊃ (p⊃r))   (1)
(1), A3 × D : Θ1

Θ2. p ⊃ ((p⊃r) ⊃ (q⊃r))

PROOF:

Θ1 ((p⊃r) ⊃ (q⊃r)/r) : ((q⊃p) ⊃ ((p⊃r) ⊃ (q⊃r))) ⊃
                                   (p ⊃ ((p⊃r) ⊃ (q⊃r)))   (1)
(1), A1 (q/p, p/q) × D   : Θ2.

In this proof the object of the substitution in Θ1, giving line (1), was to produce an expression of the form

$$X ⊃ Θ2$$

where X would be a known thesis or easily obtained, so that Θ2 could be proved by detachment. We could therefore have written line (1) more economically as

$$((q⊃p) ⊃ ((p⊃r) ⊃ (q⊃r))) ⊃ Θ2$$

In future we shall use this device whenever it is convenient.

Θ3. p ⊃ p [Id]

PROOF:

A1((p⊃q) ⊃ p/q, p/r) :
                 (p ⊃ ((p⊃q) ⊃ p)) ⊃ [(((p⊃q) ⊃ p) ⊃ p) ⊃ Θ3]   (1)
A3(p⊃q/q)   : p ⊃ ((p⊃q) ⊃ p)   (2)
(1),(2) × D   : (((p⊃q) ⊃ p) ⊃ p) ⊃ Θ3   (3)
(3), A2 × D   : Θ3

Θ4. p ⊃ (p ⊃ (p⊃p))

PROOF:

A3(p ⊃ (p⊃p)/p, p/q) : (p ⊃ (p⊃p)) ⊃ Θ4   (1)
(1), A3(p/q) × D   : Θ4

Θ5. (p ⊃ (p⊃q)) ⊃ (p⊃q)

PROOF:

A1(p⊃(p⊃q)/p, ((p⊃q)⊃q)⊃(p⊃q)/q, p⊃q/r) :
            [(p ⊃ (p⊃q)) ⊃ (((p⊃q) ⊃ q) ⊃ (p⊃q))] ⊃
                  [((((p⊃q) ⊃ q) ⊃ (p⊃q)) ⊃ (p⊃q)) ⊃ Θ5]   (1)
A1(p⊃q/q, q/r) : (p ⊃ (p⊃q)) ⊃ (((p⊃q) ⊃ q) ⊃ (p⊃q))   (2)

(1),(2) × D   : $((((p⊃q) ⊃ q) ⊃ (p⊃q)) ⊃ (p⊃q)) ⊃ Θ5$ (3)

A2(p⊃q/p)   : $(((p⊃q) ⊃ q) ⊃ (p⊃q)) ⊃ (p⊃q)$ (4)

(3),(4) × D   : $Θ5$

Θ6. $((p⊃q) ⊃ p) ⊃ ((p⊃q) ⊃ q)$

PROOF:

A1((p⊃q)⊃p/p, (p⊃q)⊃((p⊃q)⊃q)/q, (p⊃q)⊃q/r) :
$$[((p⊃q) ⊃ p) ⊃ ((p⊃q) ⊃ ((p⊃q) ⊃ q))] ⊃$$
$$[(((p⊃q) ⊃ ((p⊃q) ⊃ q)) ⊃ ((p⊃q) ⊃ q)) ⊃ Θ6]\ \ (1)$$
A1(p⊃q/p, p/q, q/r) : $((p⊃q) ⊃ p) ⊃ ((p⊃q) ⊃ ((p⊃q) ⊃ q))$ (2)

(1),(2) × D : $(((p⊃q) ⊃ ((p⊃q) ⊃ q)) ⊃ ((p⊃q) ⊃ q)) ⊃ Θ6$ (3)

(3), Θ5(p⊃q/p) × D : $Θ6$

Θ7. $p ⊃ ((p⊃q) ⊃ q)$

PROOF:

A1((p⊃q)⊃p/q, (p⊃q)⊃q/r) : $(p ⊃ ((p⊃q) ⊃ p)) ⊃$
$$[(((p⊃q) ⊃ p) ⊃ ((p⊃q) ⊃ q)) ⊃ Θ7]\ \ (1)$$
A3(p⊃q/q) : $p ⊃ ((p⊃q) ⊃ p)$ (2)

(1),(2) × D : $Θ6 ⊃ Θ7$ (3)

(3),Θ6 × D : $Θ7$

Θ8. $(((p⊃q) ⊃ q) ⊃ r) ⊃ (p⊃r)$

PROOF:

A1((p⊃q)⊃q/q), Θ7 × D : $Θ8$

Θ9. $(p ⊃ (q⊃r)) ⊃ (q ⊃ (p ⊃ r))$ [Perm]

PROOF:

A1(p⊃(q⊃r)/p, ((q⊃r)⊃r)⊃(p⊃r)/q, q⊃(p⊃r)/r) :
$$[(p ⊃ (q⊃r)) ⊃ (((q⊃r) ⊃ r) ⊃ (p⊃r))] ⊃$$
$$[((((q⊃r) ⊃ r) ⊃ (p⊃r)) ⊃ (q ⊃ (p⊃r))) ⊃ Θ9]\ \ (1)$$
(1), A1(q⊃r/q) × D : $[(((q⊃r) ⊃ r) ⊃ (p⊃r)) ⊃ (q ⊃$
$$(p⊃r))] ⊃ Θ9\ \ (2)$$
Θ8(q/p,r/q,p⊃r/r) : $(((q⊃r) ⊃ r) ⊃ (p⊃r)) ⊃ (q ⊃ (p⊃r))$ (3)

(2),(3) × D   : $Θ9$

We know from our experience of PM that certain theses are extremely useful in constructing proofs of others. Two of these are Syll and Simp which we have as axioms – to these we have now added Perm, and as each such useful thesis is obtained we can expect the others to be easier to prove.

Θ10.   (q⊃r) ⊃ ((p⊃q) ⊃ (p⊃r))

Θ11.   q ⊃ (p⊃p)

Θ12.   (q ⊃ (p⊃r)) ⊃ (p ⊃ (q⊃r))

Θ13.   (p ⊃ (q ⊃ (r⊃s))) ⊃ (q ⊃ (p ⊃ (r⊃s)))

Θ14.   (p ⊃ (q ⊃ (r⊃s))) ⊃ (p ⊃ (r ⊃ (q⊃s)))

Θ15.   (p ⊃ (q ⊃ (r ⊃ (s⊃t)))) ⊃ (p ⊃ (q ⊃ (s ⊃ (r⊃t))))

None of Θ10–15 are difficult to prove, and you should construct proofs of them for yourself at once. Θ10 is the permuted form of Syll in its A1 form, and where we want to refer to it by name, but distinguish it from the axiom, we shall call it 'Syll Θ'. Θ13–15 are extended forms of Perm.

An extremely useful theorem is:

Θ16.   (p ⊃ (q⊃r)) ⊃ ((r⊃s) ⊃ (p ⊃ (q⊃s)))

PROOF:

SyllΘ(s/p,p/q,q⊃r/r) : (p ⊃ (q⊃r)) ⊃ ((s⊃p) ⊃ (s ⊃ (q⊃r)))   (1)

(1) × Θ15   : (p⊃ (q⊃r)) ⊃ ((s⊃p) ⊃ (q ⊃ (s⊃r)))   (2)

(2)(q⊃r/p, r⊃s/q, q⊃s/r, p/s)

                 [(q⊃r) ⊃ ((r⊃s) ⊃ (q⊃s))] ⊃ Θ16   (3)

(3), A1(q/p,r/q,s/r) × D : Θ16

Θ17.   p ⊃ (q ⊃ (p⊃q))

PROOF:

A3(q⊃(p⊃q)/p, p/q) : (q ⊃ (p⊃q)) ⊃ Θ17   (1)

(1), A3(q/p,p/q) × D : Θ17

Θ18.   (p⊃q) ⊃ ((q⊃r) ⊃ ((r⊃s) ⊃ (p⊃s)))

PROOF:

Θ16(p⊃q/p, q⊃r/q, p⊃r/r, (r⊃s)⊃(p⊃s)/s) :

               A1 ⊃ [((p⊃r) ⊃ ((r⊃s) ⊃ (p⊃s))) ⊃ Θ18]   (1)

(1),A1 × D : ((p⊃r) ⊃ ((r⊃s) ⊃ (p⊃s))) ⊃ Θ18   (2)

(2), A1(r/q,s/r) × D : Θ18

Θ18 is an extended form of Syll. Further extensions of Syll, to five or more variables, are quite simple.

Consistency and completeness

It is easy to show that every thesis of TB is valid, by showing that the axioms are valid and the Rules of Transformation preserve validity. But of course it cannot follow from this that TB is consistent with respect to negation, except in the most vacuous sense, since TB contains no negation-operator. However, since no wff consisting of a single propositional variable is valid, it does follow that TB is consistent in the sense of Post – and, since this provides us with a wff which is not a thesis, it is therefore absolutely consistent.

If you are interested in consistency as a guarantee of freedom from contradiction then you are hardly likely to find these results worth while. For you will either feel that the guarantee has already been given by the lack of a negation in TB; or you will still want a guarantee but feel that it is not given by consistency in the two senses available. But if you are interested in consistency as a guarantee that the system is not one in which 'anything goes' – as a guarantee of freedom from triviality – then these results provide the guarantee. And if your interest in consistency and completeness is an interest in the adequacy of a system as an axiomatization of a certain field – if you want to know whether the set of theses coincides with the set of valid wffs – then the general result, that every thesis is valid, gives one half of the answer. The other half is given by the completeness result, that every valid wff of the implicational fragment of PC is a thesis of TB. This result, which we shall not prove here, was obtained by M. Wajsberg in 1937.

EXERCISES 20

Prove the following in TB:

20.1 $p \supset ((p \supset p) \supset p)$
20.2 $((p \supset p) \supset p) \supset p$
20.3 $((q \supset (r \supset p)) \supset q) \supset q$
20.4 $(r \supset s) \supset (q \supset (r \supset s))$
20.5 $(p \supset (q \supset s)) \supset (((q \supset s) \supset r) \supset (p \supset r))$
20.6 $(p \supset q) \supset (p \supset ((q \supset r) \supset r))$
20.7 $(q \supset p) \supset (p \supset p)$
20.8 $(p \supset q) \supset (((p \supset q) \supset q) \supset q)$
20.9 $(p \supset s) \supset (p \supset (q \supset s))$
20.10 $(p \supset q) \supset ((r \supset s) \supset ((q \supset r) \supset (p \supset s)))$
20.11 $(p \supset q) \supset ((q \supset r) \supset ((r \supset s) \supset ((s \supset t) \supset (p \supset t))))$
20.12 $(((p \supset q) \supset q) \supset q) \supset ((q \supset s) \supset (p \supset s))$
20.13 $(((p \supset q) \supset r) \supset q) \supset ((p \supset r) \supset (q \supset s) \supset (p \supset s)))$

CHAPTER 21

Extensions of TB : The System W

TB contains no definitions, since it is simply an axiomatization of the implicational fragment of PC. But there is one definition we could add – for disjunction is definable in terms of material implication alone.

Consider the truth-table:

p	q	p⊃q	(p⊃q) ⊃ q
1	1	1	1
1	0	0	1
0	1	1	1
0	0	1	0

'(p⊃q) ⊃ q' has the same truth-table as 'pvq', and so we could formulate the definition

$$(X \lor Y) =_{Df} ((X \supset Y) \supset Y)$$

If we add this definition to TB, we obtain an axiomatization of a larger fragment of PC – viz. that in which the only operators are '⊃' and 'v'. It can be seen that the completeness of this extended system is a consequence of the completeness of TB. For, by the definition, every valid wff in the implication/disjunction fragment of PC can be transformed into a valid wff of TB. For example, the Commutative Law:

$$(pvq) \supset (qvp)$$

is a definitional transform of:

Θ19. $((p\supset q) \supset q) \supset ((q\supset p) \supset p)$

PROOF:

Θ16((p⊃q)⊃q/p, q⊃p/q, (p⊃q)⊃p/r, p/s) :

   $(((p\supset q) \supset q) \supset ((q\supset p) \supset ((p\supset q) \supset p))) \supset (A2 \supset \Theta 19)$ (1)

A1(p⊃q/p, p/r)   : $((p\supset q) \supset q) \supset ((q\supset p) \supset$

   $((p\supset q) \supset p))$ (2)

(1),(2) × D), A2 × D   :   Θ19

149

However, no further extensions of this sort are possible. It is easy to show, for example, that conjunction is not definable in terms of material implication alone. For in order to define it we should have to find some implicational wff, $X \supset Y$, with the truth-table:

p	q	$X \supset Y$
1	1	1
1	0	0
0	1	0
0	0	0

But now consider the consequent, Y. For $X \supset Y$ to have this truth-table, Y's truth-table must be either

$$(a) \ 1, 0, 0, 0$$
$$\text{or } (b) \ 0, 0, 0, 0.$$

In case (a), the same problem is just posed again.

Case (b) is impossible, since *no purely implicational wff can have a truth-table consisting entirely of 0's.* For either Y is a single variable, which cannot have such a table; or Y is an implication whose consequent also has such a table; and so on until a single variable is reached.

Although we cannot extend TB further by adding definitions, other extensions are possible, which will produce an axiomatization of the whole of PC. The crucial lack in TB is negation. If we were to add '$\sim$' as a further primitive symbol, we could define all the other operators. However we must also add suitable axioms involving negation – for otherwise the only PC laws in negation provable would be those which are substitution instances of theses of TB, which would exclude, e.g., '$p \supset (\sim p \supset q)$'.

An alternative way to extend TB would be to make additions which would enable us to *define* negation in the extended system. (Again we would expect to have to add to the axioms.) Now we have already seen that no purely implicational wff can have a truth-table entirely of 0's. But suppose, for the moment, that there were such a wff, say X_o. Then consider the expression

$$p \supset X_o$$

Now, if $p = 1$, $p \supset X_o = 1 \supset 0 = 0$
and if $p = 0$, $p \supset X_o = 0 \supset 0 = 1$

Then 'p $\supset$ X$_o$' is false or true as 'p' is true or false, so we could formulate the definition:

$$\sim Y =_{Df} (Y \supset X_o)$$

Now although there is no implicational wff with the characteristics demanded of X$_o$, it is easy enough to add to TB something else that has the characteristic of always being false. The simplest thing to do is to add a *propositional constant* which denotes some false proposition. For the new primitive symbol we shall, naturally enough, choose '0'. By saying that this is a propositional constant we mean that although it may be substituted for propositional variables, it cannot itself have substitutions made for it. In addition, we must amend the Formation Rules so that '0' can appear in wffs, and add suitable definitions, including:

$$\sim X =_{Df} (X \supset 0)$$

Finally when we add one new axiom:

$$A4. \quad 0 \supset p$$

the resulting system is a complete axiomatization of the whole of PC. This extension of TB was devised by M. Wajsberg (1937) and we therefore call it 'W'. We set out its basis in the usual way:

The System W

Primitive symbols

1. p, q, r, . . . [Propositional variables]
2. 0 [Propositional constant]
3. $\supset$ [Dyadic operator, material implication]
4. (,) [Brackets]

Formation rules

F1. A propositional symbol (variable or constant) standing alone is a wff.
F2. If X and Y are wffs, then (X $\supset$ Y) is a wff.

Axioms

A1. (p$\supset$q) $\supset$ ((q$\supset$r) $\supset$ (p$\supset$r))
A2. ((p$\supset$q) $\supset$ p) $\supset$ p
A3. p $\supset$ (q$\supset$p)
A4. 0 $\supset$ p

Transformation rules

R1. Substitution [as in PM]
R2. Detachment [as in PM]

Definitions

1. [∼] ∼X =$_{Df}$ (X ⊃ 0)
2. [v] (X v Y) =$_{Df}$ (∼X ⊃ Y)
3. [.] (X.Y) =$_{Df}$ (∼(X ⊃ ∼Y)
4. [≡] (X ≡ Y) =$_{Df}$ ((X ⊃ Y).(Y ⊃ X))

Notice that Formation Rule F1 is so framed that '0' is a wff, in just the way that 'p' is. Notice too that A3 expresses one of the 'paradoxes of material implication' – viz. that a true proposition is implied by any proposition – and that A4 expresses the other – viz. that a false proposition implies any proposition. The choice of definitions is to some extent arbitrary. We could, for example, replace 2 and 3 by:

$$2'. \ (X \ v \ Y) =_{Df} ((X ⊃ Y) ⊃ Y)$$
$$\text{and } 3'. \ (X.Y) =_{Df} (∼(∼X \ v \ ∼Y)$$

We adopt our usual conventions about bracketing.

Some theorems of W

Since W is an extension of TB, so that all theorems of TB are theorems of W, we shall number the theorems of both systems in a single sequence, the next being Θ20.

Θ20.   0 ⊃ 0

PROOF:

Id(0/p)   : Θ20

Θ21.   ∼0

PROOF:

Θ20 × Def ∼   : Θ21

Θ22.   p v ∼p

PROOF:

Id(∼p/p)   : ∼p⊃∼p   (1)
(1) × Def v   : Θ22

Θ23.   p ⊃ ∼∼p

PROOF:

Θ7	: p ⊃ ((p⊃q) ⊃ q)	(1)
(1)(0/q)	: p ⊃ ((p⊃0) ⊃ 0)	(2)
(2) × Def ∼ (twice)	: Θ23	

Θ24.   ∼∼p ⊃ p

PROOF:

Θ19 × Perm	: (q⊃p) ⊃ (((p⊃q) ⊃ q) ⊃ p)	(1)
(1)(0/q)	: (0⊃p) ⊃ (((p⊃0) ⊃ 0) ⊃ p)	(2)
(2),A4 × D	: (((p⊃0) ⊃0) ⊃ p)	(3)
(3) × Def ∼ (twice)	: Θ24	

Θ25.   (∼p⊃p) ⊃ p   [Consequentia mirabilis]

PROOF:

| A2(0/q) | : ((p⊃0) ⊃ p) ⊃ p | (1) |
| (1) × Def ∼ | : Θ25 | |

Θ25 was known to be valid by certain Polish Jesuits in the sixteenth century, and was called by them the *consequentia mirabilis* since it asserts that if a proposition is implied by its own negation it is true. Łukasiewicz names it 'The Law of Clavius' after one of these Polish Jesuits.

Θ26.   (p⊃∼q) ⊃ (q⊃∼p)   [Transp]

PROOF:

Perm(0/r) × Def ∼   :   Θ26

Θ27.   (p⊃q) ⊃ (∼q⊃∼p)   [Transp]

PROOF:

A1(0/r) × Def ∼   :   Θ27

Θ28.   (∼p⊃q) ⊃ (∼q⊃p)   [Transp]

PROOF:

Θ27(∼p/p)	: (∼p⊃q) ⊃ (∼q⊃∼∼p)	(1)
SyllΘ(∼q/p, ∼∼p/q, p/r)	: (∼∼p⊃p) ⊃ ((∼q⊃∼∼p) ⊃ (∼q⊃p))	(2)
(2),Θ24 × D	: (∼q⊃∼∼p) ⊃ (∼q⊃p)	(3)
(1),(3) × Syll	: Θ28	

Θ29. (~p⊃~q) ⊃ (q⊃p)   [Transp]

PROOF:

Θ26(~p/p)   : (~p⊃~q) ⊃ (q⊃~~p)   (1)
Θ16(~p⊃~q/p, ~~p/r, p/s) :
              ((~p⊃~q) ⊃ (q⊃~~p)) ⊃ ((~~p⊃p) ⊃ Θ29)   (2)
(2),(1) × D   : (~~p⊃p) ⊃ Θ29   (3)
(3),Θ24 × D   : Θ29

Θ30. p ⊃ (q ⊃ (p.q))   [Adj]

PROOF:

Θ7   : p ⊃ ((p⊃q) ⊃ q)   (1)
(1) × Transp × Syll   : p ⊃ (~q ⊃ ~(p⊃q))   (2)
(2)(~q/q)   : p ⊃ (~~q ⊃ ~(p⊃~q))   (3)
(3) × Def .   : p ⊃ (~~q ⊃ (p.q))   (4)
(4) × Perm   : ~~q ⊃ (p ⊃ (p.q))   (5)
(5), Θ23(q/p) × Syll   : q ⊃ (p ⊃ (p.q))   (6)
(6) × Perm   : Θ30

Θ31. (p ⊃ (q⊃r)) ⊃ ((p⊃q) ⊃ (p⊃r))

PROOF:

SyllΘ(p⊃r/r)   : (q ⊃ (p⊃r)) ⊃ ((p⊃q) ⊃ (p ⊃ (p⊃r))) (1)
Θ5(r/q)   : (p ⊃ (p⊃r)) ⊃ (p⊃r)   (2)
(1),(2) × Θ16   : (q ⊃ (p⊃r))⊃ ((p⊃q) ⊃ (p⊃r))   (3)
Perm, (3) × Syll   : Θ31

Although Θ31 is a not uninteresting implicational law, it is included here chiefly to facilitate the proof of the Law of Composition (Θ32).

Θ32. (p⊃q) ⊃ ((p⊃r) ⊃ (p ⊃ (q.r)))   [Comp]

PROOF:

Adj(q/p,r/q)   : q ⊃ (r ⊃ (q.r))   (1)
SyllΘ(r⊃(q.r)/r)   : (q ⊃ (r ⊃ (q.r))) ⊃
                                      ((p⊃q) ⊃ (p ⊃ (r ⊃ (q.r))))   (2)
(2),(1) × D   : (p⊃q) ⊃ (p ⊃ (r ⊃ (q.r)))   (3)
Θ31(r/q, q.r/r)   : (p ⊃ (r ⊃ (q.r))) ⊃
                                      ((p⊃r) ⊃ (p ⊃ (q.r)))   (4)
(3),(4) × Syll   : Θ32

Θ33. (p ⊃ (q⊃r)) ⊃ ((p.q) ⊃ r)   [Imp]

PROOF:

Θ16(0/s)	:	(p ⊃ (q⊃r)) ⊃ ((r⊃0) ⊃ (p ⊃ (q⊃0)))	(1)
(1) × Def ∼	:	(p ⊃ (q⊃r)) ⊃ (∼r ⊃ (p ⊃ ∼q))	(2)
(2) × Transp × Syll	:	(p ⊃ (q⊃r)) ⊃ (∼(p⊃∼q) ⊃ r)	(3)
(3) × Def .	:	Θ33	

Θ34. (p.q) ⊃ p

PROOF:

Imp(p/r), A3 × D   :   Θ34

Θ35. (p.q) ⊃ q

PROOF:

Imp(q/r), Θ11(q/p,p/q) × D   :   Θ35

EXERCISES 21

21.1 Prove the following in W:

(a) ∼∼∼0

(b) 0 ⊃ ∼0

(c) (0 ⊃ q) ⊃ (0 ⊃ 0)

(d) ∼p ⊃ (p⊃q)

(e) ((p⊃q) ⊃ q) ⊃ (p∨q)

(f) (p⊃∼q) ⊃ (p ⊃ (q⊃s))

(g) p ⊃ (p.p)

(h) p ≡ (p.p)

(i) p ≡ (p∨p)

(j) (p.0) ≡ 0

(k) ((p.q) ⊃ r) ⊃ (p ⊃ (q⊃r))

(l) (p⊃q) ⊃ ((p.r) ⊃ (q.r))

21.2 Let Classical Positive Logic (CPL) be the system formed by adding to TB

(a) conjunction as a primitive (with suitable change in the Formation Rules)

(b) the axioms: A4. (p.q) ⊃ p

A5. (p.q) ⊃ q

A6. (p⊃q) ⊃ ((p⊃r) ⊃ (p ⊃ (q.r)))

(c) definitions of '∨' and '≡'.

Obtain the following as theorems of CPL:

(a) (p.q) ⊃ (q.p)

(b) p ⊃ (pvq)

(c) q ⊃ (pvq)

(d) (p.q) ⊃ (pvq)

(e) ((p.q).r) ⊃ p

(f) ((p.q).r) ⊃ q

(g) ((p.q).r) ⊃ (p.(q.r))

(h) p ⊃ (q ⊃ (p.q))

CHAPTER 22

Consistency and Completeness of W

It is easily established that every thesis of W is valid. (Note that wffs containing '0' present no problem: in testing them for validity each occurrence of '0' is always assigned the value *false*.) The consistency of W with respect to negation then follows by the definition of negation and the consideration that for any wff, X, at most one of X and X ⊃ 0 can be valid. It then follows that W is also consistent absolutely and in the sense of Post.

As regards completeness, it is possible to show directly that every valid wff of W is a thesis of W. However, we shall show this indirectly by showing that every thesis of PM is a thesis of W – i.e. that W contains PM. This result provides a basis for proving that W is weakly complete.

To show that every thesis of PM is a thesis of W, we notice that the theses of PM are the axioms of that system together with their transforms under Substitution and Detachment. Then since the Transformation Rules of the two systems are the same, we know that if the axioms of PM are theses of W, so are all their transforms under those rules. So the first step is to obtain the PM axioms as theorems of W.

Θ36. (pvp) ⊃ p   [= PM 1]

PROOF:

Θ25 [i.e. consequentia mirabilis] × Def v   :   Θ36

Θ37.   q ⊃ (pvq)   [= PM 2]

PROOF:

A3(q/p,∼p/q) × Def v   :   Θ37

Θ38.   (pvq) ⊃ (qvp)   [= PM 3]

PROOF:

Θ28 × Def v   :   Θ38

Θ39. (p v (qvr)) ⊃ (q v (pvr))   [= PM 4]

PROOF:

Perm($\sim$p/p,$\sim$q/q) × Def v   :   Θ39

Θ40. (q⊃r) ⊃ ((pvq) ⊃ (pvr))   [= PM 5]

PROOF:

SyllΘ($\sim$p/p) × Def v   :   Θ40

Note that it was really unnecessary to prove Θ39 for these purposes, since the fourth axiom of PM was shown to be non-independent.

Now in order to establish that PM is contained in W, in the sense that every thesis of PM is a thesis of W, we need to take account of the fact that the *definitions* differ in the two systems. In particular we have in PM, but not in W:

$$(X \supset Y) =_{Df} (\sim X \vee Y)$$
$$\text{and } (X.Y) =_{Df} \sim(\sim X \vee \sim Y)$$

We need to show that anything obtainable by their use in PM can be obtained in some way in W. A little reflection will show that this is so provided that we have in W:

(*a*) the Rule for Substitution of Equivalents.
(*b*) the theorems:

  (i) (p⊃q) ≡ ($\sim$pvq)
  (ii) (p.q) ≡ $\sim$($\sim$pv$\sim$q)

Accordingly we shall show that both these conditions are satisfied.

The Rule for substitution of equivalents

The proof that this rule holds for W is very similar in structure to the earlier proof that it holds for PM. We shall therefore set out the proof more sketchily in this case.

You will recall that the Rule is:

If X, Y, Z, W are wffs such that:

1. Z is a part of X
2. ⊢(Z ≡ W)   } then ⊢Y.
3. Y = X[W/Z]
4. ⊢X

and that the proof proceeds via the Lemma:

> If X, Y, Z, W are wffs such that:
>
> 1. Z is a part of X
> 2. $\vdash (Z \equiv W)$ $\Big\}$ then $\vdash (X \equiv Y)$
> 3. Y = X[W/Z]

To prove the Lemma for the system W we need to consider the cases:

> 1. X is Z
> 2. *a.* X is Z ⊃ U
>   *b.* X is U ⊃ Z where U is some wff.

Notice that Case 2*a* has as a special case that in which X is Z ⊃ 0, which is equivalent to the case in which X is ∼Z which had to be considered separately for PM.

In Case 1, the Lemma is obvious. In Case 2, the Lemma asserts that under the hypothesis

$$\vdash (Z \equiv W)$$

we have, in Case 2*a*, $\vdash ((Z \supset U) \equiv (W \supset U))$
and in Case 2*b*, $\vdash ((U \supset Z) \equiv (U \supset W))$

Thus, in order to show that the Lemma holds in Case 2, it is sufficient to obtain as theorems of W:

Θ41. $(p \equiv q) \supset ((p \supset r) \equiv (q \supset r))$
Θ42. $(p \equiv q) \supset ((r \supset p) \equiv (r \supset q))$

To prove Θ41:

Θ34(p⊃q/p, q⊃p/q), A1 × Syll   :

$$((p \supset q).(q \supset p)) \supset ((q \supset r) \supset (p \supset r)) \quad (1)$$

Similarly, use Θ35 to get   : $((p \supset q).(q \supset p)) \supset ((p \supset r) \supset (q \supset r)) \quad (2)$
(1),(2) × Comp × Def ≡   :   Θ41

Θ42 is proved in similar fashion.

Now Θ41 yields $(Z \equiv W) \supset ((Z \supset U) \equiv (W \supset U))$ so that if $\vdash (Z \equiv W)$, as we have by hypothesis, then

$$\vdash ((Z \supset U) \equiv (W \supset U))$$

Thus the Lemma holds in Case 2*a*; and by similar argument from Θ42, it holds in Case 2*b* also.

But every wff of W can be expressed with '⊃' as the only operator. Therefore every well-formed part of a wff of W must imply or be implied by some other well-formed part of the wff. Therefore, since the Lemma holds in Cases 1 and 2, it holds in every case.

If the Lemma holds in W, so does the Rule.

For Θ34 enables us to obtain ⊢ ((X ≡ Y) ⊃ (X ⊃ Y)).

But if the Lemma holds, then ⊢ (X ≡ Y)

and therefore ⊢ (X ⊃ Y).

The Rule adds the hypothesis, ⊢ X

which gives, by Detachment, ⊢ Y.

Thus given the conditions of the Rule, its conclusion follows. Therefore, *the Rule for substitution of equivalents holds in W*.

Equivalence Theorems

Θ43. $p \equiv \sim\sim p$

PROOF:

Θ23, Θ24 × Adj × Def ≡ : Θ43

Θ44. $p \equiv p$ [Id]

PROOF:

Θ43, Θ43 × Eq : Θ44

Here we use the same notation as in PM to indicate use of the Rule for Substitution of Equivalents.

Θ45. $(p \supset q) \equiv (\sim p \vee q)$

PROOF:

Θ44(p⊃q/p)	: $(p \supset q) \equiv (p \supset q)$	(1)
(1), Θ43 × Eq	: $(p \supset q) \equiv (\sim\sim p \supset q)$	(2)
(2) × Def v	: Θ45	

Θ46. $(p.q) \equiv \sim(\sim p \vee \sim q)$

PROOF:

Θ44(p.q/p)	: $(p.q) \equiv (p.q)$	(1)
(1) × Def .	: $(p.q) \equiv \sim(p \supset \sim q)$	(2)
(2), Θ43 × Eq	: $(p.q) \equiv \sim(\sim\sim p \supset \sim q)$	(3)
(3) × Def v	: Θ46	

Θ45 and Θ46 are of course the two equivalence theorems which will enable us, by use of Substitution of Equivalents, to obtain in W anything we could obtain by use of the corresponding definitions in PM. Thus we have shown that every thesis of PM is also a thesis of W. So we have:

THEOREM 1 : W contains PM.

It follows that W is a complete axiomatization of PC as defined by the Formation Rules of PM. But the question remains open whether W is complete in the sense that every valid wff *of W* is a thesis of W – for the wffs of W containing '0' are not wffs of PM, although every wff of PM, is a wff of W.

We shall therefore prove that every valid wff of W is provable in W.

Since W contains PM, we have in W all the machinery for putting any wff – including those containing '0' – into CNF.[1] Therefore every wff in W has a CNF.

Consider then the conjuncts of any valid CNF. Each one is a valid disjunction which is either

> (*a*) a thesis of PM, or obtainable by substitution in such a thesis,

or else (*b*) not obtainable by substitution in a thesis of PM.

In case (*a*), the disjunction is provable in W, since W contains PM. And in case (*b*), the disjunction is also provable in W. For then the only way for the disjunction to be valid is for it to have the form:

$$\sim 0 \vee X$$

and it is therefore provable, since

$$A4, \Theta43(0/p) \times Eq \times Def \vee \quad : \quad \sim 0 \vee p$$

Therefore every valid disjunction is provable in W; and so by adjunction every valid CNF is provable in W. Therefore, every valid wff of W is a thesis of W. So we have:

THEOREM 2 : W is weakly complete.

EXERCISES 22

22.1 Show that W is strongly complete

> (*a*) with respect to negation (i.e. there is no pair of theses with the forms X and X ⊃ 0)

[1] See the proof of Lemma A, p. 139.

(*b*) absolutely

(*c*) in the sense of Post.

[*Hint*: Let the added axiom be X, and the extended system, W+X. By the weak completeness of W, X is not valid. Thus there is some assignment of truth-values to its variables under which X = 0. Choose such a case and substitute '∼0' or '0' for each variable according to whether it gets 1 or 0 under the assignment. The resulting wff is a thesis of W+X, and plays a part analogous to that of the invalid constituent disjunction in the proof for PM.]

22.2 Show that each of these systems is contained in PM:

(*a*) TB

(*b*) CPL (see Exercise 21.2)

22.3 Show that the following system, due to Meredith (1951), is contained in PM.

Primitives, *rules* and *definitions* are as for PM.

Axioms: 1. (pvp) ⊃ p

2. p ∨ (p⊃q)

3. (pvq) ⊃ ((q⊃r) ⊃ (pvr))

(Meredith's system in fact contains PM as well as being contained in it. If you want practice in working another system with PM's primitives, you could set yourself the task of proving this.)

22.4 Show that the following system, due to Church, is contained in W:

Primitives, *rules* and *definitions* are as for W.

Axioms: 1. p ⊃ (q⊃p)

2. (r ⊃ (p⊃q)) ⊃ ((r⊃p) ⊃ (r⊃q))

3. ((p⊃0) ⊃ 0) ⊃ p

PART III

The Lower Predicate Calculus

Some General Remarks on Part III

These remarks are addressed to readers who know something about the Predicate Calculus already. Beginners in logic should omit them, at least at a first reading, and proceed straight to Chapter 23.

Our treatment of the Lower Predicate Calculus (LPC) diverges in two main ways from that found in most books on the subject.

1. We divide LPC into several strata, of increasing degrees of complexity and comprehensiveness. A considerable proportion of Part III is devoted to setting out in some detail two fragments of LPC, the second being an extension of the first. The first of these (LPC1) consists of uniform quantification theory for monadic LPC, and for it we use a simplified notation which is similar in essential respects to that employed by Von Wright in *On the Idea of Logical Truth I*,[1] in which the bound variables are omitted. The second (LPC2) is a wider fragment of monadic LPC, in which free individual-variables occur, but not within the scope of quantifiers; and we use a simplified notation here too. For each of these systems we give Decision Procedures, and also an axiomatic basis which we prove to be consistent and complete by elementary methods. We then extend our survey to include formulae with multiple quantification, the identity relation, and two- and three-place predicate variables. At this stage bound variables are explicitly introduced for the first time, and with them a more standard LPC notation. Finally we sketch the range of the full LPC, but without attempting an axiomatic presentation.

We have found that this scheme offers several advantages. For one thing, it enables practice to be given in axiomatic procedure in the Predicate Calculus without the complexities which make an axiomatic treatment of the full LPC very difficult for beginners. For another, the notation used for LPC1 and LPC2 greatly facilitates tests for validity and derivations of theorems, and enables students to handle much more intricate formulae than they could otherwise cope with. (Anyone who doubts this is invited to re-state the rules

[1] Reprinted in his book *Logical Studies*.

and work through the examples and exercises in, for example, Chapters 27, 29, 33 and 35, using a more orthodox notation such as the Russellian one.)

2. The other main way in which our treatment of LPC is somewhat unusual is that in LPC1 and LPC2 we have tried to draw a clear distinction between validity in the logic of a non-empty universe and validity in the logic of an empty universe. Most logic texts, it would appear, implicitly or explicitly work within the former logic only.

Any reader, however, who wishes to follow this more usual practice of confining himself to the logic of a non-empty universe has only to disregard all asterisks in Chapters 27–30, to neglect certain easily identifiable passages, especially in Chapter 26, and to omit Chapter 36 entirely.

CHAPTER 23

The Lower Predicate Calculus : Introduction

A limitation of PC

In the Propositional Calculus we have considered solely complete statements or propositions and some of the ways (viz. the truth-functional ways) in which these complete propositions can be combined or operated on to form complex propositions. The only variables we have used have been propositional variables, i.e. variables which take as their values whole propositions, whether simple or complex. A variable such as 'p' can be taken to represent any proposition we please, but it cannot stand for anything *less* than a complete proposition, i.e. it cannot stand for any part of a proposition, unless that part is itself a complete proposition. One result of this is a certain limitation in the applicability of PC methods. A valid inference can have its validity exhibited by the techniques of PC if, but only if, when we replace each distinct whole proposition within it by a distinct variable, the result is an inferential schema which can be shown to be valid by PC methods as described in Part I. We have seen a number of examples of this procedure in earlier chapters.

There are, however, many inferences which are obviously valid, but whose validity cannot be displayed in this way. An example is: 'There are no snakes in New Zealand; but some New Zealand animals are venomous; therefore there are some venomous animals other than snakes'; for although this is clearly valid, if we were simply to replace each whole proposition by a propositional variable, we should obtain the inferential schema

$$\frac{\begin{array}{c} p \\ q \end{array}}{\therefore\ r}$$

which is certainly not a valid one. It is clear on a very little reflection that the validity of the inference depends not only on the relation between the three propositions in it, but also on the relations between expressions such as 'snake', 'New Zealand animal' and 'venomous', which are something less than complete propositions. The Propositional Calculus by itself, therefore, cannot express the logical form of such an inference; and for this reason if for no other we need to add to our stock of logical symbolism.

Predicates and predicate variables

First of all we need a new set of variables which can take as their values expressions of the kind we have just mentioned. Such expressions are known in logic as *predicates*. We shall not attempt here to give a rigorous definition of the word 'predicate', as this would involve philosophical questions of considerable intricacy. We can however give an indication of the use of the word which will be sufficiently clear for our present purposes.

Roughly, a predicate is any expression which stands for a property which a thing or person can possess. The word 'property' here is being used in a very wide sense. Not only those characteristics of things which would ordinarily be said to be their qualities or properties, such as their colour or their shape, but also e.g. their location or their activities or their habits, are to rank as properties. Thus if we say of a man that he is an Austrian, or that he drinks more than is good for his health, or that he is on a journey, or of an object that it is an object of a certain kind, say a book, or of a number that it is divisible by 7, we shall in each case be said to be attributing a property to the person or thing in question; and the phrases '(is) an Austrian', '(is) a book', '(is) divisible by 7', and so forth, are said to be predicates. (In certain of these phrases the word 'is' has been placed in brackets, because it is sometimes regarded as part of the predicate-phrase and sometimes not. This, however, is a question for philosophical logic rather than for formal logic; and as it will not affect any of the problems or techniques discussed in this book, we shall not pursue the matter further here.)

As predicate variables (i.e. variables which take predicates as their values) we shall use the series of small letters beginning 'f', 'g', 'h', . . .

A predicate is not itself a statement or proposition: we could not, for example, sensibly ask whether 'blue' or 'in Zanzibar' is true or false. A predicate can, however, become an element in a proposition, and there are two main ways in which this may happen.

(a) Individuals and individual-variables

We may say of some specified individual thing (or person, etc.) that it has the property for which the predicate stands. To do this we typically begin with some name of the thing in question, and follow this with the appropriate predicate-phrase. We say, for example, that Socrates is wise (i.e. has the property of wisdom), and in this statement '(is) wise' is a predicate. But 'Socrates' is not a predicate: 'Socrates' does not stand for a property which some individual may possess, it stands for the individual himself. We therefore require a further set of variables which shall take as their values names of individual things, people, etc. We call such variables *individual-variables* (meaning thereby, of course, not that the variables are themselves individuals – whatever that might mean – but that they stand indifferently for the names of individual things, just as predicate variables stand indifferently for predicates and propositional variables stand indifferently for propositions.)

As individual-variables we shall use the sequence of small letters which begins with 'x', 'y' and 'z' (and continues if necessary with 'w' and then backwards through the alphabet.)

By combining predicate variables and individual-variables we can construct certain special types of propositional schemata. Thus, 'fx' is a schema which represents the form of propositions like 'Socrates is wise', i.e. propositions which assert that a certain individual possesses a certain property. You should note that we are following what is in fact the common convention of writing the predicate-expression before the individual-variable in such schemata, even though the most usual order of words in the relevant sentences in a language such as English might make us expect to find the symbols in the reverse order, with the individual-variable first.

We shall not meet schemata containing individual-variables for several chapters to come, so we shall say no more about them just now.

(b) Quantifiers

A second way in which we may incorporate a predicate in a statement is by asserting that *everything*, or *nothing*, or *something*, has the property for which the predicate stands. When we say any of these things we do not mention any individual which has or does not have the property in question. We cannot therefore express such propositions by means of individual-variables, but need some further symbolism. We shall use the symbol 'U' followed by a predicate-expression to mean that everything has the property in question. Thus 'Uf' is to mean 'Everything possess the property for which the predicate f stands'; though it will usually be more convenient (if less strictly accurate) to read it as 'Everything has the property f', or simply 'Everything is (an) f'. Similarly 'Something has the property f' will be expressed by the formula '∃f'. Alternative readings for '∃f' are 'Something is (an) f', 'There is at least one (thing which is) f', and so forth. The statement that nothing is (an) f is the negation of the statement that something is (an) f; it will therefore be symbolized by '∼∃f'.

A formula which consists of 'U' or '∃' followed by a predicate-expression we shall call a *quantified schema*. The symbols 'U' and '∃' are known as *quantifiers*, the former as *the universal quantifier* and the latter as *the existential quantifier*. (It is from the initial letters of the words 'universal' and 'existential' that the symbols 'U' and '∃' have been derived. The existential quantifier is written as an inverted 'E' partly because this is very frequently done in books on logic, and partly to avoid any possible confusion with the symbol for equivalence in the Polish notation.)

'U' and '∃' can be defined in terms of each other. To say that everything is f is the same as saying that nothing fails to be f, or that nothing is not f. We therefore have the valid equivalence

$$Uf \equiv \sim\exists\sim f$$

Similarly, to say that something is f is to say that not everything fails to be f. We therefore have the further valid equivalence

$$\exists f \equiv \sim U\sim f$$

In view of these equivalences, we can *either* take 'U' as primitive and define '∃' as '∼U∼' *or* take '∃' as primitive and define 'U' as '∼∃∼'.

Furthermore, by the law of double negation we have the following additional valid equivalences

$$\sim Uf \equiv \exists\sim f$$
$$\sim\exists f \equiv U\sim f$$

The four equivalences we have just mentioned give us the following replacement rule, which we shall call the *Rule of Quantifier Transformation*:

Either quantifier may be replaced by the other, provided that a negation sign is either inserted or deleted both immediately before and immediately after it.

It should be carefully noted that 'U' and 'Ǝ' are not variables but constants. I.e. they do not (like 'p' or 'f' or 'x') stand indifferently for any item in a certain range of values, but (like 'v' or '⊃') have a definite, determinate meaning.

Complex predicates

Something more must be said about predicates and predicate variables before we proceed. In PC we have used '∼', 'v', '.', '⊃' and '≡' solely as proposition-forming operators on propositions. It is clear, however, that the notions for which these symbols stand (in their normal interpretation) have an application to predicates just as much as to propositions. We can, for instance, say that Socrates is *both wise and ironical*, that a certain figure is *either circular or elliptical*, that a certain number is *not a prime*; and we can then say that the italicized phrases are conjunctive, disjunctive and negative predicates respectively. We therefore extend the use of the operators '∼', 'v' and '.', using them now not only as proposition-forming operators on propositions but also as predicate-forming operators on predicates. Hence we obtain predicate-expressions such as '∼f', 'fvg' and 'f.g'. Similarly we can introduce (materially) implicative, and (materially) equivalent predicate-expressions such as 'f⊃g', 'f≡g'. It would not be strictly correct to speak of these operators as *truth-functional* when they are used with predicate variables, since predicates themselves do not have a truth-value. Their use is, however, closely analogous to a truth-functional one, as may be seen from an example such as the following: for a given individual, e.g. Socrates, there are four and only four possibilities with regard to the predicates 'wise' and 'ironical'. Socrates may be (*a*) wise and ironical, (*b*) wise but not ironical, (*c*) not wise but ironical, (*d*) neither wise nor ironical. The statement that Socrates is either wise or ironical will count as true in cases (*a*), (*b*) and (*c*), but false in case (*d*). This presents a close parallel to the truth-table definition of 'v' in PC. The other operators can be dealt with similarly.

Predicate-expressions can be either well-formed (like 'f⊃(gv∼h)') or ill-formed (like 'f⊃g⊃h' or '⊃fg∼'). The formation rules for predicate-expressions are exactly parallel to those for wffs in PC. They will be stated explicitly in the next chapter.

This explanation of complex predicates leads on to some further remarks about quantified schemata. We have already drawn the distinction between propositions like 'Socrates is wise', which ascribe a property to a specified individual, and quantified propositions like 'There are tigers in India'. We may perhaps have given the impression that in the case of every sentence which is *grammatically* of the subject-predicate form, the 'subject of the sentence' should be represented in logic by an individual-variable, and only the 'predicate of the sentence' by a predicate-expression. Such an impression would be completely mistaken. In the case of the proposition 'Some swans are white', e.g., although the phrase 'some swans' is the *grammatical* subject and not the *grammatical* predicate of the sentence in which the proposition is expressed, neither 'some swans' nor 'swans' is the name of an individual thing. On the contrary '(is) a swan' is a typical example of what we have called a predicate in the logical sense; so is '(is) white'; and the word 'some' is a sign of quantification. The Predicate Calculus formula which will represent such a proposition, therefore, will contain two predicate variables and a quantifier. We can see what the formula will be if we translate 'Some swans are white' into 'There are things which are *both* swans *and* white things (at the same time.)' If we represent '(is) a swan' by 'f' and '(is) white' by 'g', the formula will be '$\exists(f.g)$'.

Now let us consider a proposition such as 'All tigers have stripes'. Once more 'all tigers' is not the name of an individual, but '(is) a tiger' is a predicate; so is 'has stripes' (or '(is) striped'); and 'all' is a sign of quantification – of universal quantification this time. By analogy with the previous example we might be inclined to express this by the formula '$U(f.g)$'. This however would not do, as it would mean 'Everything is a striped tiger' (more literally 'Everything is both a tiger and striped'), i.e. 'Nothing exists except striped tigers'. The point is not that this is manifestly false (though it is), but that it is not what we mean to assert when we say 'All tigers have stripes'. The predicate-expression should not be 'f.g' but 'f⊃g', which means in the present example 'if a tiger, then striped' or alternatively (since '...⊃—' may be replaced by '∼(... . ∼—)') 'not both a tiger and *un*striped'. And this (if we grant the truth of 'all tigers are striped') is something which applies universally to everything. *I* am not an unstriped tiger; the books on my shelves are not unstriped tigers; tigers themselves are not unstriped tigers; and so forth. So the formula for 'All tigers are striped' is '$U(f⊃g)$', or alternatively

'U∼(f.∼g)', or alternatively again (since 'U∼' can be replaced by '∼∃') '∼∃(f.∼g)' – i.e. 'nothing is a tiger but not striped', 'there are no unstriped tigers'.

The fact that 'U(f⊃g)' is equivalent to '∼∃(f.∼g)' serves to bring out one important point about the meaning of universally quantified propositions containing an implicative predicate, a point connected with the fact that the implication in question is *material* implication. When we say 'There are no unstriped tigers' we are not thereby asserting that there *are* any tigers at all, but only that there are no unstriped ones. In fact if there are no tigers at all, then *a fortiori* there are no unstriped tigers. So quite generally, '∼∃(f.∼g)' does not have as part of its meaning that there are any f's. It merely says that the properties f and not-g are never found together, and this is not to say that the property f is ever found at all. And if '∼∃(f.∼g)' does not have as part of its meaning that there are any f's, 'U(f⊃g)', since it is equivalent to '∼∃(f.∼g)', cannot have this as part of its meaning either.

It may be thought that in this respect 'U(f⊃g)' does not express the usual meaning of English sentences of the form 'All so-and-so's are such-and-such'; and in many cases it is plausible to say that this is true. If I arrive at a theatre just before the curtain rises and the theatre attendant tells me that all seats are occupied, I may naturally take him to mean that there *are* seats in the theatre, but no unoccupied ones. On the other hand, the man who puts up a notice on his property worded 'All trespassers will be prosecuted' is not asserting that there are or will be any trespassers (indeed he almost certainly hopes that there will be none at all). Such a notice is naturally interpreted simply to mean that there will be at any rate no unprosecuted trespassers, or that *any trespassers there may happen to be* will be prosecuted. The meaning of propositions of the form 'U(f⊃g)' is analogous to this case rather than to the previous one. It is not *absolutely* analogous, perhaps; for if it turned out that there were no trespassers, we should not feel inclined on that ground *alone* to say 'So what the notice said was true'; whereas if there are no f's it does follow that U(f⊃g) is true. There is a parallel here with the fact that in PC if p is false, p⊃q is true. No confusion need occur in either case so long as we keep clear about what '⊃' means in its standard interpretation; but just as in PC it is useful from time to time to remind oneself that 'p⊃q' means no more and no less than '∼pvq', or '∼(p.∼q)', so in the Predicate Calculus it is useful to remind oneself that 'U(f⊃g)' means no more and no less than '∼∃(f.∼g)'.

If however, we wish to express explicitly in Predicate Calculus symbolism an assertion to the effect that not merely are there no f-non-g's but also that there *are* some f's, there is no difficulty in doing so. We can simply conjoin '∃f' to 'U(f⊃g)' to obtain the formula '∃f.U(f⊃g)'.

You should now be in a position to write down a good many quantified schemata for yourself and to grasp their meaning. E.g. 'U(f ⊃ (g.h))' means 'Whatever is f is both g and h'; and '∃(f.∼(gvh))' means 'There is something which is f but neither g nor h'. You should also be at least beginning to have some grasp of the range of propositions whose form can be expressed by quantified schemata. You will find it extremely useful at this point to work through the exercises at the end of this chapter. These exercises require 'translation from English into logic'; but (as we remarked in connection with PC) the formulae with which we replace the English sentences do not and cannot express all the nuances of meaning of the English sentences themselves. They catch only the logical skeleton of that meaning, and only so much of that as the structure of the calculus permits. Such skeletons are not, however, to be despised, for it is on them that the validity of inferences depends, and that is no trivial matter.

Logically equivalent predicate-expressions

In our study of PC we encountered equivalence transformations. Such transformations consisted in the replacement of some well-formed part X of a wff by another expression Y which was equivalent to X. X and Y were said to be equivalent if any and every possible *uniform* substitution of actual propositions for the variables throughout X and Y was such that the result of such substitution in X necessarily had the same truth-value as the result of the substitution in Y. (By 'uniform substitution throughout X and Y' we mean the substitution of the same proposition for every occurrence of the same variable whether it occurs in X or in Y.) The test for whether X and Y were equivalent in the sense required consisted in discovering whether the formula

$$X \equiv Y$$

was valid when tested by the truth-table method or some other adequate decision procedure.

Something analogous to this obtains for predicate-expressions. Two predicate-expressions α and β will be said to be equivalent if any and every possible uniform substitution of actual predicates for the variables throughout α and β is such that anything which possessed the property for which the predicate thus obtained from α stands would be bound also to possess the property for which the predicate obtained from β stands, and *vice versa*.

In the Predicate Calculus we shall allow ourselves to replace any predicate-expression which occurs within a formula by any other predicate-expression with which it is equivalent. For example, if we are entitled to describe a man as *tall and handsome*, we are equally entitled to describe him as *handsome and tall* and *vice versa*: he logically could not have the one (conjunctive) property without having the other. And this holds good for any object and for any conjunctive predicate. Conjunction is commutative for predicates as well as for propositions. In fact, whenever any equivalence holds in PC, a corresponding equivalence holds for predicate-expressions. Thus the analogue of one of the De Morgan Laws permits us to replace 'fvg' by '∼(∼f.∼g)', and so forth.

We can put this more accurately as follows. We shall say that a predicate-expression α and a wff of PC α′ are *isomorphic with each other* if and only if α can be obtained from α′ by uniformly replacing each distinct propositional variable in α′ by a distinct predicate variable (and leaving the operators and brackets unchanged.) Then if we have two well-formed predicate-expressions α and β which are isomorphic respectively with the PC wffs α′ and β′, and if

$$\alpha' \equiv \beta'$$

is a valid formula in PC, α is equivalent to β.[1]

Although this account of the equivalence of predicate-expressions is a perfectly adequate one, it will simplify things later on if we substitute for it a somewhat differently expressed account, which will, however, yield exactly the same results.

You will be familiar from earlier chapters with the fact that if X is a valid formula in PC, and Y is derived from X by uniform

---

[1] Hitherto we have used the capital letters 'X', 'Y', as PC meta-logical variables. In this passage, however, and in some subsequent ones, we shall be dealing with the close analogy which exists between predicate-expressions and PC formulae; and since we are using 'α', 'β', . . . as meta-logical variables for predicate-expressions, we have thought it would make the argument easier to follow in such contexts if we used 'α″', 'β″', . . . as PC meta-logical variables instead of 'X','Y', ...

substitution of wffs of PC for some or all of the variables in X, then Y is also a valid formula in PC. So if we take a valid *equivalential* formula in PC, $(\alpha' \equiv \beta')$, and make any such substitutions in it, the result will be another valid equivalential formula in PC, $(\gamma' \equiv \delta')$. Therefore by the rule we have stated, γ and δ (the predicate-expressions isomorphic with γ' and δ' respectively) will be equivalent.

Now clearly we could have reached this result in one step instead of two if we had allowed ourselves to replace the propositional variables in α' and β' not only by single predicate variables but by any well-formed predicate-expressions (provided of course that such replacement is made uniformly throughout α' and β'.) We shall therefore recast our account of the equivalence of predicate-expressions as follows:

If $(\alpha' \equiv \beta')$ is a valid formula in PC, $p_1, \ldots, p_n$ the totality of the propositional variables occurring in $(\alpha' \equiv \beta')$, and γ and δ are derived from α' and β' respectively by uniformly replacing each of $p_1, \ldots, p_n$ by some well-formed predicate-expression, then γ is equivalent to δ.

To illustrate this, let us consider the PC equivalence

$$(p \supset {\sim}q) \equiv (q \supset {\sim}p) \tag{1}$$

From this, by the rule we have just stated, we can immediately obtain the equivalence of, e.g., '$(f.{\sim}g) \supset {\sim}(gvh)$' and '$(gvh) \supset {\sim}(f.{\sim}g)$' by replacing 'p' by 'f.${\sim}g$' and 'q' by 'gvh'. Now '$(f.{\sim}g) \supset {\sim}(gvh)$' is not *isomorphic* with 'p$\supset{\sim}$q', nor is '$(gvh) \supset {\sim}(f.g)$' with 'q$\supset{\sim}$p' : we reserve the term 'isomorphic' for wffs and predicate-expressions which can be derived from each other by simple replacement of variables by variables. Hence we could not obtain the required equivalence from (1) by the isomorphism rule in one step; but we could have obtained it in two, by first of all obtaining a new PC equivalence by uniform substitution of 'p.${\sim}$q' for 'p' and 'qvr' for 'q' in (1), and then applying the isomorphism rule to the equivalence thus obtained.

The practical upshot of all this is that we can manipulate predicate-expressions exactly as if they were wffs in PC, with the variables written as 'f', 'g', etc. instead of as 'p', 'q', etc.

The notion of isomorphism will play a considerable part in subsequent chapters, and you should therefore take care that you understand it thoroughly. Fortunately it is a very simple notion to grasp.

Scope of Part III

We have in this chapter introduced in an informal way most, though not all, of the concepts and symbolism which we shall find in the Predicate Calculus – and in fact all which we shall require for some little time to come. The remainder will be introduced later as they are required.

The Predicate Calculus is commonly divided into what are known as the Lower Predicate Calculus and various Predicate Calculi of higher order. We cannot here state with any accuracy what is the distinction between these Calculi. Roughly, however, it consists in this: that in the Calculi of higher order new quantifiers are introduced which enable us (to take one example) to state that all, some, or no *properties* have such and such characteristics; whereas in the Lower Predicate Calculus the only quantifiers are those used to assert that all, some, or no *things* have properties of a certain sort. Calculi of higher order lie wholly outside the range of this book. Even the full Lower Predicate Calculus (LPC) raises problems of a non-elementary nature, and we shall not attempt a systematic treatment of it. There are however certain segments of LPC (standing to the full LPC much as, e.g., the implicational fragment of PC stands to the full PC) within which a great deal of important work can be done and which are capable of discussion at a relatively elementary level. Two of these (which we shall call LPC1 and LPC2 respectively) we shall expound with some thoroughness, giving decision procedures and an axiomatic basis for each. After that we shall deal, under the heading of Multiple Quantification, with certain other segments of the Predicate Calculus, though in a less systematic way, and lead up to the point where you should at least have a grasp of the range of formulae which lie within the full Lower Predicate Calculus.

EXERCISES 23

23.1 In each of the following, pick out the predicates, assign a predicate variable to each, and express the form of the whole proposition by a quantified schema (or a truth-function of quantified schemata):

(a) All mammals are vertebrates.

(b) There are mammals in Australia which lay eggs.

(c) Not every politician is a man of sound judgment.

(*d*) A test pilot has a dangerous occupation.

(*e*) Unicorns do not exist but lions do.

(*f*) All substances are destructible except simple ones.

(*g*) Some, though not all, poets write novels.

(*h*) Only adult citizens are entitled to vote.

(*i*) No one can pass the examination unless he either works hard or is a genius.

(*j*) If all taxes are reduced but no wages are reduced, some goods will be in short supply.

(*k*) Either all the Smiths will accept the invitation or else none of them will.

(*l*) 'Every boy and every girl
That's born into the world alive
Is either a little Liberal
Or else a little Conservative' (W. S. Gilbert.)

(In (*l*) the second line should be disregarded.)

CHAPTER 24

The System LPC1

The formulae in this system contain predicate variables, operators and quantifiers, but no individual-variables. Every wff of LPC1 consists either of a quantified schema, or of a truth-function of one or more quantified schemata.

The symbols used in LPC1 are the following:

f, g, h, . . .	[predicate variables]
∼	[negation sign]
v	[disjunction sign]
•	[conjunction sign]
⊃	[implication sign]
≡	[equivalence sign]
U	[universal quantifier]
Ǝ	[existential quantifier]
(,)	[brackets]

Formation rules

Predicate-expressions on their own are not to count as *formulae*, either well-formed or ill-formed, of LPC1. The reason is as follows. Just as PC is a calculus which displays the relations between propositions regardless of their internal structure, so LPC1 is to be a calculus which displays relations between certain limited types of propositions, viz. those with a certain kind of internal structure. But in each case the relations are relations between *propositions*. In PC even the simplest wff (which in that calculus consists of a single variable) is one which takes as its values complete propositions, of which we can sensibly ask whether they are true or false. Similarly in LPC1 even the simplest expression which we shall count as a wff will be one which can take whole propositions (with a certain structure) as its values. This rules out predicate-expressions as wffs, since their values are not propositions but simply predicates, and we cannot sensibly ask of a predicate whether it is true or false. Every wff of LPC1, however, must *contain* a predicate-expression, and the symbols out of which predicate-expressions are constructed can be combined either in ways which 'make sense' or in ways which do not. Our Formation Rules will therefore begin with a set of rules which will specify the class of *well-formed predicate-expressions* ('wfpes' for short); and then with reference to this class we shall set out the rules which specify the class of wffs.

We use 'α', 'β', . . . as meta-logical variables whose values are predicate-expressions, and 'X', 'Y', . . . as meta-logical variables whose values are formulae.

Our Formation Rules are as follows:

> (*a*) A predicate variable standing alone is a wfpe.
> (*b*) If α is a wfpe, $\sim$α is a wfpe.
> (*c*) If α and β are wfpes, (α ∨ β), (α . β), (α ⊃ β) and (α ≡ β) are wfpes.
> (*d*) If α is a wfpe, then Uα and Ǝα are wffs.
> (*e*) If X is a wff, $\sim$X is a wff.
> (*f*) If X and Y are wffs, (X ∨ Y), (X.Y), (X ⊃ Y) and (X ≡ Y) are wffs.

N.B. 1. We shall usually omit the outermost pair of brackets round a wff (but not those round a wfpe).

2. We shall regard conjunctions and disjunctions with more than two terms as well-formed without any internal bracketing. This applies both to wfpes and to wffs.

These conventions are analogous to those already used in PC.

If you will recall what was said in Chapter 14 about Formal (or Uninterpreted) Systems, you will see that the Formation Rules just given have been expressed in a purely formal way, except that in Rule (*a*) the term 'predicate variable' and in several of the rules the expression 'wfpe' (i.e. 'well-formed predicate-expression') have been used. The intention in using these expressions was certainly to indicate a certain interpretation of the calculus. The rules could however quite simply be made completely formal by dropping 'predicate variable' in favour of 'small letter occurring in the list of symbols of the calculus', and by regarding 'wfpe' simply as a neutral label for a class of sequences of symbols in which we happen to be interested.

It may be helpful at this point to give a short list of formulae in

LPC1 which are well-formed in accordance with the above rules. The following examples may suffice:

$$Uf$$
$$\exists{\sim}f$$
$$\exists(f.{\sim}f)$$
$${\sim}\exists{\sim}(fvg)$$
$$Uf \supset \exists(fvg)$$
$$(U(f{\supset}g) \,.\, \exists(gvh)) \supset \exists(fvh)$$

But the following are not wffs. (Ask yourself why in each case.)

$$f \vee {\sim}g$$
$$U \supset \exists{\sim}f$$
$$\exists(f.g) \supset g$$
$$U({\sim}fvg) \,.\, h \supset \exists f \supset {\sim}\exists(gv{\sim}h)$$

Validity

The wffs of LPC1 (like those of PC) can be divided into those which are valid, those which are contingent, and those which are inconsistent. A wff of PC was said to be valid if and only if every possible uniform substitution of actual propositions for the variables in it resulted in a true proposition. We can give an analogous account of the validity of a wff in LPC1, remembering however that the variables here are predicate variables, not propositional variables. A wff of LPC1 will be said to be valid if and only if every possible uniform substitution of actual predicates for the predicate variables in it results in a true proposition. Similarly, a wff of LPC1 will be said to be inconsistent if and only if every possible uniform substitution of actual predicates for the predicate variables in it results in a false proposition. Finally, a wff of LPC1 will be said to be contingent if and only if it is possible for some uniform substitution of predicates for the variables in it to result in a true proposition and also possible for some (other) substitution to result in a false proposition.

It is intuitively evident that there *are* valid, inconsistent and contingent wffs in LPC1. This can be seen from simple examples. Thus 'U(fv∼f)' is clearly a valid formula; for no matter what predicate you substitute for 'f', everything must either possess the property it stands for or else fail to possess that property. '∃(f.∼f)' is clearly inconsistent; for it says that there is something which both possesses and does not possess a certain property; and no matter what property you take this to be, such a statement must always be false. 'Ǝ(f.g)' is clearly contingent; for you can easily think of two properties such that something possesses them both, and also of another pair of properties such that nothing possesses them both. With more complicated formulae it is often not at all obvious to which of these three classes they belong; though it is not difficult to see from the account we have given that every wff must belong to one of them and that no wff can belong to more than one.

The decision problem

The Decision Problem for LPC1 is exactly analogous to that for PC. To solve it we have to discover some general procedure, applicable to every wff of LPC1 without exception, which will in each case tell us quite unambiguously in a finite number of steps whether the wff in question is a valid formula or not. The procedure must moreover be a 'mechanical' one, i.e. it must be statable in clear and definite rules which are such that no matter what wff we are considering we always know how to begin, and always know after each step what the next step should be.

Several solutions of the Decision Problem for LPC1 are known. We shall give two of them, the first because it is important for the theoretical understanding of this branch of logic, the second because is is easy to use as a practical test.

CHAPTER 25

LPC1 : Decision Procedure I –
The Truth-Table Method [1]

Consider what you do when you draw up a matrix in order to work out the truth-table for a wff of PC. You set down all possible assignments of truth-values to the simplest propositional elements of the wff – i.e. those propositional elements of which the wff is a truth-function. Let us call these elements the *basic formulae* of the wff. In PC the basic formulae of a wff are just the propositional variables that occur in it. They are independent of one another in the sense that, in constructing the matrix, no assignment of a particular truth-value to one basic formula commits us to any particular assignment for any of the others. That is, every combination of truth-values represents a logical possibility.

It is this ability to set out all possible assignments of truth-values to the basic formulae, of which a given wff is a truth-function, that is fundamental to the method of truth-tables. For these assignments of truth-values give us the set of logical possibilities against which we compute the values of the wff. Thus we shall be able to use truth-tables as a decision procedure for LPC1 if and only if we can find some method for identifying the basic formulae of which any given wff of LPC1 is a truth-function. In fact this identification can always be carried out. Therefore we *can* construct a suitable matrix, and from that a truth-table in the usual manner, for any wff of LPC1.

Basic formulae in LPC1

We shall say straight away what these basic formulae in LPC1 are. As in PC, their number depends on the number of distinct variables in the wff to be evaluated. But whereas in PC this number is of course the same as the number of variables, in LPC1 if a wff X

---

[1] This Decision Procedure is an adaptation of one given by G. H. von Wright in 'On the Idea of Logical Truth I' (reprinted in his *Logical Studies*).

contains n predicate variables, the number of basic formulae is not n itself, but 2^n.

If $n = 1$, i.e. if X contains only one variable (say 'f'), there are two basic formulae, viz. 'Ǝf' and 'Ǝ~f'.

If $n = 2$, there are four basic formulae, viz. 'Ǝ(f.g)', 'Ǝ(f.~g)', 'Ǝ(~f.g)' and 'Ǝ(~f.~g)'.

If $n = 3$, there are eight basic formulae, viz. 'Ǝ(f.g.h)', 'Ǝ(f.g.~h)', 'Ǝ(f.~g.h)', 'Ǝ(f.~g.~h)', 'Ǝ(~f.g.h)', 'Ǝ(~f.g.~h)', 'Ǝ(~f.~g.h)' and 'Ǝ(~f.~g.~h)'.

The principle on which these lists are drawn up should be clear already. Every basic formula consists of an 'Ǝ' followed by a conjunction of *all* the variables in X, each variable being either negated or unnegated; and every complete set of basic formulae contains every possible combination of the negated and unnegated forms of the variables.

It is convenient to have a standard order of the basic formulae. You will notice that we have chosen one which runs parallel to the standard order of the *rows* in a PC matrix. You should now have no difficulty in writing down the basic formulae when $n = 4$ or some greater number.

The Law of existential distribution

In order to show that wffs of LPC1 are truth-functions of basic formulae we need one piece of apparatus which we have not yet encountered.

We begin by giving a truth-table definition of $Ǝ(\alpha \vee \beta)$ in terms of $Ǝ\alpha$ and $Ǝ\beta$, where α and β are any wfpes:

$Ǝ\alpha$	$Ǝ\beta$	$Ǝ(\alpha \vee \beta)$
1	1	1
1	0	1
0	1	1
0	0	0

This definition is based on the idea that if an object can be said to possess a certain property, it can therefore be said to possess either that property or some other property (no matter what that other property may be). Hence if there is something which possesses a certain property, there is something (that same thing, even if no other) which possesses the disjunction of that property and any other. It will make no difference whether the properties are ones that can be symbolized by a single variable or ones which are symbolized by some more complex wfpe. Hence we are entitled to say that if $\exists\alpha$ is true, or if $\exists\beta$ is true, $\exists(\alpha \lor \beta)$ is also true. This accounts for the first three 1's in the truth-table. If however there are no α's and also no β's at all, there can be nothing which is either α or β; and this accounts for the 0 at the end of the truth-table.

It should be noted that the truth-table for $\exists(\alpha \lor \beta)$ is identical with that which we obtain for $(\exists\alpha \lor \exists\beta)$ by the ordinary truth-table for '$\lor$'. Thus we arrive at the equivalence

$$\exists(\alpha \lor \beta) \equiv (\exists\alpha \lor \exists\beta)$$

(where α and β are any wfpes), an equivalence which entitles us to replace any wff of the form of the left-hand side by the corresponding wff of the form of the right-hand side, and *vice versa*. We shall call this equivalence the *Law of Existential Distribution* (*LED*).

Wffs of LPC1 as truth-functions of basic formulae

A wff of PC is always written explicitly as a truth-function of its basic formulae (i.e. of propositional variables). By contrast, many wffs of LPC1 do not superficially look like truth-functions of their basic formulae. They can, however, be expressed explicitly as truth-functions of basic formulae by the following series of equivalence transformations: 1. Use the Rule of Quantifier Transformation (p. 171) to eliminate 'U' in favour of '$\exists$'. 2. Reduce every wfpe to perfect disjunctive normal form in terms of all the variables which occur in the whole wff. 3. Apply LED to bring an '$\exists$' in front of every conjunction of variables.

Wfpes can be reduced to perfect DNF by the procedure given in Chapter 11 for wffs of PC.

To illustrate this procedure, let us take the wff

$$(\exists f . \sim U(f.g)) \supset (U(f\supset g) \supset (\sim\exists g \lor \exists\sim f)) \qquad (1)$$

There are two predicate variables here, 'f' and 'g', so the basic formulae will be '$(\exists f.g)$', '$\exists(f.\sim g)$', '$\exists(\sim f.g)$' and '$\exists(\sim f.\sim g)$'. None of these actually occurs in (1); but let us follow through our procedure.

We have two occurrences of 'U' to deal with. We replace '$\sim$U' by '$\exists\sim$', and 'U' by '$\sim\exists\sim$', to obtain

$$(\exists f . \exists\sim(f.g)) \supset (\sim\exists\sim(f\supset g) \supset (\sim\exists g \lor \exists\sim f)) \qquad (2)$$

(2) contains five wfpes, so we reduce each of these to perfect DNF in terms of 'f' and 'g'. This means that we reduce each wfpe

to a perfect DNF in which both 'f' and 'g' appear in each disjunct, regardless of whether they both occur in the wfpe in its original form or not.

The reductions are as follows:

$$f \equiv ((f.g) \vee (f.\sim g))$$
$$\sim(f.g) \equiv (\sim f \vee \sim g) \equiv ((\sim f.g) \vee (\sim f.\sim g) \vee (f.\sim g) \vee (\sim f.\sim g))$$
$$\equiv ((\sim f.g) \vee (\sim f.\sim g) \vee (f.\sim g))$$
$$\sim(f \supset g) \equiv (f.\sim g)$$
$$g \equiv ((f.g) \vee (\sim f.g))$$
$$\sim f \equiv ((\sim f.g) \vee (\sim f.\sim g))$$

Replacing the wfpes in (2) by their perfect DNFs, we obtain

$$[\exists((f.g) \vee (f.\sim g)) \;.\; \exists((\sim f.g) \vee (\sim f.\sim g) \vee (f.\sim g))] \supset$$
$$[\sim\exists(f.\sim g) \supset (\sim\exists((f.g) \vee (\sim f.g)) \vee \exists((\sim f.g) \vee (\sim f.\sim g)))] \quad (3)$$

The final step is to apply LED. This gives us

$$[(\exists(f.g) \vee \exists(f.\sim g)) \;.\; (\exists(\sim f.g) \vee \exists(\sim f.\sim g) \vee \exists(f.\sim g))] \supset$$
$$[\sim\exists(f.\sim g) \supset (\sim(\exists(f.g) \vee \exists(\sim f.g)) \vee \exists(\sim f.g) \vee \exists(\sim f.\sim g))] \quad (4)$$

(4) is a great deal longer than (1), but it is quite explicitly a truth-function of basic formulae. If we had a matrix for the basic formulae, we should find (4) no more difficult to test than a wff in PC.

Matrices for basic formulae

The matrix for a set of basic formulae must set out all possible combinations of their truth-values. If, as in PC, we write down all the arrangements of 1's and 0's that can be devised, then each matrix will have 2^{2^n} rows (where n is the number of predicate variables). The matrix when n = 1 will look like this:

$\exists f$	$\exists \sim f$
1	1
1	0
0	1
0	0

The matrix when n = 2 will look like a PC matrix for four variables and contain 16 rows, beginning with 1 1 1 1 and ending with 0 0 0 0.

The matrix when n = 3 will have 256 rows; and so on.

Are these matrices the correct ones? Unlike the basic formulae in PC, the basic formulae in LPC1 have common elements (e.g. 'f' occurs in each). It is therefore not immediately obvious whether assigning certain truth-values to some of the basic formulae always leaves us free to assign any truth-values we please to the others; i.e. it is not immediately obvious that each row represents a logical possibility. A little reflection, however, will show that no suspicion can attach to any row, with the exception of the last in each matrix – the row which consists entirely of 0's.

In the matrix for one variable set out above, the last row says that '∃f' and '∃∼f' are both false; that is, that there are no f's and no non-f's either. Surely, you may be inclined to protest, anything which is not an f must count as a non-f, so if there are no f's there must be some non-f's; i.e. if we put '∃f' = 0, we must put '∃∼f' = 1. And you would be right, on one assumption, viz. that the class of objects of which we are asking whether they are f's or not has at least some members. If this condition is not fulfilled, then '∃f' and '∃∼f' not merely may but will both be false, for there will be nothing to be an f and nothing to be a non-f either.

The same considerations apply to the other matrices we have described. If all but one of the basic formulae are false, the remaining one must be true, subject to the assumption we have stated, an assumption which is sometimes expressed by saying that our universe of discourse is not an empty one.

There is nothing in the nature of formal logic itself which forces us either to make this assumption or not to make it: we can have an equally consistent logic whichever course we choose. Most frequently – though by no means universally – expositions of the Predicate Calculus tacitly or explicitly make the assumption in question, and for the present we shall do so too. We shall, however, draw attention, as we proceed, to the consequences of not making it.

To repeat: we are going for the present to take it as a presupposition of our logic that no matter what property we consider, there is always something of which we can say that it possesses it or does not possess it. (When we make this supposition we are said to be working in *the logic of a non-empty universe*.) In conformity with this decision, we shall strike out – or more accurately not write in – the last row in each of the matrices as we have described them; for these rows conflict with the presupposition of our logic, and are therefore not to count among the possible assignments of truth-values to the basic formulae. The matrix for a wff containing one predicate variable will therefore have not 4 rows but only 3; that for a wff containing two variables, not 16 rows but only 15; and in general, where n is the number of variables, the number of rows will be $(2^{2^n}-1)$. (If we wish to work within *the logic of an empty universe* instead, we have only to restore the last row of each matrix, the row which consists entirely of 0's.)[1]

Testing for validity

Once we have expressed a wff as a truth-function of basic formulae and have drawn up a matrix for these, we can calculate a truth-table for the whole wff in the way explained in Part I. The familiar rules still apply: if the truth-table consists entirely of 1's, the wff is valid; if entirely of 0's, it is inconsistent; if of a mixture, it is contingent.

As an example take the wff we discussed earlier in this chapter. We give the calculation of its truth-table in a slightly more condensed form than we used in Part I: instead of writing various parts of the wff separately, calculating a truth-table for each, and then assembling the results bit by bit, we write the whole wff immediately and indicate the order in which the subsidiary truth-tables are calculated by numbers placed over the operators below which the columns are written. (This is purely a device to save space when we have a long formula to deal with.) As a further space-saving device let us write 'A' for '∃(f.g)', 'B' for '∃(f.~g)', 'C' for '∃(~f.g)' and 'D' for '∃(~f.~g)'. (4) can then be re-written as

$$[(A \vee B) . (C \vee D \vee B)] \supset [\sim B \supset (\sim(A \vee C) \vee C \vee D)]$$

The calculation is as follows. (At step 2 the table for '(C v D v B)' is calculated all at once.)

				1	3	2	10	4	9	6	5	8	7
A	B	C	D	[(AvB)	.	(C v D v B)]	⊃	[~B	⊃	(~(AvC)	v C	v D)]	
1	1	1	1	1	1	1	1	0	1	0	1	1	1
1	1	1	0	1	1	1	1	0	1	0	1	1	1
1	1	0	1	1	1	1	1	0	1	0	1	1	1
1	1	0	0	1	1	1	1	0	1	0	1	0	0
1	0	1	1	1	1	1	1	1	1	0	1	1	1
1	0	1	0	1	1	1	1	1	1	0	1	1	1
1	0	0	1	1	1	1	1	1	1	0	1	1	1
1	0	0	0	1	0	0	1	1	0	0	1	0	0
0	1	1	1	1	1	1	1	0	1	0	1	1	1
0	1	1	0	1	1	1	1	0	1	0	1	1	1
0	1	0	1	1	1	1	1	0	1	1	0	1	1
0	1	0	0	1	1	1	1	0	1	1	0	1	0
0	0	1	1	0	0	1	1	1	1	0	1	1	1
0	0	1	0	0	0	1	1	1	1	0	1	1	1
0	0	0	1	0	0	1	1	1	1	1	0	1	1

[1] The theme of the last few paragraphs is discussed more fully in the next chapter.

The truth-table for the whole wff (written under the main operator), consists entirely of 1's. The wff is therefore valid.

Once we have had a little practice, it will usually be unnecessary to reduce wffs to as lengthy a form as we have done in our example. We replaced '∃f' by '∃(f.g) v ∃(f.~g)'. This is the disjunction of all the basic formulae which contain 'f' unnegated, as it is in '∃f'. We could therefore have left '∃f' unexpanded and written down straight away the truth-table for the disjunction of these basic formulae, viz. twelve 1's followed by three 0's. Quite generally, a schema which consists of '∃' followed by a single predicate variable (negated or unnegated) or by a conjunction of predicate variables (negated or unnegated) is equivalent to the disjunction of all those basic formulae which contain that variable or those variables in exactly that form. Its truth-table will therefore have a 1 for every row in which any of these basic formulae has a 1, and a 0 when each of them has a 0. Thus, the table for '∃~g' has a 1 wherever either '∃(f.~g)' or '∃(~f.~g)' = 1; '∃(~f.h)' = 1 whenever either '∃(~f.g.h)' or '∃(~f.~g.h)' = 1; and so forth. If we remember this rule, we shall find it sufficient to reduce wfpes to DNF (not necessarily perfect) before applying LED.

You should be careful to note that the result of applying LED to a wff of the form

$$\sim\exists(\alpha \text{ v } \beta)$$

is not, as one might carelessly think,

$$\sim\exists\alpha \text{ v } \sim\exists\beta$$
$$\text{but } \sim(\exists\alpha \text{ v } \exists\beta)$$

and therefore, by De Morgan,

$$\sim\exists\alpha \text{ . } \sim\exists\beta$$

An exception

There is one complication which our example does not illustrate. It sometimes happens that when a wff is put into the proper form for testing, there occurs in it a schema which consists of '∃' followed by a conjunction of predicate variables in which the same variable occurs both negated and unnegated; e.g. '∃(f.~f)' or '∃(f.g.~g)'. Such a schema will resist reformulation as a truth-function of basic formulae. There can, however, be no doubt about what its truth-table should be: every such schema is obviously inconsistent, and therefore its truth-table will consist of an unbroken column of 0's. A schema of this type we shall call an *inconsistent ∃-schema*. The negation of an inconsistent ∃-schema will of course have a truth-table consisting entirely of 1's.

Universal applicability of the method

Every wff of LPC1 is (by the Formation Rules) a truth-function of quantified schemata. 'U' can always be eliminated in favour of '∃'. Since every wff of PC can be reduced to perfect DNF in terms of any set of variables which includes all those which occur in it (see Appendix 1 and Chapter 11), and the rules for transforming wfpes are the same as those for wffs of PC, every wfpe can be reduced to an analogous perfect DNF. LED can always be applied where we have '∃' followed by a disjunctive wfpe. Therefore every wff of LPC1 can be expressed as a truth-function of schemata each of which consists of '∃' followed by a conjunction of all the predicate variables which occur in the wff and/or their negations. If such a conjunction contains the same variable negated and unnegated, the schema is an inconsistent ∃-schema, and can be dealt with as explained in the previous paragraph; if it does not, the schema is a basic formula. Therefore every wff can be expressed as a truth-function of schemata whose truth-tables we are given.

EXERCISES 25

25.1 Determine the validity of the following by the truth-table method:

(a) $(\exists \sim f \,.\, U(f \supset g)) \supset \sim Ug$

(b) $(U(f \supset g) \,.\, \sim Ug) \supset (\sim \exists f \vee U(f . \sim g))$

(c) $(U(f \supset g) \,.\, U(g \supset \sim f)) \supset \sim \exists f$

(d) $\sim \exists f \supset (\sim \exists g \supset U(f \equiv g))$

(e) $((\exists \sim f \vee Ug) \supset \exists(\sim f \supset \sim g)) \vee ((\sim \exists f \,.\, \exists g) \supset \sim U(f \supset g))$

(f) $\exists((f \vee g) \,.\, (f \supset g)) \supset (U(f \supset \sim g) \supset \exists(\sim f . g))$

CHAPTER 26

Universes of Discourse – Justification of Decision Procedure I

The notion of a universe of discourse

If someone were to maintain that all non-mammals are either birds or fish, we could refute him by producing, say, a lizard, and showing that it was not a mammal, but was not a bird or a fish either. If, however, instead of a lizard we were to produce or cite the example of a lump of iron, or the number 7, and say 'Here is something that is not a mammal, but is not a bird or a fish either', he would be likely to complain that such an example was beside the point: he had intended his original remark to apply only within the field of *living creatures*.

A great many of our conversations and arguments are like this. Implicitly or explicitly, we lay it down that we are talking about some class or collection of objects (which may be finite or infinite in number), and that all our statements are for the time being to be regarded as referring only to members of that class. When we say that everything is f, we are to be taken to mean that everything within the class in question is f; and so forth. We shall call such a class our *universe of discourse*. 'Uf' is then to be taken to mean not 'everything that there is is f', but 'everything in the relevant universe of discourse is f'.

Sometimes, in a language such as English, there are special words or phrases which serve to indicate a particular universe of discourse. Words such as 'everyone', 'someone' and 'no one' commonly make it clear that the universe of discourse is human beings. 'No one is twenty feet tall' can be represented simply by '$\sim\exists f$', provided it is stipulated that the universe of discourse is human beings. More often the universe of discourse is left to be inferred or guessed at from the context. If someone says 'Everything has some colour or other', it is probable that his universe of discourse is something like *visible objects*; it is unlikely that he is trying to say that numbers, ideas, sounds and propositions, as well as trees, houses and rainbows, have some colour or other.

The most usual way of specifying a class which is to be our universe of discourse is by means of some descriptive word or phrase; e.g. 'human beings', 'integers', 'animals', 'citizens of Canada' and so forth. But obviously, specifying a class in this way does not by itself tell us how many members there are in the class in question, or whether indeed it has any members at all. Most frequently, no doubt, in our actual statements and inferences, we work within a universe of discourse which has members; but there is no objection in principle to having a universe of discourse which has no members at all. A class which has no members, such as (presumably) the class of unicorns, is said to be an *empty* class, and one which has members – however many or however few – is said to be a *non-empty* class. So when such classes form our universes of discourse, we speak of empty and non-empty universes of discourse respectively.

Validity within a universe of discourse

Suppose we take some wff X in LPC1, and consider some particular universe of discourse. By successive substitutions of predicates for the variables in X, we can obtain an indefinitely large number of propositions within that universe of discourse, i.e. propositions which are to be regarded as being about the objects in that universe of discourse. If, no matter what substitutions we make for the variables in X, the resulting proposition is always true within the universe of discourse in question, X will be said to be *valid within that universe of discourse*.

It is possible for a wff to be valid within one universe of discourse but not within another. For example, suppose we have a universe of discourse which contains only one member; then one wff which will be valid within it is

$$\exists f \supset Uf \qquad (1)$$

For, no matter what property we take 'f' to represent, if something within that universe has that property, it must be its one and only member which has it, and in that case *everything* in the universe of discourse has that property. But if the universe of discourse we are considering has even two distinct members, (1) will not be valid within it.

Validity in LPC1

Because of the above-mentioned restriction on the sphere of its validity, we do not regard (1) as a valid wff in LPC1, or in the Predicate Calculus generally. By contrast with (1), the formula

$$\text{Uf} \supset \exists \text{f} \tag{2}$$

is valid not merely within a universe of discourse which has only a single member, but also in universes of discourse with two, three . . . or an infinite number of members. (2) has a general validity, independent of the nature of particular universes of discourse, in a way in which (1) has not. We shall therefore regard (2), but not (1), as deserving of the title 'valid in LPC1'.

There is however, just one type of universe of discourse in which even (2) fails to hold. We refer to those universes of discourse which have no members at all, i.e. to empty universes of discourse. For in such a universe of discourse, no matter what f may be, the assertion that there is something which is an f is bound to be *false*; and so is the assertion that there is something which is a non-f. So '∃f' and '∃~f' will both be false; and by consequence their negations, viz. '~∃f' and '~∃~f', will both be true. But of course, '~∃~f' may be rewritten as 'Uf'; so in any empty universe of discourse, the antecedent of (2) is true and its consequent false, and hence (2) is not valid. Quite in general, within an empty universe of discourse, every (affirmative) existentially quantified proposition will be false, and every (affirmative) universally quantified one will be true.

(If you are inclined to complain at this point that it seems strained or unnatural to say that everything is f in a case where there is nothing to be f at all, you should remember that 'U' is to be taken to mean nothing more and nothing less than '~∃~'. Within non-empty universes of discourse, 'everything is (an) f' is a natural and idiomatic reading of 'Uf'; in the case of empty universes of discourse, this reading may seem strained; but in each case the translatability of 'U' into '~∃~' is preserved, and that is the important thing here.)

By contrast with both (1) and (2) consider the wff

$$\text{U(f.g)} \supset \text{Uf} \tag{3}$$

This means that if everything possess both of a certain pair of properties, then everything possesses the first of them. (3) is valid, not merely, as (2) is, within every non-empty universe of discourse, but within every empty one as well.

We are now ready for the expressions 'the logic of a non-empty universe' and 'the logic of an empty universe'.

A wff will be said to be *valid in the logic of a non-empty universe* if and only if it is valid, in the sense we have explained, within *every* non-empty universe of discourse, regardless of whether or not it is also valid in an empty universe of discourse. Thus (2) and (3) are both valid in the logic of a non-empty universe.

A wff will be said to be *valid in the logic of an empty universe* if and only if in addition to being valid within every non-empty universe of discourse it is valid within every empty universe of discourse as well. Thus, (3), but not (2), is valid in the logic of an empty universe.

We shall frequently abbreviate the phrases 'the logic of a non-empty universe' and 'the logic of an empty universe' to 'LNEU' and 'LEU' respectively.

It is important to distinguish clearly between saying that a wff is *valid within an empty universe of discourse*, and saying that it is *valid in the logic of an empty universe*. Let us look again at the formula we numbered (1), viz. '∃f ⊃ Uf'. This formula is in fact valid within every empty universe of discourse, since in such a universe of discourse '∃f' is always false and 'Uf' is always true, and $0 \supset 1 = 1$. So indeed is the simpler wff 'Uf'. But we do not regard such wffs as *valid in LEU*; in order to qualify for that title a wff must be valid within every non-empty universe as well.

You will see that we have so defined the two phrases that every wff which is valid in LEU is also valid in LNEU. Many wffs, however, are valid in the latter but not in the former; they may be said to be valid *only* in LNEU. To count as valid in LEU a wff has to pass all the tests for validity in LNEU, and more besides.

In Chapter 25 we showed how to construct matrices for wffs in LPC1, by which we could test their validity in LNEU. In drawing up these matrices we 'missed out the last row', the row in which every basic formula has the value 0. Now all the basic formulae simultaneously have the value 0 if and only if the universe of discourse is empty; so a wff which had a 1 in its truth-table for such a row would be valid within an empty universe of discourse. If therefore we were to add this row to our matrices, and require that for a wff to be valid its truth-table must show a 1 for this row as well as for every other, we should have a test for validity in LEU.

In succeeding chapters, unless we explicitly specify to the contrary, 'valid' is to be taken to mean 'valid in LNEU'. We shall, however, mark with an asterisk (*) those formulae, rules and so forth which are valid in LNEU *only*, and are invalid in LEU. By noting such starred items you should be able to obtain a grasp of the differences between the two logics.

Validity and truth-tables

In the previous chapter we offered as a test of the validity of a wff in LPC1 that it should have the value 1 for every possible assignment of truth-values to the relevant basic formulae. We have, however, given a definition of 'valid in LPC1' in apparently quite different terms from these, firstly in a somewhat rough and ready form in Chapter 24, and now more precisely in the present chapter. Our definition has been in terms of yielding a true proposition in every universe of discourse for every substitution of actual predicates for the predicate variables which occur in the wff. The question therefore arises: have we any right to assert that the test of validity offered in Chapter 25 *is* a test of validity as we have defined 'validity'?

To establish that we have such a right we have to show that if and only if a wff X has the value 1 for every row of the relevant matrix, there could be no predicates, which, when substituted for the variables in X, would turn X into a false proposition.

We have already shown that every wff in LPC1 is a truth-function of the relevant basic formulae; i.e. that its truth-value depends on their truth-values and on nothing else. Now every basic formula asserts simply that some predicate (affirmative or negative), or some conjunction of predicates (affirmative or negative), has an instance. So the truth-value of any proposition which has the form of a wff in LPC1 depends solely on whether the predicates occurring in it, or conjunctions of these predicates (and/or their negations), have instances or not; or, as we may put it, on the *instance-pattern* of its predicates.

Every row in an LPC1 matrix can be regarded as representing a certain instance-pattern for a predicate or group of predicates. An example or two may make it clearer what we mean by this.

(*a*) In the matrix for one variable, 'f', the first row – 1 1 – represents the case in which f has an instance and not-f also has an instance. (An alternative way of saying that not-f has an instance is to say that f has a *counter-instance*.) So any wff which has the value 1 for this row of the matrix will yield a true proposition in any given universe of discourse whenever we put for 'f' any predicate which has in that universe both an instance and a counter-instance.

(*b*) In the matrix for two variables, 'f' and 'g', the row 1 1 1 0 represents the following instance-pattern for predicates f and g : f and g have a joint instance (i.e. there is something which is both f and g); so do f and not-g, and so do not-f and g; but not-f and not-g do not (i.e. there is nothing which is neither f nor g). So any wff which = 1 for this row will yield a true proposition in any given universe of discourse whenever we put for 'f' and 'g' any pair of predicates which have this instance-pattern in that universe of discourse.

We have shown that the truth-value of a proposition in LPC1 depends solely on the instance-pattern of its predicates. It follows that if a wff X has the value 1 for every row of its matrix, then in order to make X yield a false proposition we should have to substitute for its variables predicates with an instance-pattern different from any which are represented in the matrix.

It is, however, impossible that there should be such predicates. For (*a*) in LNEU every conceivable instance-pattern is represented in the matrix, with the single exception of that which would be represented by taking each and every basic formula as false. But in any non-empty universe of discourse, if a certain predicate f does not have an instance, then it must have a counter-instance, for every object in that universe (and by hypothesis there are some) which is not an f will be a non-f. So in any non-empty universe and for any predicate f, if all the basic formulae which contain 'f' (unnegated) are false, at least one of those which contain '∼f' must be true; and therefore at least one basic formula must be true. Hence no group of predicates with the instance-pattern represented by every basic formula's being false could be found in any non-empty universe of discourse.

And (*b*): in LEU, even *this* instance-pattern is also represented in the matrix: so no group of predicates could fail to have one or other of the instance-patterns expressed in the matrix.

Hence any wff in LPC1 which has a truth-table consisting entirely of 1's must be valid in the sense in which we have defined validity.

Finally, any wff in LPC1 whose truth-table contains a 0 will not be valid as we have defined 'valid'. For every row of every matrix represents a possible instance-pattern for some group of predicates in some universe of discourse. Hence if a wff X has a 0 for a certain row of the matrix, we can always think of a universe of discourse and a set of predicates such that the predicates have in that universe the instance-pattern represented by that row; and if we put these predicates for the variables in X, the result will be a false proposition in that universe of discourse, i.e. X is not valid.

CHAPTER 27

LPC1 : Decision Procedure II – Exposition

This decision procedure will be found much easier to apply in practice than the previous one, especially when we have to deal with a wff containing more than two predicate variables.

A new standard form

We have again to begin by reducing wffs to a certain standard form, but a different one this time. A wff is in the standard form for Decision Procedure II if

- (a) it consists of a disjunction of quantified schemata, or a conjunction of such disjunctions;
- (b) no quantifier is immediately preceded by '$\sim$';
- (c) '$\exists$' occurs at most once in any disjunction.

The standard form is a kind of CNF, with certain restrictions as to the nature of the disjuncts.

We can always reduce a wff of LPC1 to the standard form by equivalence transformations in the following way:

Firstly, taking each quantified schema as an indivisible unit – treating each as if it were a single propositional variable – reduce the whole wff to CNF by ordinary PC methods.

Secondly, replace every occurrence of '$\sim\exists$' by '$U\sim$', and every occurrence of '$\sim U$' by '$\exists\sim$'.

Thirdly, if any disjunction contains more than one existentially quantified schema, use Assoc and Comm[1] if necessary to make these schemata adjacent, and then apply LED (in reverse, so to speak), disjoining all their wfpes under one single existential quantifier. E.g. replace '$\exists(f \supset g) \vee \exists(f \vee h) \vee \exists(g.\sim h)$' by '$\exists((f \supset g) \vee (f \vee h) \vee (g.\sim h))$'.

---

[1] In future the abbreviation 'Comm' will be used for the Commutative Law (for Disjunction or Conjunction, as the context requires).

Unlike Decision Procedure I, Decision Procedure II does not require any special form for the wfpes; this is one of its great advantages.

Testing for validity

We shall now show how to test wffs in the standard form.

We already know that a conjunction is valid if and only if *each* conjunct is valid. The only task, therefore, is to give rules for testing the validity of conjuncts in the standard form. (If the wff consists simply of a disjunction of quantified schemata we regard it as a conjunct in a degenerate conjunction.)

Each conjunct will consist of a disjunction – again possibly degenerate – of one or other of the following four types:

(i) $\exists\alpha$ (a single existentially quantified schema)
(ii) $U\alpha$ (a single universally quantified schema)
(iii) $U\alpha \lor U\beta$ . . . (a disjunction of two or more universally quantified schemata)
(iv) $\exists\alpha \lor U\beta_1 \lor \ldots \lor U\beta_n$ ($n \geq 1$) (a disjunction of one existentially quantified schema and one or more universally quantified schemata)

The rules for determining the validity of formulae of these four types are as follows (where α', β', . . . are the PC wffs isomorphic with α, β, . . . respectively):

*Rule (i): $\exists\alpha$ is valid if and only if α' is valid.[1]

Rule (ii): $U\alpha$ is valid if and only if α' is valid.

Note that the tests for formulae of types (i) and (ii) are identical.

Rule (iii): $U\alpha \lor U\beta$ . . . is valid if and only if at least one of α', β', . . . is valid.

Rule (iv): $\exists\alpha \lor U\beta_1 \lor \ldots \lor U\beta_n$ is valid if and only if at least one of $\beta_1, \ldots, \beta_n$, say β_j, is such that $(\alpha' \lor \beta_j')$ is valid.

Rule (iv) is more complicated than the others, so we shall re-state it in another way. To test a formula of the form $\exists\alpha \lor U\beta_1 \lor \ldots \lor U\beta_n$, form n disjunctions of PC wffs (i.e. as many as there are universal quantifiers in the formula being tested); each disjunction is to have α' as one of its disjuncts and *one* of $\beta_1', \ldots, \beta_n'$ as the

[1] In LEU no formula of type (i) is ever valid, but Rules (ii), (iii) and (iv) hold as stated.

other. Then if and only if at least one of these disjunctions is valid, $\exists\alpha \lor U\beta_1 \lor \ldots \lor U\beta_n$ is valid. E.g. if the formula is of the form

$$\exists\alpha \lor U\beta \lor U\gamma \lor U\delta \qquad (1)$$

we form the three disjunctions: (*a*) $(\alpha' \lor \beta')$, (*b*) $(\alpha' \lor \gamma')$, (*c*) $(\alpha' \lor \delta')$. If and only if at least one of (*a*), (*b*) and (*c*) is valid, (1) is valid.

(In the special case of type (iv) where $n = 1$ – where the formula is simply of the form $(\exists\alpha \lor U\beta)$ – we have of course only one disjunction to form, so the Rule becomes: $(\exists\alpha \lor U\beta)$ is valid if and only if $(\alpha' \lor \beta')$ is valid.)

You should note carefully that whereas with formulae of type (iv) we have first to form certain disjunctions of PC wffs and then test these disjunctions for validity, in the case of formulae of type (iii) we must not form any such disjunctions, but must test each of α', β', ... on its own.

It is of course easy to test any wff in PC for validity by one or other of the methods explained in Part I. The Reductio test explained on pp. 58–61 is usually the quickest and most convenient.

To summarize: we first of all reduce the wff to be tested to the standard form described; we then test each conjunct by Rules (i)–(iv); finally we apply the general rule that a conjunction is valid if and only if each conjunct is valid.

An illustrative example

We shall now work through an example, and we shall choose a fairly complicated one, which would require an enormous amount of working to test by Decision Procedure I. The formula we shall test is

$$[U(f \supset (g \lor {\sim}h)) . (\exists h \equiv \exists(i.{\sim}f))] \supset [{\sim}\exists(g \lor i) \supset \exists({\sim}f.{\sim}h)] \quad (1)$$

We are going to leave the wfpes alone, and also (for the present) the quantifiers, but otherwise reduce (1) to CNF.

The first step is to remove implication signs and equivalence signs between quantified schemata. Employing the law of double negation on the way, we thus obtain:

$$\begin{aligned}{\sim}[U(f \supset (g \lor {\sim}h)) . ((\exists h.\exists(i.{\sim}f)) \lor ({\sim}\exists h.{\sim}\exists(i.{\sim}f)))] \lor \\ [\exists(g \lor i) \lor \exists({\sim}f.{\sim}h)] \quad (2)\end{aligned}$$

By De Morgan, applied successively, we reach

$\sim$U(f $\supset$ (gv$\sim$h)) v (($\sim$∃h v $\sim$∃(i.$\sim$f)) . (∃h v ∃(i.$\sim$f))) v

∃(gvi) v ∃($\sim$f.$\sim$h)   (3)

The square brackets have now been dropped since they no longer do any useful work. (3) has the form of a four-termed disjunction, of which the second term is conjunctive. Therefore the associative and distributive laws will take us to the following formula in CNF:

[$\sim$U(f $\supset$ (gv$\sim$h)) v ∃(gvi) v ∃($\sim$f.$\sim$h) v $\sim$∃h v $\sim$∃(i.$\sim$f)] .

[$\sim$U(f $\supset$ (gv$\sim$h)) v ∃(gvi) v ∃($\sim$f.$\sim$h) v ∃h v ∃(i.$\sim$f)]   (4)

Next we get rid of negative quantifiers. In practice it would have been easy to combine this with the last step, but we are setting out the moves one by one. We now have:

[∃$\sim$(f $\supset$ (gv$\sim$h)) v ∃(gvi) v ∃($\sim$f.$\sim$h) v U$\sim$h v U$\sim$(i.$\sim$f)] .

[∃$\sim$(f $\supset$ (gv$\sim$h)) v ∃(gvi) v ∃($\sim$f.$\sim$h) v ∃h v ∃(i.$\sim$f)]   (5)

Our one remaining task is to bring all wfpes in existentially quantified schemata under a single '∃' in each conjunct. In (5) these schemata lie conveniently grouped together, but if they had not been we could have changed the order of the disjuncts without affecting validity. We thus reach home at last with

[∃($\sim$(f $\supset$ (gv$\sim$h)) v (gvi) v ($\sim$f.$\sim$h)) v U$\sim$h v U$\sim$(i. $\sim$f).

∃($\sim$(f $\supset$ (gv$\sim$h)) v (gvi) v ($\sim$f.$\sim$h) v h v (i.$\sim$f))   (6)

Now we can test for validity. (6) is a two-termed conjunction, and therefore if it is to be valid each conjunct must be valid. So let us consider each conjunct separately.

The first conjunct is of type (iv), with two universal quantifiers. We therefore have to form two disjunctions of PC wffs in accordance with Rule (iv). Instead of putting 'p' for 'f' and so on throughout, however, it is easier in practice and liable to lead to fewer mistakes if we simply pretend for the moment that 'f', 'g', etc., are propositional variables. The two disjunctions will therefore be (dropping unnecessary brackets):

(a) $\sim$(f $\supset$ (gv$\sim$h)) v g v i v ($\sim$f.$\sim$h) v $\sim$h

(b) $\sim$(f $\supset$ (gv$\sim$h)) v g v i v ($\sim$f.$\sim$h) v $\sim$(i.$\sim$f)

The rule states that if *either* (a) *or* (b) is valid, the first conjunct in (6) is valid. A Reductio test will easily show that although (a) is not valid, (b) is. Therefore the first conjunct in (6) is valid.

We turn to the second conjunct. This is of type (i), so we have simply a single formula to test, viz. that isomorphic with the one long wfpe which occurs in it. A Reductio test will show that this is not valid. Therefore the second conjunct in (6) is not valid.

So the result is that (6), and therefore our original formula (1), is not valid.

This completes our account of the method. Its justification will be given in the next chapter.

Addendum

Rules (i)–(iv) enable us to test *disjunctions* of quantified schemata for *validity*. Sometimes, however, it is useful to be able to test *conjunctions* of such schemata for *inconsistency*. Since the negation of a valid formula is inconsistent, and the negation of a disjunction can always be expressed (by de Morgan) as a conjunction, we might expect the tests for the inconsistency of conjunctions to bear a close relation to those for the validity of disjunctions. In fact they are what are known as *duals* of the latter; i.e. they may be obtained from Rules (i)–(iv) by the systematic interchange of certain pairs of terms.

For disjunction we have the familiar LED,
$$(\exists\alpha \vee \beta) \equiv (\exists\alpha \vee \exists\beta)$$
For conjunction we have a corresponding equivalence
$$U(\alpha \cdot \beta) \equiv (U\alpha \cdot U\beta)$$

which enables us to bring all the wfpes in a conjunction of universally quantified schemata under a single universal quantifier.

The four types of conjunctive formulae, corresponding to (i)–(iv), will therefore be:

  (ia) $U\alpha$
  (iia) $\exists\alpha$
  (iiia) $\exists\alpha \cdot \exists\beta \ldots$
  (iva) $U\alpha \cdot \exists\beta_1 \ldots \ldots \exists\beta_n \ (n \geq 1)$

The Rules are:
  *(ia) $U\alpha$ is inconsistent if and only if α' is inconsistent.
  (iia) $\exists\alpha$ is inconsistent if and only if α' is inconsistent.

(iiia) ∃α . ∃β ... is inconsistent if and only if at least one of α',
β', ... is inconsistent.

(iva) Uα . ∃β₁ ..... ∃βₙ is inconsistent if and only if at least one
of β₁, ..., βₙ, say βⱼ, is such that (α' . βⱼ') is inconsistent.

You can easily see that Rules (ia)–(iva) are the same as Rules
(i)–(iv) respectively, with 'inconsistent' replacing 'valid', '.' replacing
'v', 'U' replacing '∃' and '∃' replacing 'U' throughout.

EXERCISES 27

27.1 Determine the validity of the following by Decision Procedure II.

(a) (U(f⊃g) . U(g⊃h)) ⊃ U(f⊃h)

(b) ∃(f.~g) ⊃ (~∃(f.~h) ⊃ ∃(g.~h))

(c) U(f⊃g) ⊃ (∃(g.~h) v ∃(f.h))

(d) U(f ⊃ ~(g.h)) ⊃ (∃(f.g) ⊃ ∃(f.~h))

(e) (∃(fvg) . ∃(fvh)) ⊃ ∃(gvh)

(f) (∃f v U(g⊃h)) ⊃ (∃g v U(f⊃h))

(g) (U(f ⊃ (gvh)) . ∃(~g.~h)) ⊃ ~Uf

(h) (~U(f.~g) ⊃ ~∃(~fv~h)) ⊃ ~U(g.h)

(i) U((fv~g) ⊃ (h.i)) ⊃ (∃(~f.h) ⊃ U(gvi))

(j) ∃((fv~g) ⊃ (h.i)) ⊃ (U(~f.h) ⊃ U(gvi))

27.2 Set out the forms of the following arguments by means of
LPC1 formulae, and test their validity:

(a) No one can be a good cartographer unless he understands
trigonometry and is a careful observer. Some people, however,
who understand trigonometry are quite ignorant of the
integral calculus; and some who are careful observers cannot
draw well. So neither a knowledge of the integral calculus
nor the ability to draw well is a necessary condition of being
a good cartographer.

(b) To write a tragedy one needs both an understanding of
human nature and a sense of the sublime, but of these two
qualities only the former is necessary for the writing of a
comedy. Therefore anyone who can write a tragedy can *a
fortiori* write a comedy too.

(c) If all industrious members of the class can construct truth-tables, some members of the class are not industrious. Either everyone who understands consistency proofs can construct truth-tables and is industrious, or there is no one in the class who understands consistency proofs.

Therefore:

If everyone in the class who does not understand consistency proofs can construct truth-tables, there are some people who can construct truth-tables without being industrious.

27.3 Which of the following are inconsistent?

    (a) $\exists f . \exists {\sim} f$

    (b) $\exists f . U{\sim} f$

    (c) $U(f \supset g) . U(g \supset h) . \exists(f . {\sim} h)$

    (d) $\exists(f v (g.h)) . U({\sim} h \supset f) . \exists({\sim} g . {\sim} f)$

    (e) $U(f.g) . \exists({\sim} f v h) . U(g.{\sim} h)$

CHAPTER 28

LPC1 : Decision Procedure II –
Justification

Universal applicability of the method

Every wff of LPC1 is a truth-function of quantified schemata; i.e. it has the form of a wff of PC, with quantified schemata taking the place of propositional variables. Hence since very wff of PC can be reduced to CNF (see Appendix 1), so can every wff of LPC1, the quantified schemata within it remaining unchanged in the process. The rules for the transformation of quantifiers always enable us to remove a negation sign in front of a quantifier; and LED can be applied to any disjunction of unnegated existentially quantified schemata. Therefore every wff of LPC1 can be reduced to the required standard form.

That a conjunction is valid if and only if each of its conjuncts is valid follows straightforwardly from the truth-table definition of conjunction.

What remains therefore is to justify the rules we have numbered (i)–(iv), by which we test the validity of disjunctions of affirmatively quantified schemata. We shall do this by showing that all such disjunctions which fulfil the conditions stated in these rules would also turn out valid if tested by truth-tables (Decision Procedure I), and all which do not fulfil those conditions would turn out invalid if tested by that method. Decision Procedure I has already been established as a sound test of validity.

Before we approach the rules directly, we shall recapitulate and develop some of the points already made in Chapter 25.

Some observations on the truth-table method

Consider what we do when we test a wff of the form $\exists \alpha$ by the truth-table method. We replace α by its perfect DNF, and then we apply LED to place an '$\exists$' before each disjunct in that perfect DNF. The resulting formula, which is of course equivalent to $\exists \alpha$ itself, we shall call the *distributed perfect DNF* ('DPDNF' for short) of $\exists\alpha$. As reference to Chapter 25 will show, it consists in all cases of a disjunction of basic formulae and/or inconsistent $\exists$-schemata. The principle on which we learnt to calculate the truth-table for $\exists\alpha$ can now be expressed as follows:

A. $\exists\alpha$ has the value 1 for every row of the matrix in which at least one of the basic formulae in its DPDNF has the value 1; and $\exists\alpha$ has the value 0 when all of these basic formulae have the value 0 (or when there are no such basic formulae).

Clearly if any basic formula whatsoever occurs in the DPDNF of $\exists\alpha$ (i.e. if its DPDNF does not consist solely of a disjunction of inconsistent $\exists$-schemata), there will be some row or rows of the matrix for which $\exists\alpha = 1$, and so $\exists\alpha$ will not be an inconsistent wff. We can therefore state a second principle:

B. $\exists\alpha$ is inconsistent if and only if every disjunct in its DPDNF is an inconsistent $\exists$-schema.

Thirdly, consider the basic formulae (if any) which do *not* occur in the DPDNF of $\exists\alpha$. As A makes clear, assigning the value 1 to any of these does not give $\exists\alpha$ the value 1; i.e. it does not ensure that there is something which is an α. What such an assignment does mean is that there is something which is *not* an α, i.e. that $\exists{\sim}\alpha = 1$. For just as, to put it roughly, we can think of the basic formulae in the DPDNF of $\exists\alpha$ as representing the various possible ways in which there may be an α, so we can think of the remaining basic formulae as representing the various possible ways in which there may be a non-α. (Examination of actual matrices will make this clearer.) So we can formulate a third principle:

C. $\exists{\sim}\alpha$ has the value 1 for any row of the matrix in which at least one basic formula which is *not* in the DPDNF of $\exists\alpha$ has the value 1. If all such basic formulae have the value 0 (or if there are no such basic formulae), $\exists{\sim}\alpha = 0$.

In Chapter 25 we also saw that the perfect DNF of a wfpe α is isomorphic with the perfect DNF of α' (the PC wff isomorphic with α). We can therefore think of the DPDNF of $\exists\alpha$ as consisting of the perfect DNF of α', but with a basic formula taking the place of each consistent conjunction of variables, and an inconsistent $\exists$-schema taking the place of each inconsistent conjunction of variables. For example, if the perfect DNF of α' is

$$(p.q.\sim r) \vee (\sim p.q.r) \vee (\sim p.q.\sim q.\sim r)$$

then the DPDNF of ∃α will be

$$\exists(f.g.\sim h) \vee \exists(\sim f.g.h) \vee \exists(\sim f.g.\sim g.\sim h)$$

Now we showed in Chapter 11: (i) that a wff of PC is inconsistent if and only if every disjunct in its DNF (perfect or non-perfect) is an inconsistent conjunction of variables; and (ii) that a wff of PC is valid if and only if every possible consistent conjunction of variables occurs in its perfect DNF. We therefore draw the following conclusions:

D. If and only if α′ is inconsistent, every disjunct in the DPDNF of ∃α is an inconsistent ∃-schema.

E. If and only if α′ is valid, every basic formula occurs in the DPDNF of ∃α. (Equivalently, we may say: if and only if α′ is *not* valid, there is some basic formula which does *not* occur in the DPDNF of ∃α.)

Some Lemmas

On the basis of the five principles we have just stated, we now prove four Lemmas. Once these have been established, the justification of the rules will be comparatively straightforward. In what follows, you should bear in mind that, by the ordinary principles of truth-tables, if we want to show that a wff is not valid, it is sufficient to show that for at least one row of the matrix the wff has the value 0.

The Lemmas are these:

Lemma 1: If α′ is not valid, ∃α is not valid.

Lemma 2: If and only if α′ is inconsistent, ∃α is inconsistent.

Lemma 3: If and only if (α′ ∨ β′) is valid, every basic formula occurs either in the DPDNF of ∃α or in that of ∃β (or in both).[1]

Lemma 4: For any row of the matrix, Uα has the value 1 if and only if every basic formula which is not in the DPDNF of ∃α has the value 0.[2]

---

[1] Equivalent formulations of Lemma 3 are: (i) If and only if (α′ ∨ β′) is valid, any basic formula which does not occur in the DPDNF of one of ∃α and ∃β does occur in that of the other; and (ii) If and only if (α′ ∨ β′) is *not* valid, there is some basic formula which occurs neither in the DPDNF of ∃α nor in that of ∃β.

[2] An equivalent formulation of Lemma 4 is: Uα = 0 if and only if some basic formula which is not in the DPDNF of ∃α has the value 1.

Proof of Lemma 1: If α′ is not valid, then (by E) there is some basic formula which does not occur in the DPDNF of Ǝα. Now there is a row of the matrix in which every basic formula other than that one has the value 0, and in which therefore every basic formula in the DPDNF of Ǝα has the value 0. For that row, Ǝα = 0 (by A).

Proof of Lemma 2: This follows directly from D and B.

Proof of Lemma 3: By E, if and only if (α′ v β′) is valid, every basic formula occurs in the DPDNF of Ǝ(α v β). Since Ǝ(α v β) is equivalent to (Ǝα v Ǝβ), Lemma 3 follows.

Proof of Lemma 4: Since Uα is equivalent to ∼Ǝ∼α, and therefore has the opposite truth-value to Ǝ∼α, Lemma 4 follows immediately from C.

Justification of the Rules

We are now in a position to tackle Rules (i)–(iv) directly.

Rule (i): Ǝα is valid (in LNEU) if and only if α′ is valid.

Justification: (a) If α′ is valid, every basic formula occurs in the DPDNF of Ǝα (by E). Therefore (by A) Ǝα = 1 for any row of the matrix in which at least one basic formula has the value 1. But in an LNEU matrix every row is of this nature.

(b) If α′ is not valid, Ǝα is not valid (Lemma 1).

Note that (b), unlike (a), holds generally, not only in LNEU.

Rule (ii): Uα is valid if and only if α′ is valid.

Justification: If and only if α′ is valid, its negation, ∼α′, is inconsistent. If and only if ∼α′ is inconsistent, Ǝ∼α is inconsistent (by Lemma 2). And if and only if Ǝ∼α is inconsistent, its negation, ∼Ǝ∼α (i.e. Uα) is valid.

Rule (iii): (Uα v Uβ v . . .) is valid if and only if at least one of α′, β′, . . . is valid.

Justification: (a) If at least one of α′, β′, . . . is valid, then, by Rule (ii), at least one of Uα, Uβ, . . . is valid, and therefore so is any disjunction in which it is a disjunct.

(b) If none of α′, β′, . . . is valid, then for each of Ǝα, Ǝβ, . . . there is a basic formula which is not in its DPDNF (by E). In the first row of the matrix every basic formula has the value 1.

Therefore for that row (by Lemma 4) each of Uα, Uβ, ... has the value 0, and hence (Uα ∨ Uβ ∨ ...) = 0.

Rule (iv) is a little harder. To justify it we have to prove (*a*) that if any one of $(\alpha' \vee \beta_1')$, ..., $(\alpha' \vee \beta_n')$ is valid, then

$$\exists\alpha \vee U\beta_1 \vee \ldots \vee U\beta_n \qquad (1)$$

is valid; and

(*b*) that if none of $(\alpha' \vee \beta_1')$, ..., $(\alpha' \vee \beta_n')$ is valid, then (1) is not valid.

Justification: (*a*) Let β_j be any one of β_1, ..., β_n such that $(\alpha' \vee \beta_j')$ is valid. Then (by Lemma 3) every basic formula which does not occur in the DPDNF of ∃β_j does occur in that of ∃α; with the result that if every basic formula in the DPDNF of ∃α had the value 0, every basic formula *not* in that of ∃β_j would have that value, and hence Uβ_j would have the value 1 (by Lemma 4). Now in every row of the matrix, either (i) at least one of the basic formulae in the DPDNF of ∃α has the value 1, or else (ii) all such basic formulae have the value 0. If (i) obtains, ∃α = 1 (by A); if (ii) obtains, Uβ_j = 1, as we have just shown. Therefore for every row, at least one disjunct in (1) has the value 1, and hence (1) itself = 1.

(*b*) Suppose none of $(\alpha' \vee \beta_1')$, ..., $(\alpha' \vee \beta_n')$ is valid. Consider the row of the matrix in which every basic formula in the DPDNF of ∃α has the value 0 and every other basic formula has the value 1. For that row, ∃α = 0 (by A). But since $(\alpha' \vee \beta_1')$ is not valid, one of the basic formulae which is not in the DPDNF of ∃α is not in that of ∃β_1 either (by Lemma 3). For the row in question, this basic formula has the value 1, so Uβ_1 = 0 (by Lemma 4). The same holds for each of Uβ_2, ..., Uβ_n. Therefore for the row in question, each disjunct in (1), and hence (1) itself, has the value 0.

EXERCISES 28

28.1 Give the distributed perfect DNF's of the following, in each case in terms of 'f', 'g' and 'h'.

    (*a*) ∃ ∼g

    (*b*) ∃(f . (g ⊃ ∼f))

    (*c*) ∃∼((f ⊃ ∼g) ⊃ (g ⊃ ∼f))

    (*d*) ∃((f ⊃ (g ∨ h)) ⊃ ((f . ∼g) ⊃ h))

28.2 Assuming the validity of Rules (i)–(iv), prove that Rules (ia)–(iva) are also valid.

28.3 Where α', β', ... are the PC wffs isomorphic with α, β, ... respectively, show that

(a) If $(\alpha' \supset \beta')$ is valid in PC, $(U\alpha \supset U\beta)$ is valid in LPC1.

(b) If $(\alpha' \supset (\beta' \supset \gamma'))$ is valid in PC,
$(\exists\alpha \supset (U\beta \supset \exists\gamma))$ is valid in LPC1.

(c) If $((\alpha' \supset \beta') \supset (\gamma' \supset \delta'))$ is valid in PC,
$((U\alpha \supset \exists\beta) \supset (U\gamma \supset \exists\delta))$ is valid in LPC1.

CHAPTER 29

LPC1 : Axiomatization

LPC1 and PC

There are two simple ways in which, starting from a valid wff of PC, X, we can obtain a valid wff of LPC1.

1. We can make uniform substitutions of wffs of LPC1 for each of the variables in X. E.g. if X is the valid wff

$$p \supset (q \supset (p.q))$$

then by substituting 'Ǝf' for 'p' and 'U(f v g)' for 'q', we obtain

$$Ǝf \supset (U(f \lor g) \supset (Ǝf \, . \, U(f \lor g)))$$

That the result of making such substitutions is a valid wff is too obvious to need much argument.

The formulae we obtain in this way will in a sense not be interesting ones, since their validity can be determined by PC methods alone. Nevertheless they are valid, and we are looking for a system in which every valid wff will be a thesis.

2. We can form the wfpe isomorphic with X, and place a 'U' immediately before it. E.g. if X is

$$(p.q) \supset (p \lor q)$$

we can construct the LPC1 formula

$$U((f.g) \supset (f \lor g))$$

That the wffs so obtained are valid has been proved in Chapter 28, in the justification of Rule (ii).

These methods of obtaining valid wffs suggest the plan of running together PC and LPC1 into a single axiomatic system; and this is in fact what we shall do. We know from Part II that the system PM is a consistent and complete axiomatization of PC; we shall therefore incorporate the basis of PM into the basis of the system we are about to construct. To the PM basis we shall add rules which will legitimize derivations of the kinds described above, as well as whatever else may be necessary to yield all valid wffs of LPC1 as theses.

We call the system so obtained, *The System PM+LPC1*.

All valid wffs of PC, since they are theses of PM, will be theses of PM+LPC1 too, and we shall make frequent use of such theses in proofs. The only formulae we shall explicitly derive as theorems, however, will be ones which belong to LPC1 itself.

We now set out the system formally.

The System PM+LPC1

Primitive symbols

p, q, r, . . .	[propositional variables]
f, g, h, . . .	[predicate variables]
∼	[negation sign]
v	[disjunction sign]
U	[universal quantifier]
(,)	[brackets]

In stating definitions and rules we use the following meta-logical symbols:

$\alpha, \beta, \ldots$ for predicate-expressions;

X, Y, . . . for formulae; and, where greater clarity results,

$\alpha', \beta', \ldots$ for PC formulae isomorphic with the predicate-expressions $\alpha, \beta, \ldots$ respectively.

Definitions

Where X and Y are any wffs and α and β are any wfpes,

[.] $\begin{cases} (X.Y) & =_{Df} \sim(\sim X \text{ v} \sim Y) \\ (\alpha.\beta) & =_{Df} \sim(\sim\alpha \text{ v} \sim\beta) \end{cases}$

[⊃] $\begin{cases} (X \supset Y) & =_{Df} (\sim X \text{ v } Y) \\ (\alpha \supset \beta) & =_{Df} (\sim\alpha \text{ v } \beta) \end{cases}$

[≡] $\begin{cases} (X \equiv Y) & =_{Df} ((X \supset Y) . (Y \supset X)) \\ (\alpha \equiv \beta) & =_{Df} ((\alpha \supset \beta) . (\beta \supset \alpha)) \end{cases}$

[∃] $\exists\alpha \qquad =_{Df} \sim U\sim\alpha$

You will be familiar with the role of such definitions, and the transformations they permit, from Part II.

Formation rules

The wffs of PM+LPC1 consist of all the wffs of PM, as specified by the Formation Rules given in Chapter 15, together with all the wffs of LPC1, as specified by the Formation Rules given in Chapter 24.

(Note that we are not admitting into our system 'mixed' formulae, i.e. formulae which contain both propositional and predicate variables, such as

$$(\exists f \lor p) \supset (U{\sim}g \supset q)$$

There is nothing inherently objectionable about such formulae; but our main aim is to construct a deductive system of valid LPC1 formulae as these have been described in previous chapters, and for this purpose it is more convenient to omit formulae of the mixed type.)

Axioms

We include the axioms of PM (minus the redundant fourth axiom) in our axiom set. The transformation rules will not, however, enable us to derive all valid wffs of LPC1 from these axioms alone. We therefore add some further axioms, drawn from LPC1 itself. As these extra axioms we choose the formulae labelled A1 and A2 below. Note that A2 is valid in LNEU only; in fact its presence or absence in the axiom set can be used to mark the distinction between LNEU and LEU. We leave the PM axioms unnumbered, as they will not be explicitly used in proofs.

The axioms are:

$$(p \lor p) \supset p$$
$$q \supset (p \lor q)$$
$$(p \lor q) \supset (q \lor p)$$
$$(q \supset r) \supset ((p \lor q) \supset (p \lor r))$$

A1. $U(f \supset g) \supset (Uf \supset Ug)$

*A2. $Uf \supset \exists f$

Transformation rules

R1. *The Rule of Substitution for Propositional Variables*

We state this rule in such a way that it will cover both the PM rule of uniform substitution and also the substitution procedure described at the beginning of this chapter.

If (i) X is a thesis of PM,

  (ii) $p_1, \ldots, p_n$ are the totality of the variables in X,

(iii) $Y_1, \ldots, Y_n$ are all *either* (not necessarily distinct) wffs of PM *or* (not necessarily distinct) wffs of LPC1,

then $X(Y_1/p_1, \ldots, Y_n/p_n)$ is a thesis.

Note: The requirement that $p_1, \ldots, p_n$ be the totality of the variables in X is simply designed to prevent the occurrence of 'mixed' formulae. When $Y_1, \ldots, Y_n$ are wffs of PM, the rule is not in practice more restrictive than the PM rule of substitution, since the wff which we substitute for a given variable can always be that variable itself.

The use of R1 in proofs will be indicated in the way made familiar in Part II. The substitution of a variable for itself will not be noted.

R2. *The Rule of Universal Quantification* (Q)

This permits the second type of derivation described at the beginning of this chapter. It runs:

If α' is a thesis containing propositional variables, $U\alpha$ is a thesis.

When we use R2 in proofs, we shall refer to the relevant (PM) thesis and then add '$\times$Q'.

R3. *The Rule of Substitution for Predicate Variables*

This allows us to replace any predicate variable in a thesis by any wfpe, provided we do so uniformly. More than one such uniform replacement may of course be made in a single step. The rule runs:

If X is a thesis containing predicate variables, $f_1, \ldots, f_n$ and $\alpha_1, \ldots, \alpha_n$ are (not necessarily distinct) wfpes, then

$$X(\alpha_1/f_1, \ldots, \alpha_n/f_n)$$

is a thesis.

The use of R3 will be indicated in the same way as R1. The nature of the substitutions made will show which of the two rules is being employed.

R4. *The Rule of Detachment*

If X and $(X \supset Y)$ are theses, Y is a thesis.
The use of R4 will be indicated by '$\times$D'.

R1-R4 are primitive transformation rules of PM +LPC1.

Derived transformation rules

Since the whole basis of PM is included in the basis of PM +LPC1, the derived rules of PM hold good in PM +LPC1 also. In virtue of R1 and R4, these derived rules can be applied to LPC1 theses as well as to PM theses.

The *Rule of Substitution of Equivalent wffs* (established for PM in Chapter 16) is worth stating separately:

If X is a thesis which contains a *wff* (not a wfpe), Y, and (Y ≡ Z) is also a thesis, then X[Z/Y] is a thesis.

(Note that 'X[Z/Y]' means 'the result of replacing some occurrence of Y in X by Z', not 'the result of *uniformly* replacing Y in X by Z'.)

When we use this rule in proofs we shall write '×Eq1'. Otherwise the employment of the derived rules of PM will be indicated as in Part II.

In PM +LPC1 we can derive additional transformation rules. Two of these we can establish immediately.

The first is one of a series of *Rules of Distribution of Quantifiers*, and we label it 'DQ1'.

DQ1: If $(\alpha' \supset \beta')$ is a thesis (of PM), then $(U\alpha \supset U\beta)$ is a thesis.

Derivation: If $(\alpha' \supset \beta')$ is a thesis, then, by Q, $U(\alpha \supset \beta)$ is a thesis. By substituting α for 'f' and β for 'g' in A1, we obtain

$$U(\alpha \supset \beta) \supset (U\alpha \supset U\beta)$$

Hence, by Detachment, $(U\alpha \supset U\beta)$ is a thesis.

The other derived rule which we shall establish here is one which we shall use with great frequency. It entitles us to substitute equivalent *wfpes* for each other, and runs parallel to the rule of substitution of equivalent *wffs* mentioned above (with which, however, it must not be confused).

We introduced and defined the term 'equivalent predicate-expressions' towards the end of Chapter 23. In subsequent chapters we have assumed the right to replace any wfpe by any other wfpe which is equivalent to it, and this has seemed an intuitively reasonable thing to do. In particular, whenever we make such a replacement in a valid wff, the result is always valid too. We now want to assure ourselves that whenever we make such a replacement in a *thesis*, the result is always a thesis.

In Chapter 23 we defined 'equivalent predicate-expressions' in terms of valid equivalential wffs of PC. Since, however, all valid equivalential wffs of PC are theses of PM +LPC1, we state the rule in terms of such theses.

The Rule of Substitution of Equivalent Predicate-expressions.

If (i) X is a thesis containing a wfpe α,
   (ii) (Y ≡ Z) is a thesis containing propositional variables (i.e. a thesis of PM),
   (iii) (α ≡ β) is a wfpe obtainable by uniform replacement of the variables in (Y ≡ Z) by any wfpes,
then X[β/α] is a thesis.

We refer to this rule as 'Eq2'. When we use it in proofs, we shall refer to the relevant PM thesis, note the replacements to be made therein, and add '×Eq2'.

Derivation of Eq2. Every substitution made under Eq2 occurs within a quantified schema, i.e. a schema of the form Uα or of the form ∃α. It consists of replacing some well-formed part of α by a wfpe which is equivalent to that part. We can always think of this as replacing the whole of α by a wfpe, β, which is equivalent to α; or more precisely, which is such that (α′ ≡ β′) is a thesis. If, therefore, we can show that whenever (α′ ≡ β′) is a thesis (of PM),

  (a) (Uα ≡ Uβ) is a thesis
and (b) (∃α ≡ ∃β) is a thesis,

then the rule of substitution of equivalent *wffs* will give us the result we want for the whole formula in which Uα or ∃α occurs.

The proofs of (a) and (b) are as follows. (We use '⊢ X', as we did in Part II, to mean 'X is a thesis'.)

If ⊢ (α′ ≡ β′), then by Def ≡, and '(p.q) ⊃ p' and '(p.q) ⊃ q' respectively, we have

	⊢ (α′ ⊃ β′)	(1)
and	⊢ (β′ ⊃ α′)	(2)
(1)×DQ1:	⊢ (Uα ⊃ Uβ)	(3)
(2)×DQ1:	⊢ (Uβ ⊃ Uα)	(4)
(3), (4) ×Adj, ×Def ≡:	⊢ (Uα ≡ Uβ)	(a)
(1)×Transp:	⊢ (∼β′ ⊃ ∼α′)	(5)
(5)×DQ1:	⊢ (U∼β ⊃ U∼α)	(6)
(6)×Transp:	⊢ (∼U∼α ⊃ ∼U∼β)	(7)
(7)×Def ∃:	⊢ (∃α ⊃ ∃β)	(8)
Similarly, from (2):	⊢ (∃β ⊃ ∃α)	(9)
(8), (9) ×Adj, ×Def ≡:	⊢ (∃α ≡ ∃β)	(b)

This completes the derivation of Eq2.

Setting out of proofs

We shall set out proofs of theorems in the same way as in Part II, with certain easily understood modifications. When we make use of PM theses, we shall not offer proofs of them. We know from the Completeness Proof for PM that all valid wffs of PC can be derived as theorems; and in fact every PM thesis we shall use will either have been proved, or be easily derivable from some theses which have been proved, in Part II. If the PM thesis is one of the more familiar ones - roughly, if it is one of those to which a name has been attached – we shall for the most part simply refer to it by its name in the justification column. If less familiar theses are used, we shall list them at the beginning of the proof and attach a temporary number to each, by which it will be referred to throughout that proof (though not in other proofs).

The abbreviations 'de M' and 'DN', which have not yet appeared in justification columns, will be used for the de Morgan Laws (in one form or another) and the Law of Double Negation, respectively.

Theorems which are not valid in LEU will be starred.

Proofs of theorems

T1. $Uf \equiv \sim\!\exists\sim\!f$

PROOF:

$Id(\sim\!\exists\sim\!f/p)$	:	$\sim\!\exists\sim\!f \equiv \sim\!\exists\sim\!f$	(1)
(1) $\times$ Def $\exists$	:	$\sim\!\sim\!U\!\sim\!\sim\!f \equiv \sim\!\exists\sim\!f$	(2)
(2), DN(f/p) $\times$ Eq2	:	$\sim\!\sim\!Uf \equiv \sim\!\exists\sim\!f$	(3)
(3), DN(Uf/p) $\times$ Eq1	:	T1	

T2. $U\!\sim\!f \equiv \sim\!\exists f$

PROOF:

T1 $(\sim\!f/f)$	:	$U\!\sim\!f \equiv \sim\!\exists\sim\!\sim\!f$	(1)
(1), DN(f/p) $\times$ Eq2	:	T2	

T3. $\exists\sim\!f \equiv \sim\!Uf$

PROOF: $(p \equiv \sim\!q) \supset (q \equiv \sim\!p)$ (i)

(i)(Uf/p, $\exists\sim\!f$/q)	:	$(Uf \equiv \sim\!\exists\sim\!f) \supset (\exists\sim\!f \equiv \sim\!Uf)$	
			(1)
(1), T1 $\times$ D	:	T3	

T4.   U(f.g) ⊃ (Uf.Ug)

PROOF: (p.q) ⊃ p   (i)
           (p.q) ⊃ q   (ii)

(i) ×DQ1   :   U(f.g) ⊃ Uf   (1)
(ii) ×DQ1   :   U(f.g) ⊃ Ug   (2)
(1),(2) ×Comp   :   T4

T5.   (Uf.Ug) ⊃ U(f.g)

PROOF: p ⊃ (q ⊃ (p.q))   (i)

(i) ×DQ1   :   Uf ⊃ U(g ⊃ (f.g))   (1)
A1(g/f, f.g/g)   :   U(g ⊃ (f.g)) ⊃ (Ug ⊃ U(f.g))   (2)
(1),(2) ×Syll   :   Uf ⊃ (Ug ⊃ U(f.g))   (3)
(3) ×Imp   :   T5

T6.   U(f.g) ≡ (Uf.Ug)

PROOF: T4, T5 ×Adj, ×Def ≡

In future we shall usually write one-line proofs in this abbreviated form, without repetition of the theorem number.

T7.   ∼∃(f ∨ g) ≡ (∼∃f . ∼∃g)

PROOF:

T6(∼f/f,∼g/g)   :   U(∼f.∼g) ≡ (U∼f.U∼g)   (1)
(1), deM(f/p, g/q) ×Eq2   :   U∼(f ∨ g) ≡ (U∼f.U∼g)   (2)
(2), T2 ×Eq1   :   T7

T8.   ∃(f ∨ g) ≡ (∃f ∨ ∃g)   [LED]

PROOF: (∼p ≡ q) ⊃ (p ≡ ∼q)   (i)
(i)(∃(fvg)/p, ∼∃f.∼∃g/q)   :

                   T7 ⊃ (∃(f ∨ g) ≡ ∼(∼∃f.∼∃g))   (1)
(1), T7 ×D   :   ∃(f ∨ g) ≡ ∼(∼∃f.∼∃g)   (2)
(2), deM(∃f/p, ∃g/q) ×Eq1 :   T8

T9.   ∃f ≡ (∃(f.g) ∨ ∃(f.∼g))

PROOF: p ≡ ((p.q) ∨ (p.∼q))   (i)

Id(∃f/p)   :   ∃f ≡ ∃f   (1)
(1), (i)(f/p,g/q) ×Eq2   :   ∃f ≡ ∃((f.g) ∨ (f.∼g))   (2)
(2), T8 ×Eq1   :   T9

*T10. ∃∼f v ∃f

PROOF:

| A2 ×Def ⊃ | : | ∼Uf v ∃f | (1) |
| (1), T3 ×Eq1 | : | T10 | |

*T11. ∼∃f ⊃ ∃∼f

PROOF:

| A2 ×Transp | : | ∼∃f ⊃ ∼Uf | (1) |
| (1), T3 ×Eq1 | : | T11 | |

T12. U(f ⊃ f)

PROOF: Id ×Q.

T13. U(f v ∼f)
T14. ∼∃(f.∼f)

Proofs are left to the reader.

T15. ∃(f ⊃ g) ≡ (Uf ⊃ ∃g)

PROOF:

T8(∼f/f)	:	∃(∼f v g) ≡ (∃∼f v ∃g)	(1)
(1), T3 ×Eq1	:	∃(∼f v g) ≡ (∼Uf v ∃g)	(2)
(2) ×Def ⊃	:	T15	

T16. (Uf ⊃ ∃g) ≡ (U∼g ⊃ ∃∼f)

PROOF:

| Transp(Uf/p, ∃g/q) | : | (Uf ⊃ ∃g) ≡ (∼∃g ⊃ ∼Uf) | (1) |
| (1), T3 ×Eq1, T2 ×Eq1 | : | T16 | |

T17. U(f ⊃ g) ⊃ (∃f ⊃ ∃g)

PROOF:

A1(∼g/f, ∼f/g)	:	U(∼g ⊃ ∼f) ⊃ (U∼g ⊃ U∼f)	(1)
(1), Transp ×Eq1	:	U(∼g ⊃ ∼f) ⊃ (∼U∼f ⊃ ∼U∼g)	(2)
(2), Transp ×Eq2	:	(U(f ⊃ g) ⊃ (∼U∼f ⊃ ∼U∼g)	(3)
(3) ×Def ∃	:	T17	

*T18. U(f ⊃ g) ⊃ (Uf ⊃ ∃g)

PROOF:

| A2(f⊃g/f) | : | U(f ⊃ g) ⊃ ∃(f ⊃ g) | (1) |
| (1), T15 ×Eq1 | : | T18 | |

From T17 and T18 we derive two further Rules of Distribution of Quantifiers (DQ2 and DQ3 respectively.)

By Q, if $(\alpha' \supset \beta')$ is any (implicative) thesis of PM, $U(\alpha \supset \beta)$ is a thesis. By substituting α for 'f' and β for 'g' in T17 and T18, we obtain

$$(U(\alpha \supset \beta) \supset (\exists\alpha \supset \exists\beta))$$
and
$$(U(\alpha \supset \beta) \supset (U\alpha \supset \exists\beta))$$

respectively. Hence, by Detachment, $(\exists\alpha \supset \exists\beta)$ and $(U\alpha \supset \exists\beta)$ are theses. We therefore have the rules:

DQ2: If $(\alpha' \supset \beta')$ is a thesis (of PM), then
$(\exists\alpha \supset \exists\beta)$ is a thesis.

*DQ3: If $(\alpha' \supset \beta')$ is a thesis (of PM), then
$(U\alpha \supset \exists\beta)$ is a thesis.

T19. $\exists(f \,.\, g) \supset (\exists f \,.\, \exists g)$

PROOF: $(p.q) \supset p$ (i)
$(p.q) \supset q$ (ii)

(i) $\times$ DQ2   : $\exists(f \,.\, g) \supset \exists f$ (1)
(ii) $\times$ DQ2   : $\exists(f \,.\, g) \supset \exists g$ (2)
(1), (2) $\times$ Comp   :   T19

T20. $(Uf \vee Ug) \supset U(f \vee g)$

PROOF:

T19($\sim$f/f,$\sim$g/g) $\times$ Transp : $\sim(\exists\sim f \,.\, \exists\sim g) \supset \sim\exists(\sim f \,.\, \sim g)$ (1)
(1), de M $\times$ Eq1, $\times$ Eq2 : $(\sim\exists\sim f \vee \sim\exists\sim g) \supset \sim\exists\sim(f \vee g)$ (2)
(2), T1 $\times$ Eq1   : T20

T19 and T20 form a pair and should be compared and contrasted with T6 and T8, which also form a pair. T6 and T8 are equivalences, but T19 and T20 are only implications: their converses are not theses. With '$\exists$' and 'v' we can move from the undistributed to the distributed form or vice versa. So we can with 'U' and '.'. But with '$\exists$' and '.' we can move in one direction only, from the undistributed to the distributed form. And with 'U' and 'v' we can move in the other direction only, from the distributed form to the undistributed.

A couple of examples will make it clear that the converses of T19 and T20 are not valid. Two properties may each have an instance yet have no joint instance. There are pigs and there are creatures with wings, but there are no pigs with wings. So we cannot infer '∃(f.g)' from '∃f.∃g'. Again, in the field of the ordinary whole numbers everything is either-even-or-odd; but we cannot infer from this that either everything is even or else everything is odd, for both disjuncts here are false. So we cannot safely move from 'U(f v g)' to 'Uf v Ug'.

Although the converses of T19 and T20 are not theses, the next two theorems should be noted and compared with them.

T21.   U(f v g) ⊃ (Uf v ∃g)

PROOF:

T17(∼f/f)	:	U(∼f ⊃ g) ⊃ (∃∼f ⊃ ∃g)	(1)
(1), Def⊃	:	U(∼∼f v g) ⊃ (∼∃∼f v ∃g)	(2)
(2), DN ×Eq2, T1 ×Eq1	:	T21	

T22.   (∃f . Ug) ⊃ ∃(f . g)

PROOF:

T21(∼f/f,∼g/g) ×Transp	:	∼(U∼f v ∃∼g) ⊃ ∼U(∼f v ∼g)	(1)
(1), T2, T3 × Eq1	:	∼(∼∃f v ∼Ug) ⊃ ∃∼(∼f v ∼g)	(2)
(2), Def .	:	T22	

T23.   U(f ⊃ g) ⊃ (U(h ⊃ f) ⊃ U(h ⊃ g))

PROOF:	(p ⊃ q) ⊃ ((r ⊃ p) ⊃ (r ⊃ q))		(i)
(i) × DQ1	:	U(f ⊃ g) ⊃ U((h ⊃ f) ⊃ (h ⊃ g))	(1)
A1(h⊃f/f, h⊃g/g)	:	U((h ⊃ f) ⊃ (h ⊃ g)) ⊃	
		(U(h ⊃ f) ⊃ U(h ⊃ g))	(2)
(1), (2) × Syll	:	T23	

T24.   (U(f ⊃ g) ⊃ (∃(h.∼g) ⊃ ∃(h.∼f))

PROOF:	∼(p ⊃ q) ≡ (p.∼q)		(i)
T23, Transp × Eq 1	:	U(f ⊃ g) ⊃ (∼U(h ⊃ g) ⊃ ∼U(h ⊃ f))	(1)
(1), T3 × Eq1	:	U(f ⊃ g) ⊃ (∃∼(h ⊃ g) ⊃ ∃∼(h ⊃ f))	(2)
(2), (i) × Eq2	:	T24	

If you are familiar with traditional syllogistic logic you may recognize T23 and T24 as analogous to the exported forms of the moods Barbara and Baroco respectively. Analogues of many other syllogistic moods can be proved without difficulty.

EXERCISES 29

29.1 Construct proofs of the following theorems. Any theorems or derived rules proved in this chapter may be used in the proofs; but starred theorems and rules should not be used in the proofs of unstarred theorems.

(a) $\sim\exists f \supset U(f \supset g)$

(b) $(Uf \supset Ug) \equiv (\exists \sim g \supset \exists \sim f)$

(c) $(Uf.\exists g) \supset \exists(f.g)$

(d) $(\sim\exists f.\sim\exists g) \vee \exists(f \vee g)$

(e) *$(\exists \sim f.\exists \sim g) \vee \exists(f \vee g)$

(f) $\exists f \supset (U(f \supset g) \supset \exists g)$

(g) $(\sim\exists(f.g) . \exists(f.h)) \supset \exists(\sim g.h)$

(h) *$(Uf.U(g \vee h)) \supset (\exists(f.g) \vee \exists(f.h))$

(i) *$(Uf.U(f \supset g)) \supset (\sim\exists h \supset \exists(g.\sim h))$

(j) $\exists(f \supset (g.h)) \supset ((Uf \supset \exists g).(Uf \supset \exists h))$

29.2 Explain why the axioms of PM alone (with the primitive transformation rules of PM+LPC1) do not suffice for the derivation of all valid wffs of LPC1.

CHAPTER 30

LPC1 : Consistency and Completeness

Consistency

We shall show that PM + LPC1 is *consistent with respect to negation*. That is, we shall show that from the basis we have stated, it is impossible to derive both X and ∼X, where X is any wff.

The theses of PM+LPC1 fall into two classes: those which are wffs of PM, and those which are wffs of LPC1. Clearly X and ∼X must both belong to the same class. We have already proved in Part II that X and ∼X cannot both be PM theses. All that remains to be shown, therefore, is that X and ∼X cannot both be LPC1 theses.

If we look at the only axioms which are not theses of PM, viz.

A1. U(f⊃g) ⊃ (Uf ⊃ Ug)
A2. Uf ⊃ ∃f

we can see that each has the following characteristic: it consists of a wfpe isomorphic with a PM thesis, into which is inserted either 'U' or '∃' at one or more places. Let us call this characteristic, for short, *characteristic C*. An alternative way of explaining characteristic C is to say that a wff of LPC1 possesses characteristic C if and only if the deletion of all the quantifiers in it would result in a wfpe isomorphic with a thesis of PM. The PM theses in question are in fact extremely simple ones: '(p⊃q) ⊃ (p⊃q)' for A1, and 'p⊃q' for A2. Of course not every wff which possesses characteristic C is an axiom or even a thesis at all: e.g. '∃(f.g) ⊃ (Uf v Ug)' has characteristic C but is not a thesis. But A1 and A2 do possess characteristic C; and our next task is to show that all other LPC1 theses possess it too.

We show this by a survey of the transformation rules.

R1. We are concerned with R1 only in so far as it generates LPC1 theses from PM theses. The formation rules guarantee that every wff of LPC1 would become, when quantifiers are deleted, a wfpe isomorphic with a wff of PM. But any formula obtained by uniform substitution of wffs of PM for variables in a thesis of PM is itself a thesis of PM. Therefore if we take any wffs of LPC1, substitute them uniformly for the variables in a thesis of PM and then delete the quantifiers, the result will be a wfpe isomorphic with a thesis of PM. I.e., every thesis of LPC1 obtained by R1 possesses characteristic C.

R2. This rule (Q) calls for no comment.

R3. *The Rule of Uniform Substitution for Predicate Variables.* Every formula to which this rule is applied already possesses characteristic C, and every wfpe is isomorphic with a wff of PM; therefore, since the uniform substitution of PM wffs for variables in a PM thesis results in a further PM thesis, every LPC1 formula derived by R3 also possesses characteristic C.

R4. *The Rule of Detachment.* Suppose this rule is applied to two formulae, each of which already possesses characteristic C. Let α and $(\alpha \supset \beta)$ be the wfpes which these two formulae become when all quantifiers are deleted and, α' and $(\alpha' \supset \beta')$ the PM formulae isomorphic with α and $(\alpha \supset \beta)$ respectively. Then α' and $(\alpha' \supset \beta')$ are both theses of PM, and therefore β' is also a thesis of PM. But the LPC1 formula derived by the rule consists of β with quantifiers inserted into it; therefore it possesses characteristic C. Now R4 can be applied only to pairs of formulae each of which is either an axiom, or a formula obtained by the previously considered rules, or a formula derived from such formulae by a previous application of R4. So it will always be applied to formulae each of which possesses characteristic C; and therefore every formula derived by it will possess characteristic C.

The other transformation rules are derived rules and therefore do not require separate treatment, since any thesis obtained by a derived rule could have been obtained by the primitive rules alone.

If follows that every LPC1 thesis possesses characteristic C, and therefore that no LPC1 formula which does *not* possess characteristic C can be a thesis of PM +LPC1.

Now if X is a wff of LPC1 which possesses characteristic C, $\sim$X cannot possess characteristic C, for the following reason: let α' be the PC formula isomorphic with the wfpe obtained from X by deletion of quantifiers; then $\sim\alpha'$ will be the PC formula isomorphic with the wfpe obtained from $\sim$X by deletion of quantifiers. But if X possesses characteristic C, then α' is a thesis of PM; and (as we proved in Part II) if α' is a thesis of PM, $\sim\alpha'$ is not a thesis of PM.

Therefore if X possesses characteristic C, $\sim$X does not, and so cannot be a thesis.

The gist of the foregoing argument is this: we have found a characteristic which we have shown must belong to every LPC1 thesis of PM + LPC1, and we have further shown that if any formula possesses this characteristic, the formula which consists of that formula preceded by '$\sim$' does not possess that characteristic. Therefore if we have any pair of LPC1 wffs, X and $\sim$X, it is impossible for them both to be theses; and this is what remained to be shown in order to prove that PM + LPC1 is consistent.

Weak completeness

An axiomatic basis is said to be weakly complete if every valid wff is derivable as a thesis.

We already know, from the Completeness Proof for PM, that every valid wff of PM is derivable in PM + LPC1. What we have still to show is that every valid wff of LPC1 is also derivable.

We prove this by making use of the material in Chapters 27 and 28, where Decision Procedure II was expounded and justified. We showed there that every wff of LPC1 can be reduced by equivalence transformations to a conjunction of wffs each of which is of one of the types (i)–(iv) listed on p. 199. Since validity is preserved throughout equivalence transformations, every valid wff can be reduced to a *valid* conjunction of this kind; and a conjunction of this (or indeed any other) kind is valid if and only if each of its conjuncts is valid.

Our axiomatic basis will therefore be complete if from it there can be derived

(a) all valid formulae of any of types (i)–(iv);
(b) all conjunctions of such valid formulae; and
(c) all the equivalences used in the reduction of formulae to the standard form.

(a) We shall consider each of types (i)–(iv) separately.

(i) A formula of the form $\exists\alpha$ is valid if and only if α' is valid. Now every valid wff in PC is a thesis of PM; and by Q, if α' is a thesis of PM, Uα is a thesis of PM + LPC1. By putting α/f in A2, we obtain (by Detachment) $\exists\alpha$ as a theorem. Therefore all valid wffs of type (i) are derivable from our basis.

(ii) A formula of the form Uα is valid if and only if α' is valid.

Since if α' is valid it is a thesis of PM, Q will give us as theorems all valid formulae of type (ii).

(iii) A formula of the form $(U\alpha \lor U\beta \lor \ldots)$ is valid if and only if at least one of α', β', ... is valid. By Q, if α' is valid (and therefore a thesis of PM), $U\alpha$ is derivable; and if $U\alpha$ is derivable, then by 'p $\supset$ (pvq)', R1 and Detachment, so is $(U\alpha \lor U\beta \lor \ldots)$. Similarly, if β' is valid, $(U\beta \lor U\alpha \lor \ldots)$ is derivable, and hence, by Comm and Eq1, $(U\alpha \lor U\beta \lor \ldots)$ is again derivable; and so on for any other disjuncts there may be in a wff of type (iii). Therefore every valid wff of type (iii) is derivable.

(iv) A wff of the form $(\exists\alpha \lor U\beta_1 \lor \ldots \lor U\beta_n)$ is valid if and only if at least one of $(\alpha' \lor \beta_1')$, ..., $(\alpha' \lor \beta_n')$ is valid. Let β_j be any one of $\beta_1, \ldots, \beta_n$. If $(\alpha' \lor \beta_j')$ is valid (and therefore a thesis of PM), then by Comm and Q, $U(\beta_j \lor \alpha)$ is a thesis; therefore, by T21, $(U\beta_j \lor \exists\alpha)$ is a thesis. It is then a simple matter to derive any disjunction which contains both $U\beta_j$ and $\exists\alpha$ among its disjuncts. Hence every valid wff of type (iv) is derivable.

(*b*) Adj is a derived rule of PM+LPC1, and provides for the derivability of all conjunctions of derivable formulae.

(*c*) The only equivalences used in reduction to the standard form are: (i) Substitution-instances of PC equivalences used in reduction to CNF; PM theses and R1 provide these, and Eq1 allows us to use them. (ii) Equivalences used in eliminating negative quantifiers; T2 and T3 provide these. (iii) LED; and T8, with R3, makes this available in all cases.

The basis of PM+LPC1 is therefore (weakly) complete.

Moreover, if we delete A2 from the basis of PM+LPC1, the basis is complete for LEU. This can be proved quite simply.

The only difference between the tests for validity in LNEU and in LEU by Decision Procedure II is that in LEU a formula of type (i) is never valid. But the only point in the Completeness Proof we have just given at which A2 or any thesis dependent on it was appealed to, was in showing the derivability of formulae of type (i). Therefore every wff of LPC1 which is valid in LEU can be derived from the basis of PM+LPC1 without A2.

Strong completeness

Our basis, though weakly complete, is not strongly complete.

To say that an axiomatic basis is strongly complete is to say that the addition as an extra axiom of *any* wff which is not derivable from the original basis would make the system inconsistent. We can therefore show that our basis for PM +LPC1 is *not* strongly complete by finding a wff not derivable from it, whose addition to the axiom set would *not* make the system inconsistent.

Such a wff is

$$\exists f \supset Uf \tag{1}$$

The proof that the addition of (1) to the axiom set would not result in inconsistency is simple. (1), as is easily seen, possesses characteristic C; and as we saw in the Consistency Proof, no set of axioms each of which either possesses characteristic C or is a thesis of PM can yield a pair of mutually contradictory theorems.

But (1) cannot be derived from our original basis. (It would, indeed, be tragic if it could; for then by conjoining it with A2 we should be able to obtain as a theorem

$$\exists f \equiv Uf$$

and thereby the distinction between 'some' and 'all' would be obliterated.)

We shall not give a formal proof that (1) is not derivable in PM + LPC1, but an informal proof can be given quite easily. The axioms of PM +LPC1 are all valid wffs either of PC or of LPC1. The transformation rules are all validity-preserving, in the sense that if they are applied to any valid formula or set of valid formulae, the formulae derived by means of them will all be valid too. But (1) is not valid, as can easily be seen, e.g. by working out its truth-table. Therefore (1) cannot be derived from the axiomatic basis of PM + LPC1.

EXERCISE 30

30.1 Construct an alternative proof of consistency with respect to negation for PM +LPC1, by showing that every thesis is valid. (Cf. the consistency proof for PM given in Chapter 19.)

CHAPTER 31

The System LPC2 : Introductory

In Chapter 23 we said that predicates can enter into propositions in either of two fundamentally different ways. One is by quantification, and of that we have by now said a good deal. The other occurs when we assert that some specified object has (or lacks) a certain property. We said a little, but only a little, about this in Chapter 23; we must say more now.

In order to express the forms of propositions of this second sort, we need some symbols not found in LPC1, viz. *individual-variables*, for which we use the sequence of small letters beginning 'x', 'y', . . . These variables take as their values *names of individuals*; more accurately, their values are the names or other designations of the individuals (objects, people, numbers – whatever they may be) in the relevant universe of discourse. A wff can always be formed by prefixing any wfpe, enclosed in brackets, to any single individual-variable. (The brackets may be omitted when the wfpe consists simply of a single predicate variable negated or unnegated.) But an individual-variable on its own is not a wff, any more than a wfpe is.

A wff constructed in the way we have just described we shall call an *individual-schema* ('IS' for short). The term 'quantified schema', with which we are already familiar, we shall frequently abbreviate to 'QS'.

We are going to extend our system to include as wffs all truth-functions of IS's and/or QS's. The system so obtained we call *LPC2*. Clearly every wff of LPC1 is also a wff of LPC2.

Formation rules

The symbols used in LPC2 consist of all those used in LPC1, with the addition of

$$x, y, . . . \quad \text{[individual-variables]}$$

We shall use 'x_1', 'x_2', . . . and 'y_1', 'y_2', . . . as meta-logical variables whose values are individual-variables.

228

The Formation Rules are as follows:

The rules for the construction of wfpes are exactly as stated for LPC1 in Chapter 24.

The rules for the construction of wffs are the same as for LPC1, with one addition:

(g) If α is a wfpe and x_1 is an individual-variable, αx_1 is a wff.

We continue to observe the practice of dropping brackets when no confusion will thereby be caused.

Validity in LPC2

Every wff of LPC2 becomes a proposition in some universe of discourse if for every individual-variable in it there is uniformly substituted a name or other designation of some object in that universe of discourse, and for every predicate variable in it there is uniformly substituted an expression designating some property which objects in that universe of discourse can be said to possess or to lack.

A wff of LPC2 is valid in the logic of a non-empty universe if and only if every such uniform substitution in every non-empty universe of discourse results in a true proposition.

We shall consider LPC2 only from the point of view of the logic of a non-empty universe. The question of how (if at all) IS's can be interpreted in an empty universe of discourse is a difficult and complex one. We shall have something, tentatively, to say about it in Chapter 36; but for the present, 'valid' is to mean simply 'valid in LNEU'. We shall therefore, in dealing with LPC2, drop the practice of starring.

Single predicate form

You will remember that in LPC1 we have two Distributive Laws for quantified formulae, one for existentially quantified formulae and another for universally quantified ones. These are:

$$\exists(f \vee g) \equiv (\exists f \vee \exists g)$$
and
$$U(f \cdot g) \equiv (Uf \cdot Ug)$$

For IS's something analogous to *each* of these Laws holds, viz.

$$(f \vee g)x \equiv (fx \vee gx) \tag{1}$$
and
$$(f \cdot g)x \equiv (fx \cdot gx) \tag{2}$$

The validity of (1) and (2) is intuitively evident. If Smith is in his 20's or in his 30's, then either Smith is in his 20's or Smith is in his

30's, and *vice versa*. And if Smith is both tall and blue-eyed, then Smith is tall and Smith is blue-eyed, and *vice versa*.

Two other valid equivalences are:

$$(f \supset g)x \equiv (fx \supset gx) \qquad (3)$$

and
$$(f \equiv g)x \equiv (fx \equiv gx) \qquad (4)$$

In virtue of equivalences (1)–(4) we can always very simply transform any IS into a truth-function of IS's in each of which the wfpe is a single predicate variable only. When this is done we shall say that the formula is in *single predicate form*. The method is this: we simply delete the individual-variable at the end of the IS, and instead write that same variable immediately after each predicate variable in the original wfpe.

For example,

$$[((\sim f.g) \vee h) \supset (\sim h \equiv f)]x$$

will become

$$((\sim fx.gx) \vee hx) \supset (\sim hx \equiv fx)$$

which is in single predicate form. ('$\sim fx$' and '$\sim hx$' are here regarded as the negations of 'fx' and 'hx' respectively, not as IS's in which the wfpes are '$\sim f$' and '$\sim h$'.) Similarly,

$$(\sim f \vee g)x \supset (f.h)y$$

can be expressed in single predicate form as

$$(\sim fx \vee gx) \supset (fy.hy)$$

In view of all this, it is in a sense a luxury to allow ourselves to use any wfpe other than a single predicate variable with an individual-variable. Most logicians, in fact, insist that an individual-variable shall be preceded by a single predicate variable only, and thus write all wffs containing individual-variables in what we have called single predicate form. We shall, however, permit ourselves the luxury of prefixing any wpfe we please to an individual-variable, since many calculations are simplified thereby and rules of substitution become easier to state and to apply.

There is one important principle about wffs of LPC2 which contain no quantifiers and are in single predicate form, which applies no matter how many distinct individual-variables such wffs contain. Every wff, whether in single predicate form or not, which can be obtained by uniform substitutions in a valid wff of PC, is of course valid; but in the case of wffs in single predicate form no wff which *cannot* be obtained in this way is valid. It follows that every valid wff of LPC2 which contains no quantifiers is either a substitution-instance of some valid wff of PC, or is equivalent by (1)–(4) to a wff which is such a substitution-instance.

Such wffs are, of course, in a sense uninteresting. The interesting wffs of LPC2 are those which contain at least one QS and at least one IS. A simple example of a valid wff of this kind is

$$fx \supset \exists f \qquad (5)$$

which states that if x has a certain property f, then there is at least one thing which has that property. (5) can, indeed, be regarded as the key principle relating IS's with QS's.

Another important law, closely related to (5), is

$$Uf \supset fx$$

i.e., if everything is f, then x is f.

We have said enough to introduce LPC2. In the next three chapters we shall show how the Decision Procedures we have given for LPC1 can be extended to deal with the wffs of LPC2.

EXERCISES 31

31.1 Give LPC2 formulae to express the forms of the following.
   (*a*) Mary is wearing a hat but John is not.
   (*b*) Shakespeare wrote plays but not novels; Dickens wrote novels but not plays.
   (*c*) If anyone will pass the examination, Smith will.
   (*d*) If Smith and Jones both pass the examination, all the examiners will be surprised.
   (*e*) If India is a republic, and no republic is a monarchy, then some countries in the Commonwealth are not monarchies.
   (*f*) Stars are self-luminous, but planets are not. The moon is a heavenly body which is neither self-luminous nor a planet. Therefore there are heavenly bodies which are neither stars nor planets.

CHAPTER 32

LPC2 : Decision Procedure I

We are going to show how the truth-table procedure set out for LPC1 in Chapter 25 can be extended to deal with the wffs of LPC2. As in the case of LPC1, this decision procedure is given more for its theoretical importance than for practical use in the testing of formulae, since the matrices mostly turn out to be very long ones indeed. A decision procedure which is much more workable in practice will be given in the next chapter.

Basic formulae

The basic formulae for a wff X in LPC2 will comprise the basic formulae used in LPC1, together with every formula which consists of a single predicate variable occurring in X followed by an individual-variable occurring in X.

Thus if X contains one predicate variable ('f') and two individual-variables ('x' and 'y'), there will be four basic formulae, viz. 'Ǝf', 'Ǝ∼f', 'fx' and 'fy'.

If X contains two predicate variables and three individual-variables, there will be the following ten basic formulae: 'Ǝ(f.g)', 'Ǝ(f.∼g)', 'Ǝ(∼f.g)', 'Ǝ(∼f.∼g)', 'fx', 'gx', 'fy', 'gy', 'fz' and 'gz'.

Matrices

We shall now show how to draw up a matrix for any such set of basic formulae.

Let us call those basic formulae which begin with 'Ǝ', *existential basic formulae* (EBF's for short), and those which contain an individual-variable, *individual basic formulae* (IBF's for short).

All IBF's are logically independent of each other: the fact that x is f tells us nothing about whether or not x is g, or about whether y is f, etc. So under the IBF's in a set of basic formulae we can enter all possible combinations of 1's and 0's.

The EBF's, however, are not in general independent of the IBF's. In the previous chapter we took note of the principle

$$fx \supset \exists f$$

and this principle involves a limitation on the possible truth-values of EBF's, given certain truth-values of the IBF's.

An example will illustrate the point here. Suppose we are drawing up a matrix for a wff with two predicate variables and one individual-variable. We adopt the convention of writing the IBF's to the left of the EBF's. We begin by writing '1' under each of 'fx' and 'gx'. Since this means that x is both f and g, we cannot consistently write a '0' under '$\exists(f.g)$', for that would mean that nothing is both f and g. So if 'fx' $= 1$ and 'gx' $= 1$, '$\exists(f.g)$' must also have the value 1. The other three EBF's, however, can take either value, 1 or 0. We thus have eight rows of our matrix, which we can summarize as follows:

fx	gx	$\exists(f.g)$	$\exists(f.\sim g)$	$\exists(\sim f.g)$	$\exists(\sim f.\sim g)$
1	1	1	1/0	1/0	1/0

This is simply a space-saving way of indicating what should be written out as eight distinct rows, each beginning '1 1 1...' and continuing with three further figures, each of which can be either '1' or '0'.

Similarly, if we assign 1 to 'fx' and 0 to 'gx', we must put '$\exists(f.\sim g)$' $= 1$, but each of the other three EBF's may be either 1 or 0. Since there are four possible combinations of values for 'fx' and 'gx', each of which will yield eight rows, there will be 32 rows in all.

Suppose now the formula for which we are drawing up a matrix contains 'y' as well as 'f', 'g' and 'x'. We shall then have 4 IBF's, with 16 truth-value combinations. It would take too long to work through these in detail, but we shall give examples of the limitations on the values of the EBF's that arise.

One set of values for the IBF's is: 'fx' $=1$, 'gx' $=1$, 'fy' $=1$, 'gy' $=0$. The first pair of these state that x is both f and g; the second pair state that y is f but not g. Therefore we cannot put a '0' under *either* '$\exists(f.g)$' *or* '$\exists(f.\sim g)$', but must give each of these the value 1; though each of the other two EBF's can have either value. Therefore this assignment of values to the IBF's will yield *four* rows, which may be indicated thus:

fx	gx	fy	gy	$\exists(f.g)$	$\exists(f.\sim g)$	$\exists(\sim f.g)$	$\exists(\sim f.\sim g)$
1	1	1	0	1	1	1/0	1/0

If however we assign the same pattern of truth-values to the two pairs of IBF's – if, e.g., we put 'fx'=0, 'gx'=1, 'fy'=0, 'gy'=1 – then we have only one EBF (in this case 'Ǝ(∼f.g)') whose value is determined. Thus we have 8 rows for such an assignment of values to the IBF's. In our example these will be

$$0 \quad 1 \quad 0 \quad 1 \quad 1/0 \quad 1/0 \quad 1 \quad 1/0$$

The general principle, and the way to apply it to other LPC2 matrices, should now be clear. The principle can be stated as follows: Any assignment of truth-values to those IBF's which contain the same individual-variable necessitates placing a '1' in that row under *one* of the EBF's but leaves the others free to take either truth-value. The EBF whose value is determined as 1 is that one which contains *unnegated* every predicate variable which occurs in the IBF's to which 1 is assigned, and contains *negated* every predicate variable which occurs in the IBF's to which 0 is assigned.

Subject to this limitation, every combination of truth-values for all the basic formulae is to be written down, to form the matrix.

Matrices for formulae containing only one predicate variable follow the same principles, though here their application is a simpler one, as we never have more than one IBF for any individual-variable. We shall write down the complete matrix for a wff with one predicate variable and two individual-variables.

fx	fy	Ǝf	Ǝ∼f
1	1	1	1
1	1	1	0
1	0	1	1
0	1	1	1
0	0	1	1
0	0	0	1

In each of the first two rows, 'fx'=1 determines 'Ǝf'=1, but leaves 'Ǝ∼f' free to be 1 or 0; and 'fy'=1 does likewise. In the fifth and sixth rows, 'fx'=0 determines 'Ǝ∼f'=1 but leaves 'Ǝf' free, and 'fy'=0 does likewise. But in the third row, 'fx'=1 determines 'Ǝf'=1, and 'fy'=0 determines 'Ǝ∼f'=1, so the values of *both* EBF's are determined; as, for similar reasons, they are in the fourth row too.

Testing for validity

It needs very little argument to show how every wff in LPC2 can be expressed as a truth-function of the relevant basic formulae. Every wff in LPC2 is a truth-function of QS's and/or IS's. We transform all QS's in the way explained in Chapter 25; they can then be treated as truth-functions of the EBF's. We then reduce all IS's to single predicate form. The whole wff is now displayed as a truth-function of some or all of the basic formulae, and can have a truth-table drawn up for it against the appropriate matrix in the usual way.

The familiar rules still apply: if the truth-table consists entirely of 1's, the wff is valid; if entirely of 0's, it is inconsistent; if of a mixture, it is contingent.

EXERCISES 32

32.1 Make a list of the basic formulae

 (*a*) for a wff containing three predicate variables and two individual-variables.

 (*b*) for a wff containing two predicate variables and five individual-variables.

32.2 Calculate the number of rows in the matrix for a wff containing two predicate variables and two individual-variables.

32.3 With what assignments of truth-values to the EBF's are the following assignments of values to the IBF's compatible?

	fx	gx	fy	gy	fz	gz	fw	gw
(*a*)	1	0	0	1	1	0	1	0
(*b*)	0	0	1	0	0	0	0	0
(*c*)	0	1	1	1	1	0	0	0

32.4 Reduce each of the following to an explicit truth-function of the relevant basic formulae:

 (*a*) (U∼(fvg) v (f.∼g)x) ⊃ (∃(f.g) . (∼g⊃f)x)

 (*b*) ((fx ⊃ (gvh)y) ⊃ U(∼f ≡ (g.∼h))) ⊃ (∼fx v ∼hy v ∃g)

 (*c*) (Uf ⊃ (∃g ⊃ hx)) ⊃ (Uh ⊃ (∃f ⊃ gy))

32.5 'Valid in LPC2' was defined in Chapter 31. Write a justification of the claim that Decision Procedure I provides a test of validity as thus defined. (Refer to the analogous argument for LPC1 in the later part of Chapter 26, and make what use of it you find convenient.)

CHAPTER 33

LPC2 : Decision Procedure II –
Exposition

We shall now show how the Decision Procedure for LPC1 given in Chapter 27 can be extended to LPC2.

Standard form

In Chapter 27 we reduced LPC1 formulae to a standard form as follows: taking each QS as an indivisible unit, we reduced the whole wff to CNF by PC methods. Secondly, we made every quantifier affirmative. Finally, within each conjunct we disjoined all the wfpes in existentially quantified schemata under a single existential quantifier, by LED.

The extension of this procedure for LPC2 is as follows:

1. Taking each QS and each IS as an indivisible unit, reduce the whole wff to CNF by PC methods.
2. Make every quantifier affirmative, as in LPC1.
3. *Within each conjunct*, apply LED as in LPC1.
4. *Within each conjunct*, disjoin all the wfpes which are followed by the *same* individual-variable under a single occurrence of that variable, by '(fvg)x ≡ (fx v gx)'. E.g. replace

    fx v (g⊃h)x v ~gy v (~h.f)y

    by

    (f v (g⊃h))x v (~g v (~h.f))y

The result is a conjunctive formula (possibly degenerate), each conjunct of which is a disjunction (again, possibly degenerate) of unnegated QS's and/or IS's; moreover in each such disjunction 'Ǝ' will occur at most once, and each individual-variable will occur at most once. Such a formula is in the required standard form.

Testing for validity

Whether a formula in this standard form is valid or not can be tested as follows.

A conjunctive formula, as we know, is valid if and only if each and every conjunct is valid. All that is needed, therefore, is a way of testing disjunctions of the kind we have just described. The method of doing this can in fact be very simply stated as follows:

In every IS, replace the individual-variable at the end by a universal quantifier at the beginning, and then apply Rules (i)–(iv) exactly as stated in Chapter 27.

This rule may strike you as surprising, and indeed its soundness is far from evident at first sight. But you are asked to take our word for it in the meantime, while we work through an example; if you still have doubts, the next chapter should set your mind at rest.

An illustrative example

We shall test the formula:

$$[(\exists(f.{\sim}g) \vee gx) \supset ({\sim}hy \supset U({\sim}f \supset (g.h))] \supset (fx \supset (fvh)y) \qquad (1)$$

Step 1: We reduce (1) to CNF by PC methods. It should be unnecessary by now to go through the details of the reduction. The result is:

$$(\exists(f.{\sim}g) \vee gx \vee {\sim}fx \vee (fvh)y).$$
$$({\sim}hy \vee {\sim}fx \vee (fvh)y).$$
$$({\sim}U({\sim}f \supset (g.h)) \vee {\sim}fx \vee (fvh)y) \qquad (2)$$

Step 2 requires only a single change: in the third conjunct we replace '${\sim}U$' by '$\exists{\sim}$'.

Step 3 is inapplicable, as no conjunct contains more than one '$\exists$'.

Step 4 requires two changes: (*a*) in the first conjunct we have two schemata containing 'x', viz. 'gx' and '${\sim}fx$'. So we replace 'gx $\vee$ ${\sim}fx$' by '(g $\vee$ ${\sim}f$)x'. (*b*) in the second conjunct we have two schemata containing 'y', viz. '${\sim}hy$' and '(fvh)y'. We use Comm to make them adjacent, and then replace '${\sim}hy \vee (fvh)y$' by '(${\sim}h \vee (fvh))y$'.

The final form of (1) is therefore:

$$(\exists(f.{\sim}g) \vee (gv{\sim}f)x \vee (fvh)y).$$
$$({\sim}fx \vee ({\sim}h \vee (fvh))y).$$
$$(\exists{\sim}({\sim}f \supset (g.h)) \vee {\sim}fx \vee (fvh)y) \qquad (3)$$

Now for the testing. (3) will be valid if and only if each of its three conjuncts is valid. We mentally replace each occurrence of 'x' or 'y' by a universal quantifier at the beginning of the wfpe attached to it, and then apply Rules (i)–(iv) for LPC1. As in Chapter 27, we pretend that 'f', 'g' and 'h' are propositional variables.

First conjunct. This would be of type (iv). It is therefore valid if and only if *either*

$$(f.{\sim}g) \vee (gv{\sim}f) \qquad\qquad (a)$$
or $\qquad (f.{\sim}g) \vee (fvh) \qquad\qquad (b)$

is valid. It is easily shown that (a) is valid (though (b) is not). The first conjunct is therefore valid.

Second conjunct. This would be of type (iii). It is therefore valid if and only if *either*

$${\sim}f \qquad\qquad (c)$$
or $\qquad {\sim}h \vee (fvh) \qquad\qquad (d)$

is valid. Now (c) is not valid, but (d) is. Therefore the second conjunct is valid.

Third conjunct. This would be of type (iv). It is therefore valid if and only if *either*

$${\sim}({\sim}f \supset (g.h)) \vee {\sim}f \qquad\qquad (e)$$
or $\qquad {\sim}({\sim}f \supset (g.h)) \vee (fvh) \qquad\qquad (f)$

is valid. Now (e) is not valid, but (f) is. Therefore the third conjunct is also valid.

So (3), and therefore (1), is valid.

EXERCISES 33

33.1 Determine the validity of the following by Decision Procedure II:

  (a) $(U(f{\supset}g) . fx) \supset gx$

  (b) $(Uf \supset \exists g) \supset (fx \supset gx)$

  (c) $(\exists f \supset Ug) \supset (fx \supset gx)$

  (d) $(fx \equiv \exists g) \supset (gy \equiv \exists f)$

  (e) $(U(f \supset (gvh)) \supset \exists({\sim}fvi)) \supset ((f.{\sim}g)x \supset ({\sim}hvi)y)$

  (f) $((\exists f.gx) \supset {\sim}gy) \supset (Uf \supset {\sim}Ug)$

33.2 Determine the validity of the following inferences:

  (a) If Mary is not at the party, all the men will be disappointed. If Mary and Tom are both at the party, some of the women will be disappointed. If Mary is at the party but Tom is not, Mary will be disappointed. Therefore someone will be disappointed.

(*b*) If all the witnesses are speaking the truth, then either Robinson is guilty but insane or else Smith is guilty but a fool. No insane man could have committed the crime, and Smith is certainly not a fool. Therefore some of the witnesses are not speaking the truth.

CHAPTER 34

LPC2 : Decision Procedure II – Justification

What we have to show is that a disjunction, some or all of whose disjuncts consist of IS's and in which no individual-variable occurs more than once, is valid under the same conditions as the same disjunction with each of the IS's replaced by the corresponding universally quantified schema.

Let Y be any disjunction of QS's, α, β, . . . any wfpes, and x_1, x_2, . . . any distinct individual-variables. Then we what have to prove is that

$$Y \vee \alpha x_1 \vee \beta x_2 \vee \ldots \tag{1}$$

is valid if and only if

$$Y \vee U\alpha \vee U\beta \vee \ldots \tag{2}$$

is valid.

(We have as specially simple cases those in which the disjunction contains only one IS, i.e. is of the form $(Y \vee \alpha x_1)$; and those in which it contains no QS's at all, i.e. is either of the form αx_1, or of the form $(\alpha x_1 \vee \beta x_2 \vee \ldots)$. The existence of such cases does not affect our argument.)

By substitutions in the valid formula

$$Uf \supset fx$$

we obtain

$$U\alpha \supset \alpha x_1$$
$$U\beta \supset \beta x_2 \quad \text{etc.}$$

whatever α, β, . . . and x_1, x_2, . . . may be.

Therefore, by '$(q \supset r) \supset ((p \vee q) \supset (p \vee r))$', if any wff of form (2) is valid, the corresponding wff of form (1) is also valid.

What remains to be shown is that if a wff of form (2) is *not* valid, the corresponding wff of form (1) is not valid either.

If a wff of form (2) is not valid, this means that there is some way of assigning values to the predicate variables in it which will make each disjunct false. Suppose such an assignment of values to be made; then Y, Uα and Uβ will all become false.

But to say that Uα is false is to say that there is at least one individual which does not possess the property α. Let x_1 represent that individual. Then $αx_1$ is also false. Similarly, if Uβ is false, there will be a value of x_2 for which $βx_2$ is false.

Since x_1 and x_2 are distinct variables, the single predicate forms of $αx_1$ and $βx_2$ will have no IBF in common. As we saw in Chapter 32, all IBF's are logically independent of each other. So $αx_1$ and $βx_2$ are logically independent of each other. And therefore if each can be false, both can be false together.

Thus if it is possible to find values for the predicate variables in (2) which will make (2) false, it is possible to find values for the predicate variables and individual-variables in (1) which will make (1) false; i.e. if (2) is not valid, neither is (1).

CHAPTER 35

LPC2 : Axiomatization

We shall extend the axiomatic basis for PM +LPC1 (Chapter 29) in such a way that we can derive all valid wffs of LPC2 as theses. We call the resulting system, *PM +LPC2*.

Primitive symbols, definitions and formation rules

To the primitive symbols of PM +LPC1 we add

x, y, z, . . .   [individual-variables]

The definitions given for PM +LPC1 remain unchanged.

The wffs of PM +LPC2 comprise all the wffs of PM together with all the wffs of LPC2 as specified in Chapter 31.

Axioms

We shall need some additional axioms, and '(f.g)x $\equiv$ (fx.gx)' and 'fx $\supset$ $\exists$f' will serve our purposes. From the former we shall be able to derive the theorems required for the reduction of IS's to single predicate form; the latter will enable us to relate IS's to QS's. If we have these two axioms, however, we can drop A2 ('Uf $\supset$ $\exists$f') as an axiom, as it will now be derivable as a theorem. To avoid confusion, we number the new axioms A3 and A4 respectively. Our axioms will therefore be:

$$(p \lor p) \supset p$$
$$q \supset (p \lor q)$$
$$(p \lor q) \supset (q \lor p)$$
$$(q \supset r) \supset ((p \lor q) \supset (p \lor r))$$

A1. U(f $\supset$ g) $\supset$ (Uf $\supset$ Ug)
A3. (f.g)x $\equiv$ (fx.gx)
A4. fx $\supset$ $\exists$f

Transformation rules

The tranformation rules given for PM +LPC1 in Chapter 29 are to be retained unchanged, except that 'LPC2' is to be read for 'LPC1' throughout. But we need one extra rule, a rule of substitution for individual-variables. Since individual-variables only occur singly in wffs of LPC2 (we do not do anything analogous to forming truth-functions with individual-variables), the only thing we can substitute for an individual-variable is another individual-variable. Such substitution is always legitimate, if uniformly carried out. We formulate the rule as follows:

R5. *The Rule of Substitution for Individual-variables.*

If Z is a thesis (of LPC2) containing distinct individual-variables $x_1, \ldots, x_n$, and $y_1, \ldots, y_n$ are (not necessarily distinct) individual-variables, then

$$Z(y_1/x_1, \ldots, y_n/x_n)$$

is a thesis.

The employment of this rule will be indicated in the familiar way.

In Chapter 29 the Rule of Substitution of Equivalent Predicate-expressions (Eq2) was established only with respect to substitutions in QS's. To make the rule generally available in PM+LPC2 we have to show that it can be applied to wfpes which occur in IS's as well. We have therefore to add to the derivation given in Chapter 29 a proof that if $\vdash (\alpha' \equiv \beta')$, then $\vdash (\alpha x_1 \equiv \beta x_1)$, where x_1 is any individual-variable.

For this purpose we make use of T27 – '$U(f \supset g) \supset (fx \supset gx)$'. This theorem is proved below, and it is important to notice that in its proof Eq2 is never applied to any IS. We proceed as follows:

$\vdash (\alpha' \equiv \beta')$ yields, in the familiar way,

$$\vdash (\alpha' \supset \beta') \tag{1}$$

and
$$\vdash (\beta' \supset \alpha') \tag{2}$$

(1) $\times$ Q:
$$\vdash U(\alpha \supset \beta) \tag{3}$$

(3),T27 $\times$ D:
$$\vdash (\alpha x_1 \supset \beta x_1) \tag{4}$$

Similarly, (2), Q and T27 give:
$$\vdash (\beta x_1 \supset \alpha x_1) \tag{5}$$

Finally we have

(4), (5) $\times$ Adj, $\times$ Def $\equiv$: $\vdash (\alpha x_1 \equiv \beta x_1)$

We can therefore apply Eq2 quite generally once we have proved T27.

Proofs of theorems

All the theorems of PM+LPC1 are also theorems of PM+LPC2. We therefore begin our numbering of the new theorems with 'T25'.

T25. Uf ⊃ fx

PROOF:

A4(∼f/f)	:	∼fx ⊃ ∃∼f	(1)
(1) ×Transp	:	∼∃∼f ⊃ fx	(2)
(2), T1 ×Eq1	:	T25	

T26. Uf ⊃ ∃f

PROOF: T25, A4 ×Syll.

(T26 is A2 in PM+LPC1. Since the rest of the basis of PM+LPC1 is included in the basis of PM+LPC2, the proof of T26 shows that PM+LPC1 is included in PM+LPC2.)

T27. U(f ⊃ g) ⊃ (fx ⊃ gx)

PROOF: (p ⊃ q) ≡ ∼(p.∼q)			(i)
T25(∼(f.∼g)/f)	:	U∼(f.∼g) ⊃ ∼(f.∼g)x	(1)
(1),A3(∼g/g) ×Eq1	:	U∼(f.∼g) ⊃ ∼(fx.∼gx)	(2)
(2),(i)(fx/p,gx/q) ×Eq1	:	U∼(f.∼g) ⊃ (fx ⊃ gx)	(3)
(3),(i)(f/p,g/q) ×Eq2	:	T27	

T28. (f ∨ g)x ≡ (fx ∨ gx)

PROOF: (p ≡ q) ⊃ (∼p ≡ ∼q)			(i)
A3(∼f/f, ∼g/g)	:	(∼f.∼g)x ≡ (∼fx.∼gx)	(1)

(i)((∼f.∼g)x/p, ∼fx.∼gx/q), (1) ×D :

$$\sim(\sim f.\sim g)x \equiv \sim(\sim fx.\sim gx) \quad (2)$$

(2), de M ×Eq2, ×Eq1 : T28

T29. (f ⊃ g)x ≡ (fx ⊃ gx)

PROOF: T28(∼f/f) ×Def ⊃.

T30. (f ≡ g)x ≡ (fx ≡ gx)

PROOF: (p≡q) ⊃ [(r≡s) ⊃ ((p.r) ≡ (q.s))]			(i)
T29(g/f, f/g)	:	(g ⊃ f)x ≡ (gx ⊃ fx)	(1)

(i)((f⊃g)x/p, fx⊃gx/q, (g⊃f)x/r, gx⊃fx/s) :

$$T29 \supset [(1) \supset (((f{\supset}g)x.(g{\supset}f)x) \equiv ((fx{\supset}gx).(gx{\supset}fx)))] \quad (2)$$

((2),T29 ×D), (1) ×D : ((f⊃g)x.(g⊃f)x) ≡ ((fx⊃gx).(gx⊃fx)) (3)

(3),A3(f⊃g/f, g⊃f/g) ×Eq1:

$$((f{\supset}g).(g{\supset}f))x \equiv ((fx{\supset}gx).(gx{\supset}fx)) \quad (4)$$

(4) ×Def ≡ : T30

Equivalence transformations carried out by successive applications of A3, T28, T29 and T30 can always transform a wff of LPC2 which contains no quantifiers into the single predicate form of that wff. Hence it is easy to derive the rule (SP):

If X is any wff of LPC2 in which no quantifiers occur, and X′ is the single predicate form of X, then $(X \equiv X')$ is a thesis.

Two rules for deriving theorems which contain both quantifiers and individual-variables are:

QI1: If $(\alpha' \supset \beta')$ is a thesis (of PM), then
$(U\alpha \supset \beta x_1)$ is a thesis;

QI2: If $(\alpha' \supset \beta')$ is a thesis (of PM), then
$(\alpha x_1 \supset \exists\beta)$ is a thesis;

where x_1 is any individual-variable.

QI1 is easily derived from DQ1 and T25 by Syll, and QI2 from DQ2 and A4 by Syll.

T31. $(U(f \supset g) . fx) \supset gx$

PROOF: T27 $\times$ Imp

T32. $Uf \supset (fx.fy)$

PROOF:

| T25(y/x) | : | $Uf \supset fy$ | (1) |
| T25, (1) $\times$ Comp | : | T32 | |

T33. $U(f.g) \supset (fx.gy)$

PROOF: $(p.q) \supset p$ (i)
$(p.q) \supset q$ (ii)

(i) $\times$ QI1	:	$U(f.g) \supset fx$	(1)
(ii) $\times$ QI1	:	$U(f.g) \supset gy$	(2)
(1), (2) $\times$ Comp	:	T33	

T34. $(U(f \supset h).U(g \supset i)) \supset ((fvg)x \supset (hvi)x)$

PROOF: $((p \supset r).(q \supset s)) \supset ((pvq) \supset (rvs))$ (i)

(i) $\times$ DQ1	:	$U((f \supset g).(g \supset i)) \supset U((fvg) \supset (hvi))$	(1)
T27(fvg/f, hvi/g)	:	$U((fvg) \supset (hvi)) \supset ((fvg)x \supset (hvi)x)$	(2)
(1),(2) $\times$ Syll	:	$U((f \supset h).(g \supset i)) \supset ((fvg)x \supset (hvi)x)$	(3)
(3), T6(f $\supset$ h/f, g $\supset$ i/g) $\times$ Eq1:		T34	

T35. $(U(f \supset h).U(g \supset h)) \supset ((fvg)x \supset hx)$

PROOF: $(p \lor p) \equiv p$ (i)

T34(h/i)   : $(U(f \supset h).U(g \supset h)) \supset ((fvg)x \supset (hvh)x)$ (1)

(1), (i)(h/p) $\times$Eq2   :   T35

T36. $(U(f \supset g).U(\sim f \supset g)) \supset gx$

PROOF: $((p \supset q).(\sim p \supset q)) \supset q$ (i)

(i) $\times$QI1   : $U((f \supset g).(\sim f \supset g)) \supset gx$ (1)

(1), T6(f $\supset$ g/f, $\sim$f $\supset$ g/g) $\times$Eq1 :   T36

T34, T35 and T36 are among the varied forms of the principle of the Dilemma.

T37. $(fx \supset gy) \supset (Uf \supset \exists g)$

PROOF: $(p \supset q) \supset ((r \supset s) \supset ((q \supset r) \supset (p \supset s)))$ (i)

A4(g/f, y/x)   : $gy \supset \exists g$ (1)

(i)(Uf/p, fx/q, gy/r, $\exists$g/s) : $(Uf \supset fx) \supset ((gy \supset \exists g) \supset T37)$ (2)

((2),T25 $\times$D), (1) $\times$D   :   T37

T38. $(\exists f \supset Ug) \supset (fx \supset gy)$

Proof similar to that of T37, using the same PM thesis.

We conclude this chapter by giving the outlines of Consistency and Completeness proofs for PM+LPC2. You should be able to fill in the details of the proofs for yourself if you have mastered the corresponding proofs for PM+LPC1.

Consistency

A proof that the basis for PM+LPC2 is consistent with respect to negation can be given along the lines of the Consistency Proof we gave in Chapter 30. Those axioms of PM+LPC2 which are not theses of PM all have the characteristic that if all quantifiers and individual-variables are deleted, the result is a wfpe isomorphic with a thesis of PM. The transformation rules guarantee that all theorems which are wffs of LPC2 also possess this characteristic. Suppose now that there were two LPC2 theorems, one of which was the negation of the other. Let us call them X and $\sim$X. Let α be the wfpe derived from X by deletion of quantifiers and individual-variables. Then $\sim\alpha$ will be the wfpe derived in the same way from $\sim$X; and α' and $\sim\alpha'$ will both be theses of PM. But this is impossible.

Completeness

A Completeness Proof can again be based on Decision Procedure II (Chapters 33 and 34).

The only equivalence used in reducing wffs of LPC2 to the relevant standard form, in addition to those used in LPC1, is

$$(f \lor g)x \equiv (fx \lor gx)$$

and this is T28. Adj is of course still available in PM +LPC2. So all that remains is to show that every valid disjunction in the standard form is derivable as a thesis.

We proved in Chapter 30 that all valid disjunctions of quantified schemata in the standard form are derivable as theses of PM +LPC1. Since every thesis of PM +LPC1 is a thesis of PM +LPC2, they are derivable in the latter system as well.

We are left therefore with disjunctions some or all of whose disjuncts are IS's. We showed in Chapter 34 that such disjunctive wffs are valid when and only when they would still be valid if all individual-variables were replaced by universal quantifiers. Since if this replacement were made they would be valid wffs of LPC1, and therefore derivable as theses, all we have still to show is that if a disjunction which contains a disjunct of the form $U\alpha$ is a thesis, the same disjunction with $U\alpha$ replaced by αx_1 is also a thesis.

And this is easily proved. Substitutions in T25 will give us every wff of the form $(U\alpha \supset \alpha x_1)$ as a thesis. And therefore, by

$$(p \supset q) \supset ((p \lor r) \supset (q \lor r))$$

and Detachment, if $(U\alpha \lor X)$ is a thesis, so is $(\alpha x' \lor X)$, where X can be any disjunction of schemata in the standard form.

EXERCISES 35

35.1 Construct proofs of the following theorems in PM +LPC2:

(a) $(fx \cdot gx) \supset \exists(f \cdot g)$

(b) $(fx \cdot gy) \supset (\exists f \cdot \exists g)$

(c) $(fx \supset (fy \supset gz)) \supset (Uf \supset \exists g)$

(d) $(\exists f \supset gx) \supset (\sim\exists g \supset \sim fy)$

(e) $(fx \equiv gy) \supset ((Uf \supset \exists g) \cdot (Ug \supset \exists f))$

(f) $U(f \supset (g \cdot h)) \supset ((fx \supset gx) \cdot (fy \supset hy))$

35.2 Fill in the details of the Consistency and Completeness Proofs for PM +LPC2.

CHAPTER 36

LPC2 and the Logic of an Empty Universe

This chapter is more exploratory than the others in this book, and raises questions of some obscurity and complexity. It can, however, be omitted entirely, since none of the later material depends on it.

In an empty universe of discourse there are no individuals to have (or for that matter to lack) any properties at all. We have seen that, when interpreted in such a universe of discourse, a wff of the form Uα always comes out true, and a wff of the form ∃α always comes out false. By consequence, wffs of the form ~Uα are always false, and those of the form ~∃α are always true. But what are we to say about the truth-value of IS's, say of 'fx' and '~fx', in an empty universe of discourse?

There are at least three possible views we could take here:

(a) We could argue that 'fx' becomes a proposition only when 'x' is replaced by the name of some individual – that the range of values of 'x' is the names of the individuals in a given universe of discourse. Since, however, there are no individuals in an empty universe of discourse, 'x' cannot take any values in such a universe; and therefore 'fx' cannot have any truth-value assigned to it at all. The same will apply to '~fx', and indeed to any wff which consists of or contains an IS: such wffs cannot have an interpretation in an empty universe of discourse. If we take this view, there is no more to be said: there will be no logic of an empty universe for LPC2.

(b) We could say that every proposition of the form 'fx' asserts of some individual that it possesses a certain property; and that any proposition which asserts this of an individual in an empty universe of discourse is *false*. In that case we shall say that 'fx' *can* be interpreted in an empty universe of discourse, and that when so interpreted it always has the value 0. What of '~fx'? If this is taken to assert that *x is a non-f*, then by parity of reasoning it will also have

248

the value 0. If, on the other hand, it is taken to assert that *it is not the case that* x *is an f*, it will be the negation of 'fx' and will therefore have the value 1. If we take view (*b*), therefore, we shall have to distinguish between '(∼f)x' – x *is* a non-f – and '∼(fx)' – it is not the case that x is an f; for in an empty universe of discourse they will have opposite truth-values.

(*c*) We could argue that 'fx' should count as valid in any given universe of discourse when *any individual there may be* in that universe is an f, and that this condition is fulfilled (vacuously) in an empty universe of discourse. We should then say, as in (*b*), that 'fx' can be interpreted in such a universe of discourse, but that when so interpreted it has the value 1. By parity of reasoning, '(∼f)x' also has the value 1; but '∼(fx)' has the value 0.

Note that if we take view (*b*), 'fx ⊃ ∃f' will be valid in LEU as well as in LNEU, but 'Uf ⊃ fx' will fail for LEU. If we take view (*c*), exactly the opposite will be the case.

From a purely formal point of view there is nothing to choose between (*b*) and (*c*): a consistent logic can be based on either, and the problems and complexities which arise do not differ in any essential way. In the remainder of this chapter we shall investigate some of the consequences of (*b*), and say no more about (*c*).

Formation rules

It is clear that we shall require a more elaborate bracketing rule than we have so far used, for IS's which begin with a negation sign. We have already pointed out that we must distinguish between '(∼f)x' and '∼(fx)', since in an empty universe of discourse they have opposite truth-values. And in general, we have to distinguish between negating an IS as a whole, and negating the wfpe which it contains. Thus the negation of '(∼f)x' will not be '(∼∼f)x' but '∼((∼f)x)'. To the former of these two expressions we can apply the Law of Double Negation and transform it into 'fx'; but to the latter we cannot–in fact in an empty universe of discourse '∼((∼f)x)' = 1, whereas 'fx' = 0.

We can to some extent reduce the welter of bracketing for which we seem to be heading, by the following notational convention. Instead of ruling out expressions such as '∼fx' or '∼(f ∨ ∼g)x' as ill-formed because of their ambiguity, we can remove their ambiguity by laying it down (quite arbitrarily) that in such expressions the initial negation sign is to be understood as operating on the *predicate-expression* only, not on the whole IS. E.g. '$\sim$fx' is to be short for '$(\sim$f)x', but not for '$\sim$(fx)'.

There are several ways in which the Formation Rules previously stated (Chapters 24 and 31) can be revised to give us the results we want. One method is to replace Rule (g) by

(g') If α is any wfpe and x_1 is any individual-variable, $((\alpha)x_1)$ is a wff;

and then to introduce conventions whereby the outer brackets may be omitted if not preceded by '$\sim$', and the inner brackets omitted if α is a single, unnegated, variable. Finally we introduce the notational convention mentioned above, by the definition:

$$(\sim\alpha x_1) =_{Df} ((\sim\alpha)x_1)$$

The version of LPC2 which observes these Formation Rules we shall call the *Elaborated Version* of LPC2. We shall, where appropriate, speak of LPC2 as expounded in Chapters 31–35 as the *Standard Version*.

In the Elaborated Version we can distinguish between wffs which are valid in LEU and those which are valid in LNEU only. We therefore revert to the practice of starring.

Some formulae

Among formulae which *fail* in LEU (though they are valid in LNEU) are the following:

$$*Uf \supset fx \tag{1}$$
$$*\sim fx \equiv \sim(fx) \tag{2}$$
$$*(f \supset g)x \equiv (fx \supset gx) \tag{3}$$
$$*(f \equiv g)x \equiv (fx \equiv gx) \tag{4}$$

The validity of (2) in LNEU but not in LEU can be regarded as marking the key distinction between the two logics. In LEU we do, however, have

$$\sim fx \supset \sim(fx)$$

The following are also valid in LEU:

$$(f \lor g)x \equiv (fx \lor gx) \tag{5}$$
$$(f.g)x \equiv (fx.gx) \tag{6}$$

That (3) fails in LEU, even though (5) holds, can be seen as follows: By Def $\supset$ the left-hand side of (3) becomes '$(\sim$f $\lor$ g)x', which, by (5), is equivalent to '$(\sim f)x \lor gx$'. The right-hand side, however, by Def $\supset$, becomes '$\sim(fx) \lor gx$'. These two formulae are equivalent only if '$(\sim f)x$' is equivalent to '$\sim(fx)$', i.e. only if (2) is valid.

In view of the failure of (2), (3) and (4), reduction to single predicate form cannot always be safely undertaken in LEU. For this reason, the admission of complex predicate-expressions in IS's, though a mere convenience in the Standard Version, is an essential feature of the Elaborated Version.

Decision procedures

In the case of wffs of LPC2 written in the notation of the Elaborated Version, the reduction to the standard forms required for Decision Procedures I and II cannot always be completed by the methods described in Chapters 32 and 33. If we wish simply to test such a wff for validity in LNEU, however, no difficulty arises; for the equivalences (2), (3) and (4), which hold in LNEU, will always enable the reduction to be completed, and the Decision Procedures then provide reliable tests for validity in LNEU. What this amounts to in practice is that we rewrite the wff in the notation of the Standard Version, by removing the brackets which the Elaborated Version requires us to insert, and then proceed as in Chapters 32 and 33.

If, on the other hand, we wish to test the wff for validity in LEU, we have to face the fact that the reduction to standard form cannot always be completed at all. It is possible to modify Decision Procedures I and II to cope with this situation. It is far simpler, however, to give a separate test for validity in an empty universe of discourse, and add this to the Decision Procedures as they stand. (To be valid in LEU, a wff must firstly be valid in LNEU, and secondly come out true when the universe of discourse is presumed to be empty.)

In an empty universe of discourse, any wff of the form αx_1 (where α is any wfpe and x_1 is any individual-variable) has the value 0, and any wff of the form $\sim(\alpha x_1)$ has the value 1. The procedure is therefore this: *firstly*, test the wff for validity in LNEU in the way outlined above. If it is invalid in LNEU, that of course is the end of the matter. But if it is valid in LNEU, then *secondly*, return to the original form of the wff, and replace every QS beginning with '$\sim U$' or '$\exists$' by '0', every QS beginning with 'U' or '$\sim\exists$' by '1', every IS of the form αx_1 by '0', and every IS of the form $\sim(\alpha x_1)$ by '1'.

Work out the truth-value of the whole expression thus obtained. If this is 1, the wff is valid in LEU; if it is 0, it is not.

(You must be careful to note that schemata such as '$\sim$fx' or '$\sim$(f v $\sim$g)y' are of the form αx_1, not of the form $\sim(\alpha x_1)$, and are replaced by '0'. By contrast, '$\sim$(fx)' and '$\sim$((f v $\sim$g)y)' are replaced by '1'.)

Axiomatization

We show first of all why the System PM +LPC2, set out in Chapter 35, requires modification if it is to cope with the distinction between LNEU and LEU.

From the point of view of the Elaborated Version, the Standard Version uses the formula '$\sim$fx' to do duty indifferently for '$\sim$(fx)' and '($\sim$f)x'. Since the Standard Version is meant to deal with LNEU only, no harm is done by this, since in LNEU the two formulae are equivalent. Now, however, we want to be able to distinguish between a logic in which they are equivalent and one in which they are not.

Let us examine the proof of T25 ('Uf $\supset$ fx') given in Chapter 35 (p. 244). First of all let us note that all the LPC2 axioms – A1, A3 and A4 – are valid in LEU, but that T25 is not. We should therefore expect to find something amiss with the steps in the proof itself if we rewrite it strictly in the notation of the Elaborated Version.

No fault can be found with the first line, which gives '$\sim$fx $\supset$ $\exists\sim$f'. But when in the second line we apply Transp to this, we obtain

$$\sim\exists\sim f \supset \sim(\sim fx)$$

This in turn yields (by T1)

$$Uf \supset \sim(\sim fx)$$

which is indeed valid in LEU, but is not T25.

We can obtain T25 from this last formula by Syll and

$$\sim(\sim fx) \supset fx \tag{7}$$

but (7) is valid in LNEU only.

Our examination of this proof illustrates the fact that in the Standard Version *the Formation Rules themselves presuppose LNEU*. As a result, the Transformation Rules are validity-preserving only for LNEU; that is, while they can never take us from theses which are valid in LNEU to theses which are not, they may very well take us from theses which are valid in LEU to theses which are valid in LNEU only.

There is a further reason why the system of Chapter 35 requires amplification. Formulae such as (7), and the equivalence (2) which we mentioned earlier, cannot even be stated in the Standard Version. They can be formulated as wffs in the Elaborated Version, but cannot be derived from the axioms of Chapter 35.

We said earlier that (2), viz.

$$*{\sim}fx \equiv {\sim}(fx)$$

can be taken as a kind of key formula to mark the distinction between LNEU and LEU. In fact, if we add (2) to the axiom set for PM+LPC2, we can then derive as theses all wffs valid in LNEU in the Elaborated Version. But we do not need to go as far as this; for the implicative thesis

$$\sim fx \supset \sim(fx) \tag{8}$$

which is valid in LEU, is derivable from T14, A3 and A4. It will be sufficient, therefore, to add the converse of (8), viz.

$$*\sim(fx) \supset \sim fx \tag{9}$$

as a new (starred) axiom.

For LEU we also need an extra axiom, though of course one which is weaker than (9). For this purpose the following formula will serve:

$$\exists g \supset (\sim(fx) \supset \sim fx) \tag{10}$$

Note that the consequent of (10) is identical with the whole of (9). Since the predicate variable in the antecedent ('g') is not repeated in the consequent, the antecedent amounts to saying simply that there is something of some kind or other; and the whole formula can be regarded as asserting that if there is anything at all, (9) holds. And *this* is valid, even in LEU.

We therefore reach an axiom set which consists of

> The axioms of PM
> A1. $U(f \supset g) \supset (Uf \supset Ug)$
> A3. $(f.g)x \equiv (fx.gx)$
> A4. $fx \supset \exists f$

plus *either* A5. $\exists g \supset (\sim(fx) \supset \sim fx)$ [LEU]

  or *A6. $\sim(fx) \supset \sim fx$ [LNEU]

The Transformation Rules stated in Chapter 35 can stand unchanged, though because of the alteration in the Formation Rules, they will not always yield the same results as they did there.

Some theorems

For the most part we state theorems either without proofs or only with a hint of the theses from which the proofs can be constructed.

T39. $fx \supset \sim(\sim fx)$

PROOF: $\sim(p.q) \equiv (p \supset \sim q)$ (i)

A4($f.\sim f/f$)	: $(f.\sim f)x \supset \exists(f.\sim f)$	(1)
(1) $\times$ Transp	: $\sim\exists(f.\sim f) \supset \sim((f.\sim f)x)$	(2)
(2), T14 $\times$ D	: $\sim((f.\sim f)x)$	(3)
(3), A3($\sim f/g$) $\times$ Eq1	: $\sim(fx.\sim fx)$	(4)
(4), (i)($fx/p, \sim fx/q$) $\times$ Eq1	: T39	

T40. $\sim fx \supset \sim(fx)$

(Proof from T39 $\times$ Transp.)

*T41. $\sim(\sim fx) \supset fx$

(Proof from A6 $\times$ Transp.)

*T42. $\sim(fx) \equiv \sim fx$
*T43. $fx \equiv \sim(\sim fx)$
T44. $\exists g \supset (\sim(fx) \equiv \sim fx)$

When a proof given in Chapter 35 does not meet the requirements of the Elaborated Version, it can always be turned into a valid (Elaborated Version) proof *in LNEU* by using A6, T41, T42 or T43 at appropriate points. We gave an example of this procedure earlier, in our discussion of T25, where T41 was required.

The following theorems in Chapter 35 required to be starred: T25, T26, T29, T30, T32, T33, T36 and T37. The proofs of T25 and T29 required reconstruction in the way just described; the proofs of the rest can be left as they are.

Because of the starring of T29 and T30, the rule SP must also be starred. So must QI1, but not QI2.

The remaining theorems given in Chapter 35 are unstarred, but T27, T28 and T38 are in a special position: although these theorems themselves are valid in LEU, the proofs given for them in Chapter

35, even if reconstructed in the way described, are valid only in LNEU, since they make use of starred theses. Alternative (though longer) proofs can be given, which do not appeal to any starred thesis at any point. The devising of these proofs is left as an exercise.

(It is worth noting that in Chapter 35 the derivation of Eq2 (as applied to IS's) was based on T27. So if Eq2 is to be fully available in LEU, a new proof of T27 must be given early in the piece, or else an alternative derivation of the rule provided.)

We add a few theorems not found in Chapter 35.

Although *T25 ('Uf ⊃ fx') is not valid in LEU, the following closely related theorems are unstarred:

T25a. $Uf \supset \sim(\sim fx)$
T25b. $Uf \supset (\exists g \supset fx)$

The following 'implicational halves' of *T29 and *T30 are unstarred:

T29a. $(f \supset g)x \supset (fx \supset gx)$
T30a. $(f \equiv g)x \supset (fx \equiv gx)$

Finally, although *'$\sim(fx) \supset \sim fx$' (A6) is a starred thesis, the following theorem is valid in LEU:

T45. $(gy \supset \sim(fx)) \supset (gy \supset \sim fx)$

(Proof from A4, A5 and '$(p \supset (q \supset r)) \supset ((p \supset q) \supset (p \supset r))$'.)

The basis from which we have been deriving these theorems can be proved to be (weakly) complete. All wffs of LPC2 (Elaborated Version) which are valid in LEU can be shown to be transforms of A1, A3, A4 and A5 (together with the axioms of PM); and all which are valid in LNEU can be shown to be transforms of the same axioms, but with A6 replacing A5. We shall not, however, prove this here.

Conclusion

The foregoing discussion has been merely a sketch of the kind of logical system which is suggested by view (*b*), mentioned near the beginning of this chapter. What we have said, however, should be enough to show that, whether or not it is 'natural' to regard IS's as having an interpretation in an empty universe of discourse, the decision to give them such an interpretation can be made to yield a coherent logical system for LPC2, with effective decision procedures and a satisfactory axiomatic basis, within which the distinction between validity in LNEU and validity in LEU can be rigorously drawn.

EXERCISES 36

36.1 Determine the validity of the following, (i) in LNEU, (ii) in LEU:

(a) $(U(f \supset g) \lor \exists(g \lor h)) \supset U(f \supset (\sim g \supset h))$

(b) $U(f \supset g) \supset (U(\sim f \supset g) \supset \exists g)$

(c) $U(f \supset g) \supset (\exists(\sim f \supset g) \supset \exists g)$

(d) $(\sim fx \supset \sim gy) \supset (\exists f \lor \sim Ug)$

(e) $(\sim(fx) \supset \sim gy) \supset (\exists f \lor \sim Ug)$

(f) $(\sim((f \lor g)x) \lor \exists f) \supset (\sim((f \lor g)y) \lor \exists(\sim f \lor g))$

36.2 Prove the following theorems in the Elaborated Version of PM + LPC2. Mark with an asterisk those theorems which are valid in LNEU only. Do not use starred theses or rules in proofs of unstarred theorems.

(a) $Uf \supset (gx \supset fy)$

(b) $(\sim \exists g . \sim fx) \supset \sim (f \lor g)x$

(c) $(\sim \exists g . \sim(fx)) \supset \sim(f \lor g)x$

(d) $Uf \supset (((f \lor g)x \supset Ug) \supset (f.g)y)$

CHAPTER 37

Multiple Quantification I

This chapter and the next three will take us beyond the limits of LPC2 but will be less systematic than previous ones have been. In particular, they will not contain any decision procedures or axiomatic bases. We shall, moreover, confine ourselves to the logic of a non-empty universe.

In this chapter we are going to show how to construct three sequences of formulae, each of which is in some way concerned with the *number* of things that possess a certain property. Then we shall discuss propositions which contain what are known as definite descriptions.

I

'At least n things are f'

We are already familiar with the use of '∃f' to mean 'at least one thing is f'. Frequently, however, we want to say that at least two, or three, or more, things have a certain property.

As a formula to express 'at least two things are f' we might at first be tempted to suggest

$$\exists f \, . \, \exists f \tag{1}$$

A moment's reflection, however, will show that this will not do. '∃f . ∃f' is of the form 'p.p'; and since 'p.p' says no more then 'p' itself, '∃f.∃f' says no more than '∃f', viz. that at least *one* thing is f.

Clearly what is missing is some way of referring to the two things which we want to say are both f. We have already (in LPC2) used 'x', 'y', . . . as variables which take individual things as values; we shall now introduce these into quantified schemata, in the following way. Instead of a single existential quantifier, '∃', we shall have a series of existential quantifiers, '∃x', '∃y', '∃z', . . .; and instead of writing '∃f', as we have hitherto done, we shall write '∃xfx' (or '∃yfy' etc.) Note that the individual-variable is written after the 'f' as well as after the '∃': we shall see the point of this later. '∃xfx' may be read, somewhat stiltedly but in a way which brings out the force of each symbol in it, as 'There is something – call it 'x' – which is such that it (viz. x) is f.' Commoner and simpler readings are: 'There is an x such that x is f'; 'There is an x such that fx'; 'There is some value of 'x' which makes 'fx' true'; and 'For some x, fx'. The last of these is to be recommended on the score of brevity.

We shall also have (though we shall not be using them immediately) an analogous series of universal quantifiers, 'Ux', 'Uy', 'Uz', . . . Each of these can be defined in terms of the existential quantifier which contains the same individual-variable. So we could form the following definition:

Where x_1 is any individual-variable,

$$Ux_1 =_{Df} \sim\exists\sim x_1$$

Alternatively, we could take 'U' as primitive and define '∃' by

$$\exists x_1 =_{Df} \sim U \sim x_1$$

where x_1 is again any individual-variable.

To return: suppose we now try to express 'At least two things are f' by

$$\exists xfx \, . \, \exists yfy \tag{2}$$

This is an advance on (1), but it still will not do, for this reason: 'x' and 'y' are variables which can stand for any individuals whatsoever, just as 'p' and 'q' can stand for any propositions whatsoever; and one possibility is that they might stand for the same individual in the former case or the same proposition in the latter. Therefore just as 'p.q' represents the conjunction of two propositions which may be distinct but may also be identical, so (2) simply asserts that there is something (x) which is f, and something (y) which is f, and this leaves open the possibility that x and y may be the same thing. What is missing is some way of asserting that x and y are *different* things, i.e. of saying 'there is something (x) and something *else* (y). . . .'

We cannot express this with our present stock of symbols. We need one further symbol, which is written ' = ' and is known as the *identity sign*. This is a dyadic operator which forms a propositional schema from a pair of individual-variables. It is written between these variables to produce wffs of the form $(x_1 = x_2)$. (In such wffs we usually omit the brackets when no confusion is likely to result from doing so.) We read 'x = y', for example, as 'x is identical with y', and we understand it to mean that 'x' and 'y' stand for the same object. The negation of 'x = y' will therefore mean that 'x' and 'y' stand for different, or distinct, objects. We can of course write this negation as '$\sim$(x = y)', but by a commoner and more convenient notation we shall write it as 'x $\neq$ y' instead.

Can we then express 'At least two things are f' by conjoining 'x $\neq$ y' to (2)? What we then have is

$$\exists xfx \,.\, \exists yfy \,.\, x \neq y \tag{3}$$

We are near to the correct formula, but one further refinement is needed. In (3), 'x $\neq$ y' is, so to speak, hanging in the air. We must make it clear that the objects which 'x $\neq$ y' declares to be distinct are the very same objects which '$\exists xfx$' and '$\exists yfy$' assert to have the property f. The most convenient way of doing this is to use brackets to indicate the *scope* of the quantifiers. Whenever we use a quantifier which contains an individual-variable, x_1, we make it a rule to enclose in brackets so much of the expression following that quantifier as contains every occurrence of x_1 to which that quantifier is intended to apply; this bracketed expression is said to be the *scope* of the quantifier, and these occurrences of x_1 are said to be *within its scope*.[1]

If we apply this rule to (3), we have to insert after '$\exists y$' a pair of brackets enclosing both 'fy' and 'x $\neq$ y', and also insert after '$\exists x$' a pair of brackets enclosing both 'fx' and 'x $\neq$ y'. (3) will then become

$$\exists x(fx \,.\, \exists y(fy \,.\, x \neq y)) \tag{4}$$

This is a perfectly correctly-written formula, and one which does mean that at least two (distinct) things are f. It is, however, both simpler and commoner to use instead of (4) the equivalent formula

$$\exists x \, \exists y(fx.fy.x \neq y) \tag{5}$$

If you spell out (4) and (5) carefully you should have no difficulty in seeing that they are equivalent. (4) can be read: 'There is something, x, such that (i) it is f and (ii) there is something, y, which is f and is a distinct object from it.' (5) can be read: 'There are two things, x and y, such that each is f and they are distinct from each other.'

It is worth noting, however, that although (4) and (5) are equi-

---

[1] This will serve as a sufficient explanation of the notion of the scope of a quantifier in the present context. A more accurate definition requires more material in quantification theory than we have at our disposal here.

valent, in (5) the two quantifiers have the same scope, but in (4) they do not. (You should say what the scopes are in each case.)

The lengthy explanation we have just given will enable us to proceed more rapidly from now on. We have found formulae for 'At least one thing is f' and 'At least two things are f'. It should now be reasonably evident how the series can be continued. 'At least three things are f' will be expressed by

$$\exists x\ \exists y\ \exists z\ (fx.fy.fz.x \neq y.y \neq z.z \neq x) \tag{6}$$

Note that it is not enough to have '$x \neq y.y \neq z$' in (6); we must include '$z \neq x$' as well. For x might be a different thing from y and y a different thing from z, yet z be the same thing as x; so if we were to omit '$z \neq x$' from (6), it would be compatible with there being only two distinct things that are f.

In general, to express the proposition that at least n things are f (where $n > 1$), we first choose n distinct individual-variables, $x_1, \ldots, x_n$; then we take each pair that can be selected from $x_1, \ldots, x_n$, write '$\neq$' between the members of each pair, and conjoin the wffs thus obtained; using 'A' to stand for this conjunction, we finally construct the formula

$$\exists x_1, \ldots, \exists x_n\ (fx_1 \ldots fx_n . A)$$

II

'At most n things are f'

The formulae in this second series are easily constructed from those in the first. To say that at most one thing is f is to say that either nothing at all is f or else just one thing is f; and this is simply to deny that two or more distinct things are f. So 'at most one thing is f' is the negation of 'at least two things are f', and may therefore be expressed by

$$\sim\exists x\ \exists y\ (fx.fy.x \neq y) \tag{7}$$

And in general, 'At most n things are f' can be expressed as the negation of 'At least (n + 1) things are f'.

We shall now apply some straightforward transformations to (7). '$\sim\exists x$' can be replaced by '$Ux\sim$', to give

$$Ux \sim\exists y(fx.fy.x \neq y) \tag{8}$$

A negation sign has now appeared before 'ꓱy', so by the same procedure as before, (8) becomes

$$Ux \ Uy \sim (fx.fy.x \neq y) \tag{9}$$

In (9) the negation sign operates on 'fx.fy.x≠y'. Since by substitution in

$$\sim(p.\sim q) \equiv (p \supset q)$$

we obtain

$$\sim(fx.fy.x \neq y) \equiv ((fx.fy) \supset x = y)$$

(9) finally becomes

$$Ux \ Uy \ ((fx.fy) \supset x = y) \tag{10}$$

which may be read: 'For all x and all y, if x and y are both f, x is identical with y'; or, more informally, 'It holds universally that if any two things are both f, they are not two *different* things but the same thing.' It is not difficult to see, therefore, that (10), like (7) expresses what we mean when we say that at most one thing is f.

Similar transformations can be applied to the other formulae in the series. Thus 'At most two things are f' is, according to our rule, expressed by the negation of (6), viz.

$$\sim ꓱx \ ꓱy \ ꓱz \ (fx.fy.fz.x \neq y.y \neq z.z \neq x)$$

('it is not the case that there are three distinct objects each of which is f'); and this, by the procedures applied to (7), together with the de Morgan Law, becomes

$$Ux \ Uy \ Uz((fx.fy.fz) \supset ((x = y) \lor (y = z) \lor (z = x)))$$

('If any three things are all f, then at least one pair of them must be identical.')

III

'Exactly n things are f'

We now reach our third series, which is to give us formulae for propositions of the form 'exactly n things are f'. Alternative ways of expressing this are: 'n things and only n things are f', and 'at least n things are f and at most n things are f'.

This last formulation makes it clear that one way of constructing the series is by conjoining corresponding members of the previous two series. Thus we could express 'Exactly one thing is f' by

$$(\exists x\ fx)\ .\ UxUy((fx.fy) \supset x=y) \qquad (11)$$

(11) is a correctly formed formula, and it expresses what we want it to express. We can, however, use a briefer formula instead. To see how this is possible, let us go back to the first of our acceptable formulae for 'At least two things are f', viz.

$$\exists x(fx.\exists y(fy.x \neq y)) \qquad (4)$$

This may be read: 'There is a certain object, x, which is f, and *another* object, y, which is also f.' Now to say that one and only one thing is f amounts to saying that 'There is a certain object x, which is f, but *no other* object which is also f.' We can express this by taking (4) and in it negating the part that begins with '∃y'. Thus we obtain

$$\exists x\ (fx.\sim\!\exists y(fy.x \neq y))$$

which by standard transformations becomes

$$\exists x\ (fx.Uy(fy \supset y=x)) \qquad (12)$$

This means: 'There is something which has the property f, and anything which has the property f is that thing.' This is clearly another way of saying that exactly one thing is f.

You should now have little difficulty in continuing the series, though the formulae become fairly complex before long. We give the formula for 'Exactly two things are f':

$$\exists x\ \exists y[fx.fy.x \neq y.Uz(fz \supset ((z=x)v(z=y)))] \qquad (13)$$

I.e. 'There are two distinct (non-identical) things each of which is f, and anything which is f is one or other of these.'

There is an important point to notice here. In formulae such as (12) or (13), each quantifier must contain a different individual-variable; thus in (13) we write 'Uz' in the place corresponding to 'Uy' in (12), since 'y' has already occurred in '∃y' earlier in the formula.

You may wonder why we should insist on this whereas we allowed (11) to contain both '∃x' and 'Ux'. The reason is that (11) is the conjunction of two quite distinct formulae, namely '∃xfx' and 'UxUy((fx.fy) ⊃ x=y)', each complete in itself and able to stand on its own: the scopes of '∃x' and 'Ux' do not overlap at any point. By the time we have reached the end of the first conjunct, the individual-variable 'x' has, we might say, finished the work assigned to it there;

we are therefore free to re-use it for a different purpose, or to choose an entirely new variable, just as we please. (Similar considerations apply to other truth-functions than conjunctions.) By contrast, in (12) the scope of '∃x' is the whole of what follows it, and thus includes the scope of '∃y'. In this formula, 'x' has been booked for a certain role which it continues to play until the end of the scope of '∃x'; so if within that scope we want an individual-variable to play any other role, we have to use another variable, such as 'y'.

The safe rule to follow is this: no two quantifiers whose scopes overlap may contain the same individual-variable.

IV

Russell's theory of definite descriptions

Early this century Russell advanced an important theory about the analysis of propositions containing what are known as *definite descriptions*. Definite descriptions are most commonly expressed by phrases of the form 'the so-and-so'; simple examples of propositions of the kind under discussion are, 'The author of *Ulysses* was an Irishman', 'The present King of France is wise', 'The mosque in Lima is large'.

One difficulty to which such propositions may be felt to give rise is this. It would seem at first sight that the contradictory (negation) of

The mosque in Lima is large   (14)

is

The mosque in Lima is not large   (15)

Now each of these two propositions seems to imply that there is a mosque in Lima. Of two mutually contradictory propositions, however, one must be true. We therefore seem to have established the existence of a mosque in Lima by pure logic alone, without making use of any empirical information about Peru; and this is absurd.

Russell's theory is – among other things – a way of avoiding such absurdities. The general effect of his analysis, expressed in terms of our example, is to grant that each of (14) and (15) implies that there is a mosque in Lima, but to deny that they are contradictories (i.e. to deny that one is the negation of the other). Hence we are no longer driven to say that one of them must be true, and so the absurd conclusion is avoided.

As an approach to the analysis, let us imagine three people, A, B and C, each of whom objects to the assertion that the mosque in Lima is large, but each on different grounds.

A says: "But there is no mosque in Lima at all."

B says: "I grant that there is a mosque in Lima. The trouble is that there is more than one. So it is incorrect to say anything about *the* mosque in Lima."

C says: "I grant that there is one and only one mosque in Lima. It is, however, not a large one."

According to Russell's theory, if what any one of these objectors says is true, (14) must be regarded as false. The analysis of (14) must therefore contain the denials of each of the three objections raised; i.e. (14) must be taken to assert firstly that there is at least one mosque in Lima (to deny A's objection), secondly that there is not more than one mosque in Lima (to deny B's objection), and thirdly that the one and only mosque in Lima is large (to deny C's objection).

Let us set this out in the notation of the Predicate Calculus. Let us abbreviate 'x is a mosque in Lima' to 'Mx' and 'x is large' to 'Lx'. The first two assertions to be included in the analysis of (14), which together amount to the assertion that there is exactly one mosque in Lima, can be symbolized by

$$\exists x(Mx \,.\, Uy(My \supset y = x))$$

The third assertion may be incorporated in this by adding 'Lx' as a further conjunct *within the scope of '$\exists x$'*, since it is the same object which we want to assert both to be the one and only one mosque in Lima and also to be large. We thus arrive at the following formula for (14):

$$\exists x(Mx \,.\, Uy(My \supset y = x) \,.\, Lx)^1 \qquad (16)$$

And in general, '*The* f is (a) g' is expressed by

$$\exists x(fx \,.\, Uy(fy \supset y = x) \,.\, gx) \qquad (17)$$

---

[1] 'M' and 'L', as they are used here, are symbols of a type known as *predicate constants*. Unlike predicate variables, predicate constants do not take values; they *are* values of predicate variables. They can be thought of as temporary abbreviations of actual predicate words or phrases. (16) is not a wff of pure LPC, though it could be called a formula in an *applied* Predicate Calculus. It expresses, not the *form* of the proposition 'The mosque in Lima is large', but *that proposition itself*. The *form* of the proposition is given not by (16) but by (17), which as we shall see *is* a wff of pure LPC.

Similar reasoning will lead us to analyse (15) – 'The mosque in Lima is not large' – as 'There is exactly one mosque in Lima and it is not large', and to symbolize it by

$$\exists x(Mx . Uy(My \supset y=x) . \sim Lx) \tag{18}$$

It should now be clear that if (14) and (15) are understood to mean what is expressed by (16) and (18) respectively, then each implies that there is a mosque in Lima; for each is of the form, 'There is something which is both a mosque in Lima and . . .' But it is also clear that they are not contradictories: they could not indeed both be true, but they could both be false; and both would be false if there were no mosque in Lima at all or if there were more than one. In fact, if (16) is taken as the analysis of (14), then (18), so far from expressing the negation of (14), merely expresses one of several assertions incompatible with it, viz. the assertion made by C. The contradictory of (16) is not (18) but

$$\sim \exists x(Mx . Uy(My \supset y=x) . Lx) \tag{19}$$

i.e. 'There is nothing which is both the one and only mosque in Lima and also large.'

(18) and (19) are certainly not equivalent, for if there is no mosque in Lima at all, (18) is false but (19) is true. Moreover (19) – the contradictory of (16) – does not imply that there is a mosque in Lima; for, as we have just seen, (19) could be true but 'There is a mosque in Lima' false.

What we have given is not a full account of Russell's theory, but only an illustrative sketch of its central thesis. It is proper to add that the theory has had its critics. The most serious criticisms have, however, been based not on any objection to the formal logic involved but on the philosophical contention that Russell's analysis does not accurately represent the normal use of sentences of the form 'The so-and-so is such-and-such'; and Russell has denied that his intention was to give an account of the normal use of such sentences. We cannot go into this controversy here; if you want to follow it up, you could not do better than begin with P. F. Strawson's article *On Referring* and Russell's reply to it.[1] But whatever the rights and wrongs of this controversy may be, the importance of Russell's theory, both as a piece of logical analysis in its own right

---

[1] *Mind*, 1950 and 1957 respectively. Strawson's article is reprinted in *Essays in Conceptual Analysis* (ed. Flew).

and for its influence on the development of logic and philosophy during the present century, is undisputed. It can, moreover, hardly be denied that it does provide an escape, even if not the only possible one, from the paradox outlined at the beginning of this Section.

(N.B. Exercises on Chapters 37–40 are grouped together at the end of Chapter 40.)

CHAPTER 38

Equivalence Transformations of Quantifiers

We are now becoming used to the idea that a wff[1] may contain a string of quantifiers, each equipped with a distinct individual-variable. A quantifier which is immediately preceded by a negation sign will be called a *negative* quantifier; one which is not, an *affirmative* quantifier. An expression which consists solely of quantifiers and negation signs we shall call a *sequence* of quantifiers. Within a sequence, any two consecutive quantifiers which are not separated by a negation sign will be said to be *adjacent*; and if no negation sign occurs between the first and the last of any number of consecutive quantifiers, these will be said to form an *adjacent group*.

$$\exists x \sim Uy\ Uz\ \exists w \sim \exists u \tag{1}$$

is a sequence of quantifiers. In it, 'Uy' and 'Uz' are adjacent, and so are 'Uz' and '∃w'; and 'Uy', 'Uz' and '∃w' form an adjacent group; but there are no other adjacent pairs or groups. Note that the fact that 'Uy' is preceded by a negation sign does not prevent it from counting as adjacent to 'Uz'.

A sequence of quantifiers is not, of course, itself a wff; but such a sequence can occur in a wff, either at the beginning or at various other positions in it. We shall say that two sequences of quantifiers are *equivalent* if the result of replacing either by the other in a wff X, is always equivalent to X itself.

We shall now state two rules whereby a sequence of quantifiers may be transformed into another sequence equivalent to it.

The first rule we have already used in the last chapter; it is a generalized form of the *Rule of Quantifier Transformation* stated on p. 171, and we shall use the same name for it.

---

[1] We are anticipating a little in speaking of *wffs* (well-formed formulae) here, since we have not yet stated the relevant Formation Rules. These are, however, given in Chapter 41.

R1. Where x_1 is any individual-variable, 'Ux_1' may be replaced by '$\exists x_1$' or vice versa, provided that a negation sign is either inserted or deleted both immediately before and immediately after the quantifier in question.

N.B. (*a*) When as a result of applying R1 to any quantifier, a new negation sign appears immediately before or after another quantifier, it may be regarded as attached to that other quantifier for the purpose of a further application of R1.

(*b*) When the result of applying R1 is the appearance of a negation sign immediately after the last quantifier in a sequence, that negation sign is to be regarded as operating on the whole expression which lies within the scope of that quantifier.

By applying R1 it is always possible to transform a sequence of quantifiers into an equivalent sequence in which the quantifiers are (*a*) all affirmative, or (*b*) all negative, or (*c*) all existential, or (*d*) all universal. We shall illustrate this by sequence (1).

(*a*) '$\sim Uy$' may be replaced by '$\exists y\sim$', to give

$$\exists x \, \exists y \sim Uz \, \exists w \sim \exists u \qquad (2)$$

In (2) we now replace '$\sim Uz$' by '$\exists z\sim$', to obtain

$$\exists x \, \exists y \, \exists z \sim \exists w \sim \exists u \qquad (3)$$

Finally, in (3) we replace '$\sim \exists w\sim$' by 'Uw', to obtain

$$\exists x \, \exists y \, \exists z \, Uw \, \exists u$$

(*b*) To obtain from (1) a sequence in which all quantifiers are negative, we first replace '$\exists x\sim$' by '$\sim Ux$', thus obtaining

$$\sim Ux \, Uy \, Uz \, \exists w \sim \exists u \qquad (4)$$

The remaining steps consist in replacing, in (4), 'Uy' by '$\sim \exists y\sim$', '$\exists w\sim$' by '$\sim Uw$', and '$\exists u$' (which has now become affirmative) by '$\sim Uu\sim$'. The result is

$$\sim Ux\sim \exists y\sim Uz\sim Uw\sim Uu\sim \qquad (5)$$

(*c*) A sequence in which all quantifiers are existential has already appeared at (3).

(*d*) A sequence in which all quantifiers are universal can easily be obtained from (5) by replacing '$\sim \exists y\sim$' by 'Uy':

$$\sim Ux \, Uy \, Uz \sim Uw\sim Uu\sim$$

The second rule concerns the order in which quantifiers occur in a sequence. We shall call it the *Rule of Quantifier Rearrangement*.

R2. If the quantifiers in any adjacent group are either all existential or all universal, they may be rearranged in any order we please.

N.B. If the first quantifier in the adjacent group is negative, the negation sign preceding it is to retain its original position when R2 is applied; i.e. it does not move with the quantifier to which it was originally attached.

In the simplest cases – when the whole sequence consists simply of two adjacent quantifiers – the soundness of R2 is obvious. It makes no difference whether we say 'There are objects, x and y, which . . .' ('∃x ∃x . . .') or 'There are objects, y and x, which . . .' ('∃y ∃x . . .'.) Similarly, 'Ux Uy' is clearly equivalent to 'Uy Ux'. (We cannot, however, replace say 'Ux ∃y' by '∃y Ux': the reason for this will become clear in the next chapter.) What obviously holds good in these simple cases in fact also holds good in the more complex cases when the adjacent group has more than two members or forms part of a longer sequence.

We give two illustrations of the application of R2. In sequence (1) the only change permitted by R2 is the interchange of 'Uy' and 'Uz', which yields

$$∃∼Uz\ Uy\ ∃w∼∃u$$

Note the position of the (first) negation sign: (1) may *not* be re-written as

$$∃x\ Uz∼Uy\ ∃w∼∃u$$

Consider secondly sequence (3). This begins with an adjacent group of three quantifiers, all of which are existential. These three quantifiers may therefore be rearranged in any order. They must, of course, remain at the beginning of the whole sequence.

A little reflection will show that by successive applications of R1 and R2 a quite considerable number of sequences, each equivalent to (1) (and therefore to each other), may be obtained.

R1 and R2 form a complete set of rules for equivalence transformations of sequences of quantifiers, in the sense that if a sequence S_1 cannot be obtained from another sequence S_2 by these rules, then S_1 and S_2 are not equivalent.

CHAPTER 39

Multiple Quantification II

Properties and relations

No doubt many men are wise, but it makes good sense to say of a single man, such as Socrates, that he is wise. Up to now, all the expressions we have called *predicates* have stood for properties which it makes sense to attribute to a single individual. Such predicates are known as *monadic*, or *one-place*, predicates.

There are, however, many expressions which we cannot meaningfully apply to single objects, but only to groups of two, three or more objects. We cannot e.g. sensibly say 'x is greater than', but only 'x is greater than y'. Nor can we say 'x is between', or even 'x is between y', but only 'x is between y and z'. We shall say that an expression such as 'greater than' or 'between' stands not for a property of an individual, but for a *relation* between individuals. Since 'greater than' stands for a relation between two individuals, we shall say that the relation in question is a *dyadic* or a *two-place* relation. Similarly, 'between' stands for a *triadic* or *three-place* relation; and we can also have four-place, five-place, etc., relations. In order to have a general term for the expressions themselves, we shall extend our earlier use of the word 'predicate' and speak of the expressions, such as 'greater than' and 'between', which stand for two-place, three-place, etc., relations, as two-place, three-place, etc., predicates respectively.

A dyadic relation holds not simply between a pair of objects, but between those objects *in a certain order*. It is one thing to say that Bill is father of Tom, and another thing to say that Tom is father of Bill. Analogous considerations apply to relations with more places than two. We can sum this up by saying that relations have a *direction*. (If Bill is Tom's father, we can think, metaphorically, of the relation of fatherhood as going *from* Bill *to* Tom, not vice versa.) There are, it is true, certain dyadic relations whose direction is unimportant, in the sense that whenever they hold between x and y, they also hold between y and x; 'parallel to' and 'cousin of' are examples. Such relations are known as *symmetrical* relations; but they form a special class, and do nothing to destroy the importance of the notion of direction in general. (Note that even symmetrical relations will be said to have a direction; for we want to be able to say e.g. that if x is parallel to y, y is parallel to x, and we could not say this if we did not allow the notion of direction to apply to such a relation. In other words, 'x is parallel to y' and 'y is parallel to x' are equivalent, not identical, propositions.)

Symbolism

We shall use 'f', 'g', . . . as variables for predicates with any number of places. The number of places will be indicated by the number of individual-variables which immediately follow the predicate variable; and the direction will be indicated by the order in which these individual-variables occur.

For example, 'x is father of y' may be represented by 'fxy'; and in that case 'fyx' will mean 'y is father of x', 'fxz' will mean 'x is father of z', and so on. Similarly, 'x prefers y to z' may be represented by 'gxyz'; and in that case 'gyzx' will mean 'y prefers z to x' and so on.

It can be seen that if we want to assign a value to a predicate variable, it is not sufficient to say, e.g. 'Let 'f' stand for 'father of''; we must also indicate the number of places and the direction. To do this we shall use 'x_1', 'x_2', . . . to mark the positions of the individual-variables. We can therefore say 'Let "fx_1x_2" stand for "x_1 is father of x_2" '. This of course is merely an interpretative 'key' to a formula; in an actual formula the place of 'x_1' and 'x_2' will be taken by any two individual-variables: the key simply means that within the formula to which it applies, any schema which consists of 'f' followed by two individual-variables is to be taken to mean that the individual represented by the first of these variables is father of the individual represented by the second.

Although a predicate variable followed by any number of individual-variables is a wff, it is necessary to stipulate that each occurrence of a given predicate variable throughout a whole formula must be followed by the same *number* of individual-variables, though these need not be distinct. Thus a formula may contain 'fxy', 'fyy', 'fxz', 'gxzy', 'gxyw' and 'gyxx'; but it may not contain, say, both 'fx' and 'fyz', or both 'gxz' and 'gyww', for if it did we could not consistently assign the same value to 'f', or to 'g', throughout the formula.

Classification of dyadic relations

Dyadic relations (and therefore two-place predicates) can be exhaustively divided into three non-overlapping classes in three distinct ways.

1 (*a*) A relation may be such that whenever it holds between one object and a second, it also holds between that second object and the first. I.e. the two-place predicate f may be such that

$$Ux \; Uy \; (fxy \supset fyx)$$

Such relations are said to be *symmetrical* relations. Examples are: 'equal to', 'sibling of'.

(*b*) A relation may be such that whenever it holds between one object and a second, it *fails* to hold between that second object and the first. I.e. f may be such that

$$Ux \; Uy \; (fxy \supset \sim fyx)$$

Such relations are said to be *asymmetrical* relations. Examples are: 'greater than', 'father of'.

(*c*) A relation may be neither symmetrical nor asymmetrical, in that sometimes when it holds between one object and a second it also holds between the second and the first, but sometimes it does not. I.e. f may be such that

$$Ex \; Ey \; (fxy.fyx) \; . \; Ex \; Ey \; (fxy.\sim fyx)$$

Such relations are said to be *non-symmetrical* relations. Examples are: 'implies', 'brother of'.

It is clear that every dyadic relation must be either symmetrical or asymmetrical or non-symmetrical.

2 (*a*) A relation may be such that whenever it holds between one object and a second and also between that second object and a third, it holds between the first and the third. I.e. f may be such that

$$Ux \; Uy \; Uz \; ((fxy.fyz) \supset fxz)$$

Such relations are said to be *transitive* relations. Examples are: 'parallel to', 'ancestor of'.

(*b*) A relation may be such that whenever it holds between one object and a second and also between that second object and a third, it fails to hold between the first and the third. I.e. f may be such that

$$Ux \; Uy \; Uz \; ((fxy.fyz) \supset \sim fxz)$$

Such relations are said to be *intransitive* relations. Examples are: 'one greater than', 'father of'.

(*c*) A relation may be neither transitive nor intransitive. I.e. f may be such that

$$\exists x \; \exists y \; \exists z \; (fxy.fyz.fxz) \; . \; \exists x \; \exists y \; \exists z \; (fxy.fyz.{\sim}fxz)$$

Such relations are said to be *non-transitive relations*. Examples are: 'one mile distant from', 'first cousin of'.

Every dyadic relation must obviously be either transitive or intransitive or non-transitive.

3 (*a*) A relation may be such that it holds between every object and itself. I.e. f may be such that

$$Ux(fxx)$$

Such relations are said to be *reflexive* relations. Examples are: 'equal to', 'of the same age as'.

(N.B. It is presupposed that the object is such that it makes sense to speak of it as a term of the relation in question. A number cannot be said to be of the same age as another number (or as itself), but this does not prevent us from calling 'of the same age as' a reflexive relation, since anything which has an age at all has the same age as itself. If we wish to free 'x' in 'Ux(fxx)' from this restriction on its range of values, we can use instead the formula

$$Ux \; (\exists y(fxy) \supset fxx)$$

– i.e. 'For all x, if there is anything at all to which x stands in the relation f, then x stands in that relation to itself.')

(*b*) A relation may be such that it never holds between any object and itself. I.e. f may be such that

$$Ux \; ({\sim}fxx)$$
or
$$\qquad {\sim}\exists x \; (fxx)$$

Such relations are said to be *irreflexive* relations. Examples are: 'greater than', 'father of'.

(*c*) A relation may be neither reflexive nor irreflexive. I.e. f may be such that

$$\exists x(fxx) \; . \; \exists x({\sim}fxx)$$

Such relations are said to be *non-reflexive* relations. Examples are:

'square of' (1 is the square of 1, but 2 is not the square of 2), 'admirer of'.

Again, every dyadic relation must be either reflexive or irreflexive or non-reflexive.

For the most part, the type to which a relation belongs with respect to one of these three classifications tells us nothing about what type it belongs to with respect to either of the others. Thus, a symmetrical relation can be transitive (e.g. 'equal to'), or intransitive (e.g. 'perpendicular to'), or non-transitive (e.g. 'one mile distant from'). There are, however, certain restrictions, of which the most important are:

1. Every relation which is both symmetrical and transitive is also reflexive.

2. Every asymmetrical relation is irreflexive.

3. Every relation which is both transitive and irreflexive is also asymmetrical.

Double quantification

We can improve our grasp of quantification theory if we take some simple schema containing two individual-variables but no quantifiers, and give a systematic account of the ways in which it can be quantified (i.e. of the sequences of quantifiers which can be prefixed to it). Such a schema might contain only monadic predicate variables (e.g. 'fx ⊃ gy'), or it might contain a dyadic predicate variable. We shall choose one of the latter type, in order to increase our grasp of dyadic predicates as well as of multiple quantification. The simplest schema of this kind will serve, viz. 'fxy'. It will be helpful to have an interpretation of this schema in mind. Let us take 'fxy' to mean 'x admires y' (the universe of discourse being human beings).

'fxy', of course, even when a determinate value, such as 'admires', has been assigned to 'f', remains a mere schema, not a proposition. We can turn it into a proposition either by replacing 'x' and 'y' by the names of individuals, or by quantification. It is with the latter method that we are concerned, and two quantifiers will be needed, one containing 'x' and the other containing 'y'. Each quantifier may be either universal or existential; each may be affirmative or negative; and the quantifier which contains 'x' may occur either before or after the quantifier which contains 'y'. We can therefore set down the following 32 sequences of quantifiers, each of which is to be understood as followed by '(fxy)':

1. UxUy	9. ∃x∃y	17. Ux∃y	25. ∃xUy
2. ~UxUy	10. ~∃x∃y	18. ~Ux∃y	26. ~∃xUy
3. Ux~Uy	11. ∃x~∃y	19. Ux~∃y	27. ∃x~Uy
4. ~Ux~Uy	12. ~∃x~∃y	20. ~Ux~∃y	28. ~∃x~Uy
5. UyUx	13. ∃y∃x	21. ∃yUx	29. Uy∃x
6. Uy~Ux	14. ∃y~∃x	22. ∃y~Ux	30. Uy~∃x
7. ~UyUx	15. ~∃y∃x	23. ~∃yUx	31. ~Uy∃x
8. ~Uy~Ux	16. ~∃y~∃x	24. ~∃y~Ux	32. ~Uy~∃x

Clearly some of these sequences are equivalent. The Rule of Quantifier Transformation (R1, p. 268) easily establishes, for example, the equivalence of 4 and 25, since '~Ux~' can be replaced by '∃x'. In fact R1 establishes the equivalence of each sequence in the list with exactly one other. Moreover, the Rule of Quantifier Rearrangement (R2, p. 269) gives us the equivalence of, e.g., 1 and 5, and 10 and 15. Applying our two rules, we are left with the following irreducible list of 12 non-equivalent ways of quantifying 'fxy':

(a)	1 = 28 = 5 = 24	(g)	9 = 20 = 13 = 32
(b)	2 = 27 = 7 = 22	(h)	10 = 19 = 15 = 30
(c)	3 = 26	(i)	11 = 18
(d)	4 = 25	(j)	12 = 17
(e)	6 = 23	(k)	14 = 31
(f)	8 = 21	(l)	16 = 29

We shall now look into the meanings of these quantifications, taking 'fxy' as before to mean 'x admires y'.

(a) We can take 1 as the most straightforward sequence here. The meaning is: everyone admires everyone (including, incidentally, himself). Following more closely the pattern of symbols in 28, we can give an alternative reading: there is no one who does not admire everyone. (Devise readings to follow the patterns of 5 and 24, and try to make the equivalence of all four sequences clear to yourself.)

(b) is the negation of (a). It means: not everyone admires everyone; or (cf. 27): there is someone who does not admire everyone. I.e. there is at least one exception to the rule of mutual admiration all round.

We shall take (g) next. The meaning is clearest in the case of 9: someone admires someone. (Satisfy yourself that 20, 13 and 32 are equivalent to 9.)

(*h*) is the negation of (*g*). It means that no one admires anyone at all.

Consider (*j*) next, in the form of 17. Translating painstakingly, we read this as: for every x there is a y such that x admires y. I.e. everyone admires someone or other.

Contrast (*j*) with (*f*). 21 contains the same quantifiers as 17, but in the reverse order. Translating 21 symbol by symbol we get: there is someone, y, such that for every x, x admires y. I.e. there is someone whom everyone admires, someone who is the object of universal admiration. (*f*) is a stronger assertion than (*j*): (*j*) will be true if everyone is an admirer of at least one person, but it need not be the same person in each case; but for (*f*) to be true there must be at least one person whom we all without exception admire. (*f*) implies (*j*) but is not implied by it.

(*i*) and (*e*) are the negations of (*j*) and (*f*) respectively. (*i*) means that there is someone who does not admire anyone at all; (*e*) that there is no one whom everyone admires.

(*d*) and (*l*) can be construed in a way analogous to (*j*) and (*f*) (*d*) means that there is someone who admires everyone without exception; (*l*) expresses the weaker (and more plausible) assertion that everybody has at least one admirer.

(*c*) is the negation of (*d*) and means: there is no one who admires everyone. (*k*) is the negation of (*l*) and means: not everyone has an admirer at all; there is at least one person whom no one admires.

It should now be clear why we cannot reverse the order of adjacent quantifiers when one is universal and the other is existential.

You will notice that (*a*)–(*l*) have been arranged in pairs of contradictories, i.e. pairs in which each is (or is equivalent to) the negation of the other.

There are also certain important relations of implication which hold among (*a*)–(*l*). We can work out what these are from two rules which we shall state in a moment. Since the rules also apply to longer sequences of quantifiers than we have under consideration at present, we shall formulate them in a quite general way. We must make it clear that the rules apply only in cases where a sequence of quantifiers occurs at the *beginning* of a formula, and then only when all the quantifiers in the sequence are affirmative.

We call these rules the *Rules of Relative Strength*, deriving this name from the fact that when one wff implies but is not implied by a second, we describe the first as *stronger* than the second (or alternatively the second as *weaker* than the first). We number the rules R3 and R4, to avoid confusion with those given in Chapter 38. They run as follows:

If a wff, X, begins with a sequence of affirmative quantifiers S, then:

R3. If X′ is obtained from X by replacing any universal quantifier in S by an existential quantifier containing the same individual-variable, X′ is weaker than X; and

R4. If S contains an existential quantifier Q_1 which stands to the left of some universal quantifier Q_2, and X′ is obtained from X by moving Q_1 to the right of Q_2, X′ is weaker than X.

To summarize these rules: Replacing 'U' by 'Ǝ' weakens, replacing 'Ǝ' by 'U' strengthens. Moving 'Ǝ' to the right of 'U' weakens, moving 'Ǝ' to the left of 'U' strengthens.

Applying these rules to those sequences in our list in which all quantifiers are affirmative, we obtain the following results:

1 implies 25 (by R3), which in turn implies 29 (by R4), which in turn implies 13 (by R3).

5 implies 21 (by R3), which in turn implies 17 (by R4), which in turn implies 9 (by R3).

Since 1 is equivalent to 5, and 9 is equivalent to 13, we can express these implications in the form of a hexagon. (We write the implication sign as an arrow for clarity.)

or, in general

The Law of Transposition will entitle us to negate each formula and then invert the whole hexagon. We then obtain the implication relations which hold among the remaining six quantifications.

or, in general

You should note that of the twelve non-equivalent ways of quantifying two individual-variables, exactly half are expressible as sequences in which both quantifiers are affirmative, and the other half are expressible as the respective negations of the first half.

The same principle holds for the quantification of any given number of individual-variables. There are, for example, 52 non-equivalent ways of quantifying three variables;[1] 26 of these are expressible as sequences of affirmative quantifiers, the remainder as their respective negations.

Where sequences of quantifiers are written in this way, (and the Rule of Quantifier Transformation always makes this possible), R3 and R4 will often enable us to tell at a glance that one quantified formula implies another. E.g. let X be any wff which contains the four individual-variables 'x', 'y', 'z' and 'w'. Then

$$ƎyUxUwUz (X) \qquad (1)$$

implies

$$ƎyUxƎwƎz (X) \qquad (2)$$

since (2) is obtained from (1) by replacing 'Uw' and 'Uz' by 'Ǝw' and 'Ǝz' respectively in an initial sequence of quantifiers. Furthermore

$$ƎzƎyUxƎw (X) \qquad (3)$$

also implies (2), since (2) can be obtained from (3) by moving 'Ǝz' to the right, crossing over 'Ux'.

In addition, (1) implies (3). Try to say why.

---

[1] It is possible to calculate the total number of non-equivalent ways of quantifying n individual-variables, where n is any natural number, though the mathematical formula involved is not a simple one. For n = 1, 2, 3 and 4, the numbers of quantifications are 4, 12, 52 and 300 respectively.

CHAPTER 40

Multiple Quantification III

More complex examples of quantification

The material introduced in Chapters 37 and 39 opens up a vast new array of propositional forms. Anything like a systematic account of these is out of the question within the limits of this book. What we shall do instead is merely to give a fairly detailed discussion of a few examples; but if you work carefully through these and then through the exercises at the end of this chapter, your grasp of quantification theory should be considerably increased.

EXAMPLE 1: *There is a father and a mother for every child.*   (1)
The first thing to do is to make a list of the predicates involved in (1), and to construct a 'key' in which a distinct predicate variable is assigned to each of them. Here there are three predicates: 'child' (one-place), 'father of' (two-place) and 'mother of' (two-place). We shall signal a one-place predicate by writing 'x_1' after the predicate variable, and a two-place predicate by writing 'x_1x_2' after the predicate variable. Our key will therefore be:

$$fx_1 = x_1 \text{ is a child}$$
$$gx_1x_2 = x_1 \text{ is father of } x_2$$
$$hx_1x_2 = x_1 \text{ is mother of } x_2$$

It is usually best next to construct what we call the appropriate *open formula*, i.e. that part of the complete formula which contains no quantifiers. We can see what the open formula should be by 'thinking away' all the quantificational elements in (1). What we are left with in the present case is something which can be expressed as 'if x is a child, then y is its father and z is its mother'; and this gives us the open formula

$$fx \supset (gyx.hzx)$$

All that remains is to prefix the quantifiers. The statement is meant to apply to every child; hence we shall have 'Ux'. On the

279

other hand every child is said simply to have *a* (i.e. some) father and *a* mother; hence we have '$\exists y$' and '$\exists z$'. The final formula is:

$$Ux\exists y\exists z \ (fx \supset (gyx.hzx)) \qquad (2)$$

which may be read: 'For every x there is a y and a z which are such that if x is a child then y is father of x and z is mother of x.'[1]

In a careless moment we might be misled by the order of the words in (1) into writing the existential quantifiers before the universal one, to give

$$\exists y\exists zUx \ (fx \supset (gyx.hzx)) \qquad (3)$$

(3) is as well-formed as (2), but what it means is: 'There are people, x and y, who are respectively the father and the mother of all the children there are.'

You should try other sequences of quantifiers with the same open formula, and work out the meanings of the resulting wffs.

EXAMPLE 2: *The Prime Minister of Great Britain is visiting the President of the United States.*

Here we have to apply the Theory of Definite Descriptions – twice in fact. The example can be re-phrased as: there is one and only one Prime Minister of Great Britain; there is one and only one President of the United States; and the former is visiting the latter.

The key will be:

$fx_1 = x_1$ is a Prime Minister of Great Britain.
$gx_1 = x_1$ is a President of the United States.
$hx_1x_2 = x_1$ is visiting x_2.

---

[1] Strictly speaking, what (2) expresses is not (1) but the *form* of (1). To express (1) itself we should have to use predicate constants in place of predicate variables. (Cf. footnote on p. 264, Chapter 37.) Thus we might abbreviate 'x_1 is a child' to 'Cx_1', 'x_1 is father of x_2' to 'Fx_1x_2', and 'x_1 is mother of x_2' to 'Mx_1x_2'. (1) would then be expressed by

$$Ux\exists y\exists z \ (Cx \supset (Fyx \ . \ Mzx)) \qquad (2')$$

Properly speaking, it is only (2'), and not (2), which should be read as we have said (2) may be read.

Similar remarks apply to the other examples in this chapter; but we give formulae containing predicate variables throughout, in order to give practice in constructing wffs of pure LPC and to concentrate attention on the forms of propositions.

What we have called a 'key' is really a set of values whose substitution for the predicate variables in the relevant formula will yield a formula expressing the proposition under consideration.

In accordance with the method explained in Chapter 37, Section IV, we symbolize 'There is one and only one Prime Minister of Great Britain' by

$$\exists x(fx \, . \, Uy(fy \supset y=x))$$

For 'There is one and only one President of the United States' we proceed similarly, except that to avoid confusion we choose new individual-variables. This gives us

$$\exists z(gz \, . \, Uw(gw \supset w=z))$$

'The former is visiting the latter' will now have to be represented by 'hxz'; and this must come within the scopes of both '$\exists x$' and '$\exists z$'. There are several ways of running these elements of the required formula together, but perhaps the clearest of them is this:

$$\exists x \exists z \, (fx \, . \, gz \, . \, Uy(fy \supset y=z) \, . \, Uw(gw \supset w=z) \, . \, hxz)$$

EXAMPLE 3: *Gentlemen prefer blondes to brunettes.*

We take this to mean: every gentleman prefers every blonde to any brunette whatever. (We are not, of course, concerned with its truth or falsity.)

'Prefers' is a three-place predicate. So the key we need is:

$$fx_1 = x_1 \text{ is a gentleman}$$
$$gx_1 = x_1 \text{ is a blonde}$$
$$hx_1 = x_1 \text{ is a brunette}$$
$$ix_1x_2x_3 = x_1 \text{ prefers } x_2 \text{ to } x_3$$

This example will enable us to study variations both in quantification and in the structure of open formulae. In order to deal with these one at a time we shall to begin with use a temporary dodge which will shorten our open formula. Instead of letting the values of all the three individual-variables we shall use be human beings in general (which is what we shall ultimately do), we shall restrict the range of values of 'x' to gentlemen, that of 'y' to blondes, and that of 'z' to brunettes. I.e. 'x' is to represent indifferently any member of the class of gentlemen, but nothing else; and analogously with 'y' and 'z'. The open formula can then be simply

$$ixyz$$

which will mean 'gentleman prefers blonde to brunette', and can remain unchanged throughout our various quantifications.

Example 3 itself means: no matter what gentleman, blonde or brunette we consider, the first prefers the second to the third. We therefore use three universal quantifiers. By the Rule of Quantifier Rearrangement (p. 269) their order is immaterial, but it is simplest to keep to the order suggested by the English sentence and write

$$Ux \ Uy \ Uz \ (ixyz) \tag{1}$$

Let us now look at some variant quantifications. If we replace 'Uy' by '∃y' we obtain

$$Ux \ \exists y \ Uz \ (ixyz) \tag{2}$$

which means: every gentleman prefers some blonde or other to any brunette whatsoever. This is a weaker assertion than (1), as the Rule of Relative Strength, R3, (p. 277) would lead us to expect: for, unlike (1), it only requires that each gentleman should rank one blonde above all the brunettes – he can rank the other blondes in any way he pleases.

If we now, in (2), move '∃y' to the beginning, we obtain

$$\exists y \ Ux \ Uz \ (ixyz) \tag{3}$$

which means: there is a certain blonde whom every gentleman prefers to all the brunettes there are. This too is a weaker assertion than (1), though it is stronger than (2), as the Rule of Relative Strength, R4, makes clear. (2) does not require that there should be any blonde whom all gentlemen without exception agree in ranking above all the brunettes, but (3) does require this.

A further variant, introducing a negative quantifier, would be:

$$\sim\!\exists z \ Ux \ Uy \ (ixyz) \tag{4}$$

which means: there is no brunette to whom every gentleman prefers all the blondes. The outlook for brunettes is further improved if we replace 'Uy' in (4) by '∃y', to give

$$\sim\!\exists z \ Ux \ \exists y \ (ixyz) \tag{5}$$

i.e. there is no brunette to whom every gentleman prefers any blonde at all; and improved still further if in addition we replace 'Ux' by '∃x', for then we have

$$\sim\!\exists z \ \exists x \ \exists y \ (ixyz) \tag{6}$$

the meaning of which you are left to work out for yourself.

We shall now look into the construction of the open formulae in their full forms. We now take the range of values of 'x', 'y' and 'z' alike to be simply *human beings*. We therefore have to bring 'f', 'g', and 'h' into our open formulae. We begin by considering the open formula

$$(fx.gy.hz) \supset ixyz \tag{7}$$

If we prefix three universal quantifiers to (7) we obtain

$$Ux\ Uy\ Uz\ ((fx.gy.hz) \supset ixyz)$$

that is: no matter what x, y and z may be, if x is a gentleman, y a blonde and z a brunette, then x prefers y to z. This means exactly the same as (1) did under our earlier conventions.

Since (7) is a well-formed open formula containing 'x', 'y' and 'z', we can prefix to it the sequences of quantifiers used in (2)–(6) and thereby obtain propositions which make good sense. They will not, however, mean quite what (2)–(6) mean. If, using the quantifiers in (2), we write

$$Ux\ \exists y\ Uz\ ((fx.gy.hz) \supset ixyz)$$

we have a formula which means: for every gentleman there is someone whom, *if* she is a blonde, he prefers to every brunette. This is weaker than it should be if it is to have the meaning we assigned to (2). What we *want* to say is: for every gentleman there is someone who *is* a blonde and whom he prefers to every brunette. We can express this by changing our open formula so that the whole formula reads

$$Ux\ \exists y\ Uz\ ((fx.hz) \supset (gy.ixyz)) \tag{2a}$$

Similarly, if we prefix the quantifiers in (3) to (7), we obtain a formula which means: there is someone who, *if* she is a blonde, is preferred by every gentleman to every brunette. Again this is too weak: we want to say that there is someone who both *is* a blonde and is preferred by every gentleman to every brunette. Our formula for this should be:

$$\exists y\ Ux\ Uz\ (gy.((fx.hz) \supset ixyz)) \tag{3a}$$

Analogous considerations give us the following formulae in place of (4), (5) and (6):

$$\sim\!\exists z\ Ux\ Uy\ (hz.((fx.gy) \supset ixyz)) \tag{4a}$$

$$\sim\!\exists z\ Ux\ \exists y\ (hz.(fx \supset (gy.ixyz))) \tag{5a}$$

$$\sim\!\exists z\ \exists x\ \exists y\ (fx.gy.hz.ixyz) \tag{6a}$$

You should try to work out what the result of using (7) as the open formula in these three cases would mean.

EXAMPLE 4: *The highest mountain in Scotland is higher than any mountain in England*   (4)

A sentence containing a grammatical superlative can usually be re-phrased as one which contains the corresponding comparative instead. Thus (4) can be re-expressed as: 'Some mountain in Scotland is higher than any other mountain in Scotland and also higher than any mountain at all in England.' So a single two-place predicate can deal both with 'highest' and with 'higher than'.

We work with the following key to begin with:

$fx_1 = x_1$ is a mountain in Scotland
$gx_1 = x_1$ is a mountain in England
$hx_1x_2 = x_1$ is higher than x_2.

The formula then is:

$$\exists x(fx \,.\, Uy((fy.y \neq x) \supset hxy) \,.\, Uz(gz \supset hxz))$$

That is: 'There is something, x, which is (*a*) a mountain in Scotland, (*b*) such that if anything *else* is a mountain in Scotland, x is higher than it, and (*c*) such that if anything *at all* is a mountain in England, x is higher than *it*'.

Fuller analyses of this example are possible. The key we have just used does not bring out the fact that 'mountain in Scotland' and 'mountain in England' have a common element, 'mountain'. We can remedy this in either of two ways:

(*a*) We can use three predicate variables for 'mountain', 'in Scotland' and 'in England' respectively. Alternatively,

(*b*) We can take 'Scotland' and 'England' as names of individuals, and represent them by individual-variables (say 'w' and 'u') which will not be quantified. We shall then have to use an additional two-place predicate variable for 'in'.

You are left to work out for yourself a key and a formula for method (*a*).

Method (*b*) gives us the following:

Our key is

$fx_1 = x_1$ is a mountain

$gx_1x_2 = x_1$ is in x_2

$hx_1x_2 = x_1$ is higher than x_2

$w =$ Scotland

$u =$ England.

The formula is

$$\exists x \, (fx \cdot gxw \cdot Uy((fy.gyw.y \neq x) \supset hxy) \cdot Uz \, ((fz.gzu) \supset hxz))$$

Which of the three formulae is to be preferred? There is no single answer to this. Everything depends on how far we need to carry the analysis; and this in turn depends on the context. If, for example, (4) occurs as part of an inference in other parts of which 'in Scotland' and/or 'in England' occur *without* the word 'mountain', the formula obtained by method (*a*) is likely to be preferable; and if the names 'Scotland' and/or 'England' occur without the preposition 'in' (or its equivalent), then the last formula is likely to be the appropriate one.

EXAMPLE 5: *There is a point within a circle which is equidistant from all points on its circumference.* (5)

We shall try to extract the last ounce from this example, partly in order to illustrate the complexity of thought which can sometimes be expressed in quite a short sentence.

By a common English idiom, the indefinite article in the phrase 'a circle' is a sign of universal, not of existential quantification. On the other hand, the indefinite article in the phrase 'a point' means simply 'at least one'. Moreover, despite the order of the words, the existential quantifier is subordinate to the universal one: the sense of the beginning of (5) clearly is, 'Every circle has at least one point within it which . . ..'[1]

Consider now the phrase 'its circumference'. Although this does not contain a definite article, it is to be ranked as a definite descriptive phrase, since it means '*the* circumference belonging to it (viz. the circle in question)'. Possessive pronouns are often used in this way. So part of what is asserted by (5) is that every circle has one and only one circumference. In expressing this part of (5) we could use a one-place predicate variable for 'is a circumference' and a two-

---

[1] In fact every circle has one *and only one* such point with in it; but (5) – perhaps fortunately – does not say this.

place one for 'has'; but we can, more economically, make do with a two-place predicate variable only, interpreted to mean 'is a circumference of'.

How shall we deal with 'equidistant from'? There are an infinite number of points on a circumference, and a certain point is said to be equidistant from all of them. We do not need, however, to invoke a predicate with an infinite number of places: a three-place one ('x_1 is equidistant from x_2 and x_3') will suffice. For we can say, 'whatever y and z may be, if both are points on the circumference, x is equidistant from each of them'; and all points on the circumference will thereby be covered.

We are now ready for the key:

$fx_1 = x_1$ is a circle
$gx_1 = x_1$ is a point
$hx_1x_2 = x_1$ is a circumference of x_2
$ix_1x_2 = x_1$ is within x_2
$jx_1x_2 = x_1$ is on x_2
$kx_1x_2x_3 = x_1$ is equidistant from x_2 and x_3

The formula will be

$$Ux\{fx \supset \exists y[(hyx.Uz(hzx \supset z=y)) \,.$$
$$\exists w(gw.iwx.UuUt((gu.gt.juy.jty) \supset kwyt))]\}$$

I.e. 'If x is any circle whatsoever, then there is something, y, which is such that

(a) it is the one and only circumference of x; and

(b) there is something, w, which is (i) a point within x, and (ii) such that if u and t are any two points on y, it (w) is equidistant from them.'

EXERCISES 40

(Based on Chapters 37–40 inclusive.)

40.1 Give a key and a formula for each of the following:

(a) There is a building in Greece which is older than any building in England.

(b) There is no greatest prime number.

(c) Every action aims at some end or other.

(*d*) There is an end at which all actions aim.

(*e*) There is one and only one end at which all actions aim.

(*f*) A sailor has a wife in every port.

(*g*) Everyone loves himself more than he loves anyone else.

(*h*) There is someone who loves everyone else more than he loves himself.

(*i*) Not more than two candidates answered the most difficult question in the examination.

(*j*) The two skyscrapers are the only buildings of architectural merit in the city.

(*k*) Everyone want to make himself happy; only some people want to make others happy.

(*l*) The play at the Opera House is better than any film in town.

(*m*) If and only if Mary is Tom's aunt, there is someone who is either Mary's brother and Tom's father or else Mary's sister and Tom's mother.

(*n*) First cousins have a common grandparent.

(*o*) At least three men are in love with Jill.

(*p*) 'Great fleas have little fleas upon their backs to bite 'em,
   And little fleas have lesser fleas, and so *ad infinitum*;
   While the great fleas themselves in turn have greater fleas
      to go on,
   And these again have greater still, and greater still, and
      so on.'

   (Augustus de Morgan.)

   (Take 'to go on' as having the same meaning as 'to be upon the back of and bite'; use a single predicate variable for this.)

40.2 Find as many sequences of quantifiers as you can which are equivalent to

$$\sim\!\exists x \; Uy \; Uz \sim\!\exists w$$

40.3 What implication relations hold among the following formulae? Which of the formulae, if any, are equivalent?

(*a*) $Ux \; \exists y \; \exists z \; Uw \; (fxyzw)$

(*b*) $\sim\!\exists x \; Uz \; Uy \; \exists w \sim\!(fxyzw)$

(*c*) $\exists z \sim\!\exists x \sim\!\exists y \; Uw \; (fxyzw)$

(*d*) $\sim\!\exists x \; Uy \; \exists w \sim\!Uz \; (fxyzw)$

(*e*) $\exists w \sim\!Ux \; Uz \sim\!\exists y \; (fxyzw)$

40.4 (a) Re-write the following formula with all quantifiers existential and no operators except '$\sim$' and '$.$'.

Ux $\sim$Ǝz Uy $\sim$Uw ((fxy ∨ gzy) ⊃ (hwz ≡ fyz))

(b) Re-write the following formula with all quantifiers affirmative and no operators except '$\sim$' and '⊃'.

$\sim$Uy Ǝx $\sim$Ǝw $\sim$Ǝy ((fx.gyx) ∨ ($\sim$hxz.$\sim$gwy))

40.5 Prove the following: If any sequence of quantifiers S contains an adjacent group of quantifiers, $Q_1, \ldots, Q_n$, and if S′ is derived from S by inserting (or deleting) a negation sign both immediately before Q_1 and immediately after Q_n, and replacing each existential quantifier in $Q_1, \ldots, Q_n$ by the corresponding universal quantifier and *vice versa*; then S′ is equivalent to S.

40.6 In Chapter 39 the following principles were stated:
1. Every relation which is both symmetrical and transitive is also reflexive.
2. Every asymmetrical relation is irreflexive.
3. Every relation which is both transitive and irreflexive is also asymmetrical.

Devise arguments to show that these principles hold.

40.7 Give two examples each of relations which are
(a) Transitive and non-symmetrical;
(b) Symmetrical and irreflexive;
(c) Transitive and non-reflexive.

40.8 (See Section headed 'Double Quantification' in Chapter 39). Suppose we have only three people to consider, A, B and C. Using 'fx_1x_2', as in the text, for 'x_1 admires x_2', we can form the following propositions:

(1) fAA	(2) fAB	(3) fAC
(4) fBA	(5) fBB	(6) fBC
(7) fCA	(8) fCB	(9) fCC

and also their negations.

Quantification (a) – 'Ux Uy (fxy)' – will then be expressible as

$$1 . 2 . 3 . 4 . 5 . 6 . 7 . 8 . 9$$

Find analogous ways of expressing quantifications (b)–(l).

40.9 Interpreting the predicate constants as follows:

$Sx_1 = x_1$ is a student

$(\text{Subj})x_1 = x_1$ is a University subject

$Gx_1 = x_1$ is a game

$Px_1x_2x_3 = x_1$ prefers x_2 to x_3

give unambiguous English readings of

   (*a*) Ux Uy Ǝz ((Sx . (Subj)y) ⊃ (Gz . Pxyz))

   (*b*) Ǝz Ux Uy (Gz . ((Sx . (Subj)y) ⊃ Pxyz))

   (*c*) Uz Ǝx Ǝy (Gz ⊃ (Sx . (Subj)y . Pxzy))

   (*d*) Ǝy ~Ǝx Ǝz ((Subj)y ⊃ (Sx . Gz . Pxyz))

40.10 In Chapter 39 we said that there are 26 non-equivalent ways of quantifying 'x', 'y' and 'z' which can be expressed by sequences of affirmative quantifiers. Make a list of these (one sequence for each of the 26 will be sufficient).

    Try to arrange the 26 sequences in an 'implication diagram' analogous to the first hexagon given in Chapter 39.

40.11 If we take 'male' and 'parent of' as primitive, and use the symbolism:

$Mx_1 = x_1$ is male

$Px_1x_2 = x_1$ is a parent of x_2

we can define 'grandfather of' as follows:

x is a grandfather of y $=_{Df}$ (Mx . Ǝz(Pxz.Pzy))

i.e. 'x is male, and there is someone (z) of whom x is a parent and who in turn is a parent of y.'

    Taking 'male', 'female', 'parent of' and 'spouse of' as primitive, give analogous definitions of (*a*) 'sister of'; (*b*) 'uncle of'; (*c*) 'brother-in-law of'; (*d*) 'step-sister of'.

CHAPTER 41

The Lower Predicate Calculus : Conclusion

Free and bound variables

Individual-variables are used in LPC formulae in two importantly different ways. (*a*) As we used them in LPC2, for example, they are straightforward variables which take names of individuals as values, in just the same way as propositional variables and predicate variables take propositions and predicates respectively as values. (*b*) Since Chapter 37, however, we have also been writing individual-variables within the scope of quantifiers which contain those same variables; used in this way, they play a different role.

When variables are used in the first of these ways, they are said to be *free* variables. When they are used in the second way, they are said to be *bound* variables; and a quantifier which contains a certain variable is said to *bind* all the occurrences of that variable which lie within its scope.

Note that it is *particular occurrences* of a variable which are said to be bound or free. As we shall see later in this chapter, a formula may contain several occurrences of a certain variable, and some of these occurrences may be within the scope of a quantifier containing that variable while other occurrences are not. In that case we say that the former occurrences are bound but the latter ones are free, and not (if we are speaking accurately) that the variable is bound or free *simpliciter*. In what follows, mention of bound or free variables must be taken to refer to bound or free occurrences of variables.

From the point of view of the formal structure of wffs, the distinction between bound and free variables is simply the one we have noted, viz. that a bound variable is one which lies within the scope of a quantifier which contains that variable, while a free variable is one which does not. From the point of view of interpretation, however, the distinction can be brought out in the following way.

A wff containing free individual variables, such as

$$fxy \qquad (1)$$

is not of course a proposition, but merely a propositional schema – something which can be turned into a proposition by making appropriate substitutions for its variables. If we merely assign a value to 'f' in (1) – suppose we let it mean 'taller than' (the universe of discourse being human beings) – we still do not obtain a proposition, but only a schema with fewer variables, viz. 'x is taller than y', which we can abbreviate to

$$Txy \qquad (2)$$

We cannot ask whether (2) is true or false: we have to replace 'x' and 'y' in (2) by names or other designations of human beings, and then for the first time we have something which can be true or false.

Contrast with (1) a somewhat similar schema, in which however the individual-variables are bound:

$$\exists x\ \exists y\ (fxy) \qquad (3)$$

(3), like (1), is a schema, not a proposition; but this time we can turn it into a proposition simply by assigning a value to 'f'. Suppose we assign it the same value as before; then (3) will become

$$\exists x\ \exists y\ (Txy) \qquad (4)$$

which means, 'There are two people, one of whom is taller than the other.' (4), unlike (2), is something of which we can ask whether it is true or false; in fact, of course, it is true.

Bound variables, then, do not require to have values assigned to them in order to turn the schemata in which they occur into propositions. But this is too weak a statement; bound variables *cannot* have values assigned to them at all. The result of replacing a bound individual-variable by the name of some individual would not be a proposition at all but simply a piece of nonsense. So although we use the same symbols for bound and free variables, they are really very different sorts of things; indeed, in a way it seems misleading to call bound variables 'variables' at all. For this reason they are sometimes called *apparent* variables, and free variables are then by contrast called *real* variables.[1]

---

[1] 'Apparent' and 'real' are the words used, e.g. in *Principia Mathematica*; 'bound' and 'free' are more common nowadays.

Note that in such a schema as

$$\exists x \, (fxy) \qquad\qquad (5)$$

'x' is bound but 'y' is free. If 'f' is interpreted as before, (5) means

There is someone who is taller than y

which remains a mere schema until we replace 'y' by someone's name.

(1), (3) and (5) are all alike in one respect: in each case a determinate value has to be assigned to 'f' if a proposition is to be obtained. That is, 'f' is a free variable in them all. In fact, the special charcteristic of the *Lower* Predicate Calculus is that in its formulae *all predicate variables are free*.

This does not mean that it makes no sense to quantify a predicate variable, but only that we are going outside LPC if we do so. A formula such as

$$Uf \, \exists x \, (fx)^1 \qquad\qquad (6)$$

cannot occur in LPC, but is well-formed in a higher-order Predicate Calculus.

One feature of (6) which makes it of interest is that every variable in it is bound. As a result it is not a mere schema but a proposition as it stands, viz. the proposition that *every property has at least one instance*.

LPC1 and LPC2 re-written

Since Chapter 37 we have been forced to use a more elaborate notation than the one we used for LPC1 and LPC2, a notation which requires, among other things, that every quantifier shall contain an individual-variable. This notation we shall call *Standard Lower Predicate Calculus notation* (*standard LPC* for short); for not only do we need it for those LPC formulae which go beyond the confines of LPC2, but most logicians use it (or some minor variant of it[2])

---

[1] The use of 'Uf' as a *quantifier* in (6) must not be confused with its use as a *wff* in LPC1.

[2] Most logicians write universal quantifiers as '(x)', '(y)', . . . and existential quantifiers as '($\exists$x)', '($\exists$y)', . . . In our version of standard LPC we have deviated from this practice, partly because 'U' is already familiar from LPC1 as a sign of universal quantification, and partly because by retaining it we can dispense with brackets round (or as part of?) quantifiers altogether. For an alternative notation see Appendix 2.

for the formulae of LPC1 and LPC2 themselves. We shall therefore show how to re-write the wffs of LPC1 and LPC2 in standard LPC.[1]

To re-write a wff of LPC1 we simply choose any individual-variable (usually 'x') and write it immediately after every occurrence of 'U' or '∃', and also immediately after every predicate variable. For example,

$$U(f \supset g) \supset (\exists f \lor U(g \lor \sim h))$$

is re-written as

$$Ux(fx \supset gx) \supset (\exists xfx \lor Ux(gx \lor \sim hx))$$

In the wffs of LPC2, as these were written in Chapters 31–35, every individual-variable is free. To re-write a wff, X, of LPC2 in standard LPC, we first reduce every IS in X to single predicate form. We then choose some individual-variable which does not occur freely (i.e. at all) in X,[2] and write it immediately after every occurrence of 'U' or '∃' and also immediately after every predicate variable which occurs within the scope of any quantifier. For example,

$$\exists(f.\sim g) \supset (((fv\sim h)x \,.\, gy) \supset Ug)$$

may be re-written as

$$\exists z(fz.\sim gz) \supset (((fx \lor \sim hx) \,.\, gy) \supset Uzgz)$$

If we prefer to have the individual-variables in alphabetical order of their first occurrences, we can of course re-letter them, to obtain

$$\exists x(fx.\sim gx) \supset (((fy \lor \sim hy) \,.\, gz) \supset Uxgx)$$

You should note that when the wffs of LPC1 and LPC2 are written in standard LPC, every predicate variable is immediately followed by an individual-variable. Since an expression so constructed counts as a wff, we have no longer any need for the notion of a wfpe as distinct from a wff; and by consequence the notion of isomorphism with wffs of PC is replaced by that of substitution-instances of wffs of PC. Moreover, axiom A4 for LPC2, and the theorems which depend on it, will no longer find a place in our system, since there is now no question of reduction to single predicate form.

---

[1] In the case of LPC2 we neglect the Elaborated Version of Chapter 36, though it would not be difficult to devise a variant of standard LPC to cope with this (see footnote to p. 294).

[2] This restriction on our choice is strictly unnecessary, but observing it is likely to avoid confusion in interpretation.

One advantage to be gained from this re-writing of LPC1 and LPC2 is that it enables us to give a single set of Formation Rules for the entire Lower Predicate Calculus. The wffs of LPC1 and LPC2 will then be seen as sub-classes of the class of wffs specified by these rules.

On the other hand, the re-writing also involves disadvantages. (*a*) An obvious one is that formulae become considerably longer, so that it is often more difficult to grasp their meaning and easier to make mistakes in working. (*b*) A less obvious but more serious disadvantage is this: although the re-writing leaves the meaning, and therefore the validity or invalidity, of wffs in LPC1 or LPC2 un-altered, it brings with it a considerable complication of our methods or working. Substitution Rules, for example, if they are to be ap-plicable to theses written in standard LPC notation, are difficult even to state with accuracy, let alone use correctly in practice; whereas with our simpler notation the Substitution Rules are no more complicated than those for PC.[1] LPC1 and LPC2 are only limited fragments of the Lower Predicate Calculus, but a great deal of logic can be done within their confines; and so long as we are working in them alone, it seems prudent to take advantage of the benefits which the simpler notation brings.

Monadic lower predicate calculus: formation rules

Ever since we advanced beyond LPC2 we have been constructing formulae on the basis of what seems intuitively to make good sense, rather than with reference to stated Formation Rules. It is time we gave such rules. We do so firstly for what is known as the *Monadic Lower Predicate Calculus*, i.e. the system in which all predicate variables are monadic ones:

1. A predicate variable immediately followed by an individual-variable is a wff.
2. If X is a wff, $\sim$X is a wff.

---

[1] A third point is that the standard notation seems to be incapable of dealing with the logic of an empty universe. How, for example, can we express the fact that '(f$\supset$g)x $\equiv$ (fx$\supset$gx)' is not valid in LEU, if we do not admit complex predicate-expressions into our formulae? This difficulty could of course be overcome by adding to the LPC Formation Rules set out below, an extra Rule recognizing any wpfe followed by an individual-variable as a wff. With such a Rule there would naturally come the reinstatement of A4 (not necessarily as an axiom). We should thereby obtain an unorthodox LPC notation; but the orthodox ones do not appear to be designed to cope with LEU.

3. If X and Y are wffs, (X v Y) is a wff.
4. If Y is a wff which contains an individual-variable x_1, but which does not contain either Ux_1 or $\exists x_1$, then Ux_1Y and $\exists x_1Y$ are wffs.

These rules are to be used in conjunction with definitions of '.', '⊃' and '≡' analogous to those in PM:

[.] $(X . Y) =_{Df} \sim(\sim X \text{ v} \sim Y)$
[⊃] $(X ⊃ Y) =_{Df} (\sim X \text{ v } Y)$
[≡] $(X ≡ Y) =_{Df} ((X ⊃ Y) . (Y ⊃ X))$

These rules and definitions carry us beyond LPC2, since they provide us with wffs such as

$$\exists x \, Uy \, (fx ⊃ gy)$$

or

$$Ux(fx ⊃ \exists y \exists z \, (gy.hz))$$

They do not, however, yield the formulae we discussed in Chapter 37. To gain these we need to make one addition to our list of primitive[1] symbols, viz:

$$= \quad \text{[Identity sign]}$$

and to give one more formation rule and one more definition, viz:

5. If x_1 and x_2 are individual variables (not necessarily distinct), then $(x_1 = x_2)$ is a wff.

[≠] $(x_1 \neq x_2) =_{Df} \sim(x_1 = x_2)$

We adopt the convention of omitting the brackets in wffs of the forms $(x_1 = x_2)$ and $(x_1 \neq x_2)$ when no confusion is likely to arise from so doing.

Note that Rule 5 takes us a step outside a strictly monadic calculus, for the identity sign stands for a dyadic relation. It is not, however, like the 'f' in 'fxy', a dyadic predicate *variable*: it has a determinate meaning, and substitutions cannot validly be made for it. '=' is therefore a *dyadic predicate constant*. Since the formulae of Chapter 37 contain no predicate variables other than monadic ones, we can describe the system to which they belong as the Monadic LPC enriched by the addition of one dyadic predicate constant.

---

[1] In *LPC* '=' must be taken as primitive (undefined). The following definition can be given in the *Second Order* Predicate Calculus (though this lies outside the scope of the present book):

$$(x_1 = x_2) =_{Df} Uf(fx_1 ≡ fx_2)$$

Here the definiens means: every property possessed by x_1 is also possessed by x_2, and vice versa.

The Formation Rules given above are so framed as not to permit what is known as *vacuous quantification*. An individual-variable is said to be quantified vacuously when it occurs in a quantifier but does not occur within the scope of that quantifier. Thus in

$$Ux \; \exists y \; \exists z \; (fx \supset (gx.hz)) \tag{1}$$

'y' is quantified vacuously, but 'x' and 'z' are quantified normally (i.e. non-vacuously). A quantifier in which a vacuously quantified variable occurs simply 'idles'. It makes no difference to the meaning of the formula whether that quantifier is there or not. According to the rules as we have stated them, (1) is ill-formed, but would become well-formed by the omission of '$\exists y$'. Nevertheless, for certain purposes it is convenient to allow vacuous quantification, and if we wish to do so we can amend our Formation Rules to provide for it by deleting the words 'which contains an individual-variable x_1, but' in Rule 4.

Full LPC: formation rules

The full Predicate Calculus differs from the Monadic Calculus only in this respect, that its wffs may contain predicate variables with any number of places. As we remarked earlier, however, an n-place predicate variable must remain as an n-place variable throughout any given wff. We can therefore construct the Formation Rules for the full LPC by simply replacing Rule 1 for the Monadic LPC by

1'. A predicate variable immediately followed by any number of individual-variables is a wff;[1] provided that if any predicate variable occurs more than once in the same formula, it must on each occurrence be immediately followed by the same number of individual-variables.

(For the purposes of this Rule, two occurrences of the same individual-variable are to count as two variables, not as one. Thus 'fxyz' and 'fxyy' can occur in the same formula, but 'fxyy' and 'fxz' cannot.)

The other Rules require no modification. We can, of course, alter Rule 4 in the way already described if we wish to admit vacuous quantification. Rule 5 can be included or not, according as we do or do not wish to make use of the identity sign in our wffs.

---

[1] We sometimes enclose a wff of this kind in brackets for greater ease of reading.

Prenex Normal Form

You will have noticed that in some formulae which contain quantifiers, all the quantifiers occur at the beginning, while in others they are scattered in various positions throughout the formula. A wff in which all the quantifiers occur at the beginning, all are affirmative, and in which their scope extends to the end of the whole wff, is said to be in *Prenex Normal Form* (PNF). (Look through Chapters 37 and 40 and pick out the wffs which are in PNF and those which are not.)

For every wff of LPC which is not in PNF it is possible to find an *equivalent* wff which is in PNF. It is often easier to compare two wffs if both are in PNF; the Rules of Relative Strength, for example, can be applied to wffs in PNF (see p. 276).

We shall state the method of reducing wffs to PNF, though without justifying it.

We consider first wffs which contain no free individual-variables, and in which every quantifier contains a different variable. (Nearly all the wffs in Chapter 37 and 40 are of this kind.) For such wffs the method is

1. Eliminate all operators except '$\sim$', 'v' and '.', by standard equivalences.

2. Eliminate all occurrences of '$\sim$' immediately before quantifiers or brackets, using the Rule of Quantifier Transformation (p. 268) and the de Morgan Laws. Negation signs will then occur only immediately before predicate variables.

3. Gather all the quantifiers into one sequence at the beginning, in the order in which they occur in the wff, and take everything which follows that sequence as its scope (i.e. enclose it in brackets if necessary).

As an example, take

$$\sim \exists x[(fx \supset \sim Uy\exists z(gy \supset hzx)) \supset \exists w\ hxw] \tag{1}$$

Step 1 transforms this into

$$\sim \exists x[\sim(\sim fx\ v \sim Uy\exists z(\sim gy\ v\ hzx))\ v\ \exists w\ hxw]$$

By step 2 we obtain (after several applications of R1 and de Morgan)

$$Ux[(\sim fx\ v\ \exists yUz(gy.\sim hzx))\ .\ Uw\ \sim hxw]$$

We now bring all the quantifiers to the beginning, by step 3:

$$Ux\exists yUzUw[(\sim fx\ v\ (gy.\sim hzx))\ .\ \sim hxw] \tag{2}$$

The brackets to indicate scope are already in place, so (2) is in PNF, and is equivalent to (1).

This procedure also applies to wffs which contain free individual-variables, *provided that the same variable never occurs both bound and free.*

For the remaining wffs the method just given is not quite adequate. These wffs are ones which exhibit either or both of the following features: (*a*) there are both bound and free occurrences of the same individual-variable; (*b*) there are two or more quantifiers which contain the same variable. Both of these possibilities are illustrated in the following wff:

$$Ux((fx \, . \, \exists y \, gxy) \supset \exists y \, hxy) \supset \exists z(fz \supset gzx) \qquad (3)$$

In (3), the 'x' at the end does not lie within the scope of any quantifier which contains 'x', and is therefore free; but all the other occurrences of 'x' are bound. Moreover '∃y' occurs twice; but this is no anomaly, since the scopes of these two quantifiers do not overlap: we could just as well have written, say '∃w hxw' instead of '∃y hxy'.

In reducing wffs with either of these two characteristics to PNF, we have a preliminary step to take: we leave the free variables as they are, but uniformly re-letter the bound variables (and of course the quantifiers which contain them) so far as may be necessary to ensure that no variable occurs both bound and free and that no two quantifiers contain the same variable. In the case of (3), this can be achieved by (i) replacing every occurrence of 'x' except the last – the free occurrence – by 'w', and (ii) replacing the third and fourth occurrences of 'y' by 'u'. (3) then becomes

$$Uw((fw \, . \, \exists y \, gwy) \supset \exists u \, hwu) \supset \exists z(fz \supset gzx) \qquad (4)$$

Once this has been done, the formula can be reduced to PNF by the method already explained.

In the case of (4) – as you can easily check for yourself – steps 1 and 2 lead to

$$\exists w((fw \, . \, \exists y \, gwy) \, . \, Uu \sim hwu) \lor \exists z(\sim fz \lor gzx)$$

This time step 3 requires, as well as the collection of the quantifiers, the insertion of an extra pair of brackets, since without these the scope of the quantifiers would not extend to the end of the formula. We thus finally obtain

$$\exists w \; \exists y \; Uu \; \exists z[((fw.gwy) \; . \; \sim hwu) \lor (\sim fz \lor gzx)] \tag{5}$$

which is in PNF and is equivalent to (3).

(We can of course, if we wish, apply equivalence transformations to the open formula in (5), e.g. to restore implication signs. (5) might then become

$$\exists w \; \exists y \; Uu \; \exists z[((fw.gwy) \supset hwu) \supset (fz \supset gzx)] \tag{6}$$

It is instructive to compare (6) with (4).)

The decision problem for the lower predicate calculus

In earlier chapters we have given decision procedures for two fragments of the Lower Predicate Calculus (LPC1 and LPC2). It is also possible – though we shall not do so – to give a decision procedure for the Monadic LPC as a whole (with or without the identity-relation); and the same is true for certain other segments of LPC.

But for the full Lower Predicate Calculus there is no solution to the Decision Problem. It is not merely that no logician has yet been clever enough to devise a decision procedure for this field: the situation is much more radical than that. For it has been demonstrated that *it is theoretically impossible that there ever should be such a decision procedure*; in more technical language, that the Decision Problem for LPC is unsolvable. This was first proved in 1936 by the American logician Alonzo Church, and is known as *Church's Theorem*. Its proof, however, lies quite outside the scope of this book.

This discovery of the impossibility of a decision procedure for LPC may strike you as both surprising and disappointing; yet its consequences are not as far-reaching as might at first be imagined. In particular, there is nothing to stop us setting up an axiomatic basis for full LPC. In fact, not merely can such a basis, and a comparatively simple one at that, be constructed, but it can even be proved to be complete, in the sense that if any wff of LPC is valid it can be derived from that basis. The only thing we lack is the ability to give an advance guarantee that no matter what wff we are presented with we shall be able to determine whether it is valid (and therefore derivable from the axiomatic basis) or not. Of course this is a serious lack, and one which differentiates LPC in an important way from the other systems we have dealt with; but it does not mean that LPC cannot be systematized in any way.

It is moreover, worth while to look further afield for a moment. Church based his proof partly on results published by Kurt Gödel in 1931, in a paper which has since been extremely influential. Gödel's paper dealt with the arithmetic of ordinary whole numbers, and about it he was able to prove something even more radical than Church subsequently proved about LPC: viz. that no axiomatic basis could ever be complete. To put it a little more precisely, he showed that no matter what consistent axiomatic basis we care to set up for this arithmetic, there will always be true arithmetical propositions which are not derivable from that basis. One might at first expect that the discoveries of Gödel and Church would act merely as barriers to further developments in their fields. Yet in fact precisely the reverse has been the case. Their work has stimulated a great deal of research into the whole question of which branches of logic (and mathematics) can, and which ones cannot, have effective decision procedures constructed for them. The results of these investigations must be regarded as among the most important logical discoveries of our own, or indeed of any, period.

EXERCISES 41

41.1 Construct Formation Rules for LPC1 and LPC2, using standard LPC symbolism.

41.2 Try to think of circumstances in which it would be convenient to allow formulae with vacuous quantifiers to count as well-formed.

41.3 Reduce the following wffs to Prenex normal form:
   (*a*) ∃x((fx ⊃ Uy gxy) ⊃ Uz hzx)
   (*b*) ~Ux ∃y((fxy . ∃z gzx) ⊃ ~∃w(gyw.fwx))
   (*c*) ∃x(~∃y(fy.gyx) ⊃ Uz(fz v gzw)) ⊃ ~Ux(fx v hx)
   (*d*) (fxy ⊃ Ux(gx ⊃ fyx)) ⊃ ∃x(~fxz ⊃ ∃ygy)

PART FOUR

Syllogistic

Introductory Note

What we call *syllogistic logic*, or more briefly *syllogistic*, is a branch of logic which takes its name from the fact that the most important forms of inference which it studies are those which are known as *categorical syllogisms*. Like the other kinds of syllogisms (hypothetical, disjunctive, etc.) which we discussed earlier in this book, a categorical syllogism contains two premises and a conclusion, but premisses and conclusion are required to be of certain special forms which we shall explain in the next chapter. In Part IV we shall use the word 'syllogism' to refer to categorical syllogisms only.

Syllogistic logic was founded by Aristotle in the fourth century B.C. His work was developed by logicians in later antiquity, during the Middle Ages, and also in more modern times; and as a result there came to be built up a certain widely-recognized body of doctrines in this field, which for a considerable period before the rise of contemporary logic was commonly regarded as the core (if not almost the whole) of formal logic, and which is still so presented in some quarters at the present day. This body of doctrines we shall call *traditional syllogistic*. It should be clear from what we have just said that while some of these doctrines go back to Aristotle himself, some others are of comparatively modern origin; but we shall follow the common practice of presenting them all as a single co-ordinated system.

There is a multitude of readily available text-books of traditional syllogistic, and it is not our intention to try to add to their number. Our aim in Part IV is to treat syllogistic logic, and some of the problems that arise in it, from the point of view of the more recent developments in logic which have been expounded in previous chapters. For the carrying out of this programme, however, it is necessary to have at least a brief statement of the relevant essentials of traditional syllogistic before us; and we give this in Chapter 42. It should be clearly realized that this chapter is not meant to give a complete or adequate account of the traditional theory. With few exceptions, we mention only what we intend to discuss later on; and topics such as Distribution of Terms, Singular Propositions, Reduction to the First Figure, and Rules of Syllogism, many of which are crucial to the standard expositions, are not dealt with at all. Moreover, although the doctrines we state in Chapter 42 are traditional ones in the sense explained, we shall occasionally present them to some extent in modern dress, where this seems likely either to result in greater precision or to make things easier for a reader who has worked through the earlier chapters of the book.

Résumé of Traditional Syllogistic Logic

The Four propositional forms

At the basis of syllogistic logic is the idea that every proposition (or at least, to be on the safe side, every proposition which syllogistic can handle) can be thought of as being of one or another of the following four types:

All ......'s are ——'s
No ......'s are ——'s
Some ......'s are ——'s
Some ......'s are not ——'s

The blanks are to be filled in in each case by a noun or noun phrase. Where normal English would lead us to use an adjective, as it frequently does in the position of the second blank in each type, a suitable noun or noun phrase is substituted; e.g. instead of saying 'Some books are blue' we say something like 'Some books are blue things'.

The words or phrases which fill the blanks are known as the *terms* of the proposition. The first of the two terms is known as the *subject-term*, the second as the *predicate-term*. (We shall sometimes call these terms the *subject* and the *predicate* respectively for short, though many logicians would reserve the words 'subject' and 'predicate' for what the terms stand for, rather than apply them to the terms themselves.)

The letters 'S', 'P' and 'M' are normally used as term variables, and as no inferential schema in syllogistic logic contains more than three terms,[1] these variables suffice. When we replace the terms in a proposition by term variables it is conventional to write the verb in the singular ('is' instead of 'are'). Using 'S' and 'P' as our variables, we thus arrive at the four fundamental propositional schemata:

---

[1] See Chapter 49 for a qualification of this statement, which however is not relevant in the present context.

All S is P
No S is P
Some S is P
Some S is not P

Propositions of these four types are known as A, E, I and O propositions respectively. A and E propositions are called *universal* propositions; I and O propositions are called *particular* propositions. A and I propositions are known as *affirmative*, and E and O propositions as *negative*, propositions. The word 'some' is to be understood in the sense of 'at least one', throughout.

For further brevity and convenience we can replace 'All . . . is', 'No . . . is', 'Some . . . is' and 'Some . . . is not' by the letters 'a', 'e', 'i' and 'o' respectively, writing these letters between the 'S' and the 'P' in each case. The fully symbolized schemata will therefore be

(i) S a P
(ii) S e P
(iii) S i P
(iv) S o P

In these schemata 'a', 'e', 'i' and 'o' are proposition-forming operators on terms. They are constants, not variables.

It should be noted that although the letters 'S' and 'P' are derived from the initial letters of the words 'subject' and 'predicate' respectively, either of them can stand in either the subject-position or the predicate-position in a schema; and so can 'M'. Thus, e.g. 'P a S' and 'M i P' are as well-formed as 'S a P'.

Syllogistic logic also recognizes negative terms, in a sense which should be easily understood by now. Every term has its corresponding negative term; thus to the term 'whales' there corresponds the negative term 'things that are not whales', or more simply 'non-whales', and so forth. If 'whales' is represented by 'S', then 'non-whales' can be represented by 'non-S', or more succinctly by 'S̄'.

The class of well-formed formulae is thus very simply given by the following Formation Rule:

If S_1 and S_2 are term variables (affirmative or negative), then S_1 a S_2, S_1 e S_2, S_1 i S_2, and S_1 o S_2 are wffs.[1]

---

[1] When convenient we shall form truth-functions of such wffs, using operators derived from PC. But traditional syllogistic is usually presented in the form of inferential schemata in which premisses and conclusion are simply A, E, I and O schemata.

Syllogistic logic is concerned with the logical relations, especially the relations of inference, which hold between schemata of the kind we have just explained. There are three main branches of the traditional doctrine about these relations:

1. The Square of Opposition.
2. The Scheme of Immediate Inferences.
3. The Theory of the Syllogism.

We shall give a brief account of each of these.

1. The Square of opposition

The Square of Opposition sets out the relations holding between the four basic schemata, 'S a P', 'S e P', 'S i P' and ' S o P', themselves. The relations are as follows. 'S a P' and 'S e P' are said to be *contraries*, i.e. if either is true the other is false (though conceivably both may be false); we can express this by means of the formula 'S a P ⊃ ∼(S e P)'. 'S i P' is said to be *subaltern* to 'S a P' (alternatively 'S a P' is said to be *superimplicant* to 'S i P');[1] i.e. if 'S a P' is true, 'S i P' is also true; and we can express this by 'S a P ⊃ S i P'. The same relation (subalternation) holds between 'S o P' and 'S e P'. 'S a P' and 'S o P' are said to be *contradictories*, i.e. if one is true the other is false, and if one is false the other is true; we can express this by 'S a P ≡ ∼(S o P)'. The same relation (contradiction) holds between 'S e P' and 'S i P'. Finally, 'S i P' and 'S o P' are said to be *subcontraries*, i.e. if either is false the other is true (though conceivably both may be true); we can express this by 'S i P v S o P'.

The expression 'Square of Opposition' is derived from the fact that we can summarize these six relations in the form of a diagram which, using our present symbolism, may be drawn as follows:

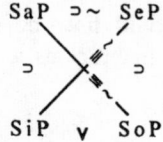

SaP ⊃∼ SeP

⊃ ⊃

SiP v SoP

2. Immediate inferences

The problem to which the scheme of Immediate Inferences presents an answer may be stated thus:

[1] The terminology of logicians varies considerably here.

Let us call the four schemata which we have already discussed *the basic schemata in 'S' and 'P'* (their characteristics are that in each of them 'S' occurs in the subject-position and 'P' in the predicate-position, and neither 'S' nor 'P' is negated); and let us call all other wffs containing 'S' and 'P' *the non-basic schemata in 'S' and 'P'* (their characteristics will be that in each of them either 'P' occupies the subject-position and 'S' the predicate-position, or either 'S' or 'P' – or both – is negated). The question to be asked is this: taking each of the basic schemata in 'S' and 'P' in turn, which of the non-basic schemata in 'S' and 'P' can be validly inferred from it? The Scheme of Immediate Inferences provides a systematic arrangement of these valid inferences.

We can explain the principle of this arrangement as follows: If we neglect for a moment the operators 'a', 'e', 'i' and 'o', and consider only the order in which the terms occur and whether each is affirmative or negative, we can easily see that there are exactly eight types of schemata, which may be symbolized thus: (i) S–P; (ii) P–S; (iii) S–$\bar{\text{P}}$; (iv) P–$\bar{\text{S}}$; (v) $\bar{\text{P}}$–S; (vi) $\bar{\text{P}}$–$\bar{\text{S}}$; (vii) $\bar{\text{S}}$–P; (viii) $\bar{\text{S}}$–$\bar{\text{P}}$. Schemata of type (i) are of course the basic schemata themselves; there are therefore seven types of non-basic schemata, among each of which we may hunt for schemata which can be validly inferred from any given basic schema. Traditional logic uses a certain technical vocabulary in this connection. For example, if a schema of type (ii) can be inferred from a certain basic schema, it is said to be the *converse* of that basic schema; and if no schema of type (ii) can be inferred from a certain basic schema, that basic schema is said to have *no converse*. The rest of the special vocabulary is set out in the table we shall give presently. (This vocabulary is not constant from logician to logician, but the form of it we shall give is probably as common as any.)

The following table should now be easy to understand. (The meanings of the numbers in brackets and of the asterisks will be explained shortly.)

Basic Schema (S-P)	SaP	SeP	SiP	SoP
Converse (P–S)	*PiS (1)	PeS (2)	PiS (3)	—
Obverse (S–$\bar{\text{P}}$)	Se$\bar{\text{P}}$ (4)	Sa$\bar{\text{P}}$ (5)	So$\bar{\text{P}}$ (6)	Si$\bar{\text{P}}$ (7)
Obverted Converse (P–$\bar{\text{S}}$)	*Po$\bar{\text{S}}$ (8)	Pa$\bar{\text{S}}$ (9)	Po$\bar{\text{S}}$ (10)	—

Basic Schema (S-P)	SaP	SeP	SiP	SoP
Partial Contra-positive (P̄–S)	P̄eS (11)	*P̄iS (12)	—	P̄iS (13)
Full Contra-positive (P̄–S̄)	P̄aS̄ (14)	*P̄oS̄ (15)	—	P̄oS̄ (16)
Partial Inverse (S̄–P)	*S̄oP (17)	*S̄iP (18)	—	—
Full Inverse (S̄–P̄)	*S̄iP̄ (19)	*S̄oP̄ (20)	—	—

These points should be noted:

(*a*) A '—' indicates that the basic schema at the top of the column in which it occurs has no converse, partial contrapositive, etc., as the case may be.

(*b*) The numbers in brackets are intended for reference. A number, however, is intended to refer not (as might be supposed) to the schema to which it is attached, but to the *inference* from the basic schema at the head of the column to that schema.

(*c*) The inferences in the table fall into two classes. In the case of inferences (2), (3), (4), (5), (6), (7), (9), (10), (11), (13), (14) and (16), the non-basic schema is not merely inferable from the basic one but is logically equivalent to it. These inferences we shall call *equivalential* immediate inferences. In the case of the remainder, the inference holds in one direction only: the non-basic schema can be inferred from the basic one, but not *vice versa*. These we shall call *implicational* immediate inferences; they have been marked with an asterisk in the table for convenience.

(*d*) In inferences (2), (4), (5), (9), (11) and (14) the conclusion is universal. But (according to the Square of Opposition) an A proposition implies the corresponding I, and an E the corresponding O. Therefore wherever a universal schema occurs as conclusion, the corresponding particular schema could also occur. There are thus six further immediate inferences, which are not written into the table. We can call these *subaltern immediate inferences*: e.g. the inference from 'S a P' to 'P̄ i S̄' is the subaltern inference corresponding to (14). They are all implicational inferences only. Subaltern inferences are omitted from the table as it is usually given, on the principle that the greater includes the lesser; their validity is not thereby meant to be denied. With the addition of these extra six inferences, the table is intended as a complete list of all the valid inferences of the type in question.

3. The theory of the syllogism

An inference is called a *syllogism* if it has the form of a syllogistic mood; and a syllogistic mood can be defined as an inferential schema in which (*a*) there are two premisses and one conclusion, each of which is an A, E, I or O schema; (*b*) premisses and conclusion together contain exactly three term variables, all unnegated; and (*c*) each term variable occurs in exactly two of the three schemata. It is conventional so to order the premisses that the premiss containing the variable which occurs as predicate in the conclusion appears first. It follows from the definition that there will be one term variable which occurs in each of the premisses but not in the conclusion; the term represented by that variable is known as the *middle term*. The terms which appear as subject and predicate in the conclusion are known as the *minor* and the *major* terms respectively.

The expression 'syllogistic mood' is a traditional one; it is convenient to use it here rather than 'syllogistic schema', as we shall thereby be freed to use the latter phrase to cover any schema in syllogistic logic in the wide sense.

How many syllogistic moods are there? We can arrive at an answer to this question quite simply. Following the usual convention, we can represent the subject and predicate of the conclusion by 'S' and 'P' respectively, and the middle term by 'M'. Then 'S' will appear in the second premiss (which is usually called the *minor* premiss), and it can appear in either, but not both, of the two places in it. 'P' will appear in the first premiss (which is usually called the *major* premiss), and again it can appear in either, but not both of two positions in it. The remaining two variable-places will both be occupied by 'M'. We have therefore four and only four possible arrangements of term variables:

I	II	III	IV
M – P	P – M	M – P	P – M
S – M	S – M	M – S	M – S
S – P	S – P	S – P	S – P

In each case the major premiss, the minor premiss and the conclusion are written in a vertical column, and the conclusion is separated from the premisses by a horizontal line. These arrangements of term-variables are known respectively as the First, Second, Third, and Fourth *Figures* of the Syllogism.

Now each Figure has three blanks, each of which may be filled by any one of the operators 'a', 'e', 'i' and 'o'. In each Figure, therefore, there are 4^3 (i.e. 64) moods; and since there are four Figures there are in all 64×4 (i.e. 256) syllogistic moods.

Since by mentioning a particular Figure we specify the arrangement of the term variables, we can indicate any of the 256 moods by stating to which Figure it belongs and which operators occur in major premiss, minor premiss and conclusion respectively. It is customary to use the capital letters 'A', 'E', 'I' and 'O' for this purpose. Thus 'AEI in Fig. III' will indicate succinctly the mood

$$M \ a \ P$$
$$M \ e \ S$$
$$\overline{S \ i \ P}$$

How many of the 256 moods are valid? Comprehensive rules for determining the validity of syllogistic moods will be found in any text-book of traditional logic. We shall not set down these rules here, but simply state the result of applying them, which is that the following moods are valid, and all the others are invalid:

In Fig. I: AAA, AAI, EAE, EAO, AII, EIO
In Fig. II: EAE, EAO, AEE, AEO, EIO, AOO
In Fig. III: AAI, IAI, AII, EAO, OAO, EIO
In Fig. IV: AAI, AEE, AEO, IAI, EAO, EIO

There are thus 24 valid moods in all, six in each Figure.

Weakened and strengthened moods

The 24 valid moods can be divided into three classes: weakened moods, strengthened moods, and those which are neither.

According to the traditional doctrine, as expressed in the Square of Opposition, 'S a P' implies, but is not implied by, 'S i P', and 'S e P' implies, but is not implied by, 'S o P', and in general, any universal proposition (affirmative or negative) implies, but is not implied by, the corresponding particular proposition (affirmative or negative). The universal proposition might be said to assert all that the corresponding particular one does, and more as well; the universal proposition is therefore said to be *stronger* than the corresponding particular proposition, the particular *weaker* than the corresponding universal.

Two things follow: (*a*) If a valid mood has as its conclusion an A or an E proposition, the mood which contains the same premisses but has an I in place of the A proposition, or an O in place of the E proposition, as its conclusion, will also be valid. Weakening the conclusion, while leaving the premisses unchanged, cannot destroy validity. In such a case the mood containing the particular conclusion is said to be a *weakened* mood, or a weakened form of the mood with the universal conclusion.

(*b*) If a valid mood contains among its premisses an I or an O proposition, then the mood obtained by substituting the corresponding A for the I proposition or the corresponding E for the O will also be valid. Strengthening a premiss cannot destroy validity. In such a case the mood containing the universal premiss in question is said to be a *strengthened* mood, or a strengthened form of the mood containing the particular premiss.

One mood can sometimes be both a weakened form of another mood and a strengthened form of a third one.

If we examine our list of 24 valid moods with all this in mind, we shall find that the following 15 moods are neither weakened nor strengthened moods:

In Fig. I:	AAA, EAE, AII, EIO
In Fig. II:	EAE, AEE, EIO, AOO
In Fig. III:	IAI, AII, OAO, EIO
In Fig. IV:	AEE, IAI, EIO.

Of the remaining 9 valid moods,

AAI in Fig. I is a weakened form of AAA and a strengthened form of AII;

EAO in Fig. I is a weakened form of EAE and a strengthened form of EIO;

EAO in Fig. II is a weakened form of EAE and a strengthened form of EIO;

AEO in Fig. II is a weakened form of AEE and a strengthened form of AOO;

AAI in Fig. III is a strengthened form of either IAI or AII;

EAO in Fig. III is a strengthened form of either OAO or EIO;

AAI in Fig. IV is a strengthened form of IAI;

AEO in Fig. IV is a weakened form of AEE;

EAO in Fig. IV is a strengthened form of EIO.

It is frequently said that the number of valid moods is 19. The list of 19 is obtained by omitting from our 24 all moods which can be regarded as weakened forms of other valid moods (whether or not they can also be regarded as strengthened moods), viz. AAI and EAO in Fig. I, EAO and AEO in Fig. II, and AEO in Fig. IV. Strengthened moods which are not also weakened moods are, however, retained in the list. The list of 19 therefore consists of the 15 moods we have already tabulated as neither weakened nor strengthened, and in addition the following four moods: AAI and EAO in Fig. III, and AAI and EAO in Fig. IV. The weakened moods are omitted because they are considered to be either trivial or already covered by the moods of which they are the weakened forms; those who omit them do not thereby wish to deny their validity.

Mnemonic names for valid syllogistic moods

In many text-books the following Latin verses are given as an aid to remembering which moods are valid in each of the four Figures. An earlier version was current at least as early as the middle of the thirteenth century.

> BARBARA CELARENT DARII FERIOque prioris;
> CESARE CAMESTRES FESTINO BAROCO secundae;
> Tertia DARAPTI DISAMIS DATISI FELAPTON
> BOCARDO FERISON habet; quarta insuper addit
> BRAMANTIP CAMENES DIMARIS FESAPO FRESISON.

The explanation of the verses is as follows. Each word printed in block capitals is the name of a valid syllogistic mood. The moods which are valid in Figures I, II, III and IV are those whose names occur in lines 1, 2, 3–4 and 5 respectively. Each name contains three vowels, which indicate the nature of the major premiss, the minor premiss, and the conclusion, in that order. Thus, BARBARA is mood AAA in Figure I, DATISI is mood AII in Figure III, and so on.

(Not only the vowels, but almost all of the consonants too, have some significance, but we have not said enough about traditional syllogistic theory to be in a position to state what their significance is. The fuller text-books of traditional logic will give the details, and will make it clear that the whole series of names forms a complicated and highly ingenious mnemonic.)

Note that only the 19 moods referred to in the preceding section are mentioned in the verses. The remaining five (weakened) moods are, however, often given the following names:

AAI in Figure I: BARBARI
EAO in Figure I: CELARONT
EAO in Figure II: CESARO
AEO in Figure II: CAMESTROP
AEO in Figure IV: CAMENOP.

Although the mnemonic names will not be used in this book, they are still in common currency. Those who can scan Latin hexameters often find that the verses provide the easiest way of memorizing the list of valid moods.

EXERCISES 42

Examples in these exercises should be re-phrased, where necessary, to give them explicitly the form of A, E, I or O propositions.

42.1 Write down, where possible, the contrary (or sub-contrary), contradictory and converse of the following:
(*a*) All Italians are Europeans.
(*b*) Lying is sometimes morally justified.
(*c*) Those who confess to crimes are not always guilty.
(*d*) No O proposition has a converse.
(*e*) Only adults may vote.

42.2 Write down, where possible, the obverse, full contrapositive and partial inverse of the following:
(*a*) Blessed are the peacemakers.
(*b*) Some birds cannot fly.
(*c*) Unjust acts are never expedient.
(*d*) A mile can be run in less than four minutes.

42.3 Given that
No vampires are vegetarians
what can be inferred about the truth or falsity of the following?
(*a*) All vegetarians are non-vampires.
(*b*) Some non-vegetarians are non-vampires.
(*c*) Some vegetarians are vampires.
(*d*) All non-vegetarians are vampires.

42.4 Set out the following inferences in proper syllogistic form.

In each case state the Mood and Figure, and say whether the inference is valid or invalid.

(a) Addled eggs are unfit for human consumption, but no new-laid eggs are addled; so no new-laid eggs are unfit for human consumption.

(b) Some Communists are not British subjects; for all Australian citizens are Communists, and some Australian citizens are not British subjects.

(c) No philosophers are morally perfect; all epistemologists are philosophers; therefore no morally perfect beings are epistemologists.

(d) All enemies of liberty support Mr. X's action; some members of the Government party support it; there are therefore enemies of liberty in the Government party.

(e) One can know the multiplication table without being awake: all John's children know the multiplication table, but none of them are awake.

42.5 In each of the four Figures of the Syllogism, supply premisses which will yield the conclusion

Some aquatic animals are not mammals.

CHAPTER 43

Syllogistic and the Predicate Calculus

What precise interpretation are we to place upon the wffs of syllogistic logic? What exactly are propositions of the form 'All S is P' and the rest supposed to assert? If you are inclined to reply, as you may be at first, that we should understand 'All S is P' simply in terms of what sentences of the form 'All so-and-so's are such-and-such' mean in ordinary English, and the other schemata in an analogous way, then what you say will be open to the objections that in the first place it is not at all clear precisely what such English sentences are used to assert, and that in the second place it is virtually certain that not all sentences of the form 'All so-and-so's are such-and-such' are used to assert the same kind of thing.

If you then try to make a more precise reply, one suggestion that may very naturally occur to you is that we should interpret term variables as predicate variables, and the wffs of syllogistic logic as quantified formulae in the Predicate Calculus. Syllogistic logic would then turn out to be a limited fragment of LPC1. The following wffs in LPC1 readily suggest themselves as possible candidates for A, E, I and O schemata respectively:

$$\text{(A)} \quad \text{U} \ (f \supset g)$$
$$\text{(E)} \quad \text{U} \ (f \supset \sim g)$$
$$\text{(I)} \quad \exists \ (f.g)$$
$$\text{(O)} \quad \exists \ (f.\sim g)$$

Comparison with the material in the previous chapter will be made easier if we modify our Predicate Calculus symbolism somewhat, by using 'S', 'P' and 'M' as our predicate variables instead of the familiar 'f', 'g' and 'h', and by using a bar above a predicate variable instead of a tilde before it as a negation sign. (We shall, however, still write '$\sim$' as a negation sign when this occurs immediately before a quantifier.) It will also simplify certain of our calculations if we make all quantifiers existential. The suggested formulae will then appear as follows:

$$S \ a \ P \quad - \quad \sim\!\exists \ (S.\bar{P}) \quad [\text{or: } U(S \supset P)]$$
$$S \ e \ P \quad - \quad \sim\!\exists \ (S.P) \quad [\text{or: } U(S \supset \bar{P})]$$
$$S \ i \ P \quad - \quad \exists \ (S.P)$$
$$S \ o \ P \quad - \quad \exists \ (S.\bar{P})$$

We can look at the suggestion we are considering as a set of rules for translating wffs of syllogistic logic into Predicate Calculus formulae. Thus the rule for translating an A schema is: omit the 'a', place a '.' between the subject-variable and the predicate-variable, place a bar over the latter (a second bar if it already has one), enclose the whole in brackets, and prefix it by '$\sim\!\exists$'. You will be able to state the other three rules for yourself quite easily.

We shall call this way of construing the meaning of A, E, I and O propositions, *Interpretation 1*. We shall now enquire how the traditional doctrines set out in the previous chapter fare when this interpretation is given.

Let us consider first the Square of Opposition.

The contradictory relations hold. This is easy to see, since '$\sim\!\exists(S.\bar{P})$' is simply the negation of '$\exists(S.\bar{P})$', and '$\sim\!\exists(S.P)$' is simply the negation of '$\exists(S.P)$'.

But the subaltern relations fail to hold. For consider the case of there being no S's at all. Then *a fortiori* there will be no S-not-P's; i.e. '$\sim\!\exists(S.\bar{P})$' will be true. But if there are no S's, '$\exists(S.P)$' will be false, since it asserts that there is something which is both S and P, and therefore that there is something which is S. It is therefore possible that '$\sim\!\exists(S.\bar{P})$' should be true but '$\exists(S.P)$' false.[1] So '$\sim\!\exists(S.\bar{P}) \supset \exists(S.P)$' (A $\supset$ I) is not valid. A similar argument will show that subalternation also fails to hold between O and E.

Moreover, A and E propositions are no longer contraries. For if there are no S's, then *a fortiori* there are no S-P's, i.e. '$\sim\!\exists(S.P)$' is true. But as we have already seen, if there are no S's, '$\sim\!\exists(S.\bar{P})$' is also true. It is therefore possible for both to be true, and hence they are not contraries.

Finally, I and O are no longer sub-contraries. For if, once again, there are no S's, '$\exists(S.P)$' and '$\exists(S.\bar{P})$' will both be false. And therefore '$\exists(S.P) \lor \exists(S.\bar{P})$' is not valid.

In summary, if we arrange the formulae under discussion in the

---

[1] This sentence should more accurately run: It is therefore possible to find two actual predicates such that when they are substituted for 'S' and 'P' respectively in '$\sim\!\exists(S.\bar{P})$' and '$\exists(S.\bar{P})$', the result is a pair of propositions of which the first is true and the second false. (And analogously in the other cases which follow.)

form of a square, the only relations remaining are those represented
by the two diagonal lines, viz. the contradictory relations, and the
square will look like this:

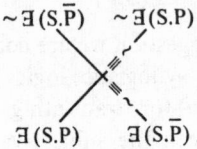

The Square of Opposition therefore fares very badly under
Interpretation 1.

Let us now turn to the table of Immediate Inferences. It would
be tedious to test all the inferences here; you will not find it at all
difficult to do so for yourself. You must first translate each of the
formulae into Predicate Calculus formulae in the way we have
already explained. Then simple applications of the laws of double
negation and commutation will show the validity of some of the
inferences, and techniques of the kind we have used in discussing
the Square of Opposition will show the invalidity of the remainder.

The upshot of examining the inferences is this: the inferences we
have numbered (1), (8), (12), (15), (17), (18), (19) and (20) turn out
to be invalid; the remaining 12 are valid. Those which are still valid
are the *equivalential* ones in the traditional theory; the invalid ones
are those which were claimed as implicational only (the ones we
marked with an asterisk in our table). The six subaltern inferences
are also invalid.

We turn thirdly to syllogisms. We can test the validity of any
syllogistic mood under the present interpretation by testing the
validity of the relevant propositional schema. To obtain this, we
first of all translate premisses and conclusion into the appropriate
Predicate Calculus formulae, then conjoin the two premisses and
place an implication sign between the conjoined premisses and the
conclusion. The result is a propositional schema in LPC1, to which
we can apply the test-procedures described in Part III.

You can, if you feel heroic, test each of the 256 moods in this way
(though, as we shall see in the next chapter, it is unnecessary to go
to such extreme lengths). The result of doing so can, however, be
stated quite briefly: fifteen moods will turn out to be valid, and the
remainder to be invalid. The fifteen moods which are valid under
Interpretation 1 are precisely those which we listed in the previous

chapter as neither weakened nor strengthened. We repeat the list here for convenience.

> In Fig. I: AAA, EAE, AII, EIO.
> In Fig. II: EAE, AEE, EIO, AOO
> In Fig. III: IAI, AII, OAO, EIO
> In Fig. IV: AEE, IAI, EIO

The nine weakened or strengthened moods which are regarded as valid in the traditional doctrine turn out to be invalid.

EXERCISES 43

43.1 Construct LPC1 schemata for each of the following, under Interpretation 1, and test for validity by the methods given in Part III.

(*a*) Partial Contrapositive of S a P

(*b*) Full Inverse of S e P

(*c*) Obverted Converse of S i P

(*d*) Mood EAO in Figure I

(*e*) Mood EIO in Figure II

(*f*) Mood AAI in Figure IV

43.2 Try to think or actual syllogisms in Mood AAI (Figure III) in which it would seem unnatural, from an intuitive point of view, to regard the inference as valid.

(This exercise may be applied to other weakened or strengthened moods.)

CHAPTER 44

Syllogistic Moods
Under Interpretation 1:
The Antilogism Theorem

We shall now give a proof of the assertion made dogmatically at the end of the last chapter, viz. that the 15 moods listed there, and no others, are valid when A, E, I and O propositions are construed in terms of Interpretation 1.

Let us call the two premisses and the conclusion of any syllogistic mood, X, Y and Z respectively. The mood will be valid if and only if

$$(X.Y) \supset Z \tag{1}$$

is valid. Now a formula is valid if and only if its negation is inconsistent. So (1) is valid if and only if

$$\sim((X.Y) \supset Z)$$

i.e. $\qquad\qquad X.Y.\sim Z$

is inconsistent.

We shall call a group of three schemata which could function as premisses and conclusion of the same syllogism (valid or invalid) a *syllogistic triad*. To state the conditions more explicitly, three schemata will constitute a syllogistic triad if (*a*) each is an A, E, I or O proposition, (*b*) between them they contain exactly three terms, (*c*) each term occurs in exactly two of the three schemata.

By the *antilogism* of a given syllogistic mood we understand the group of three schemata consisting of the premisses of that mood and the *negation* of its conclusion. Note that such a group will itself be a syllogistic triad in the sense just explained, since the negation of any syllogistic schema is (or is equivalent to) another syllogistic schema with the same terms.

So the point we made in the second paragraph can be re-phrased as follows: a syllogistic mood is valid if and only if its antilogism is an inconsistent syllogistic triad, i.e. a syllogistic triad the conjunction of whose members is inconsistent.

The importance of this can be brought out by looking at it the other way round. If we can find a syllogistic triad which is inconsistent, we can form from it a valid syllogistic mood by taking the first two schemata as premisses and the negation of the third as conclusion. (Z is the negation of $\sim$Z, by Double Negation.)

We can go further. As we know, the order of the conjuncts in a conjunction is immaterial. So if $(X.Y.\sim Z)$ is inconsistent, $(X.\sim Z.Y)$ and $(Y.\sim Z.X)$ are also inconsistent. And if these are inconsistent, $((X.\sim Z) \supset \sim Y)$ and $((Y.\sim Z) \supset \sim X)$ are valid. We can therefore say that if we have an inconsistent triad, any syllogism formed by taking *any two* schemata in the triad as premisses and the negation of the third as conclusion will be valid; and furthermore that no syllogism which cannot be derived in such a way is valid.

So instead of asking under what conditions a syllogistic mood is valid, it will do equally well to ask under what conditions a syllogistic triad is inconsistent.

We want to find out what moods are valid under Interpretation 1. We have reduced this task to that of discovering what syllogistic triads are inconsistent when they are translated into LPC1 formulae by the rules of Interpretation 1.

We now show how to solve this problem.

It is obvious that any syllogistic triad must consist of either (*a*) three universal propositions, or (*b*) three particular propositions, or (*c*) one universal and two particulars, or (*d*) one particular and two universals. So the conjunction of its members can be represented by one or other of the following:

(*a*) $U\alpha . U\beta . U\gamma$

(*b*) $\exists\alpha . \exists\beta . \exists\gamma$

(*c*) $U\alpha . \exists\beta . \exists\gamma$

(*d*) $\exists\alpha . U\beta . U\gamma$

At the end of Chapter 27 we gave rules (numbered (ia)–(iva)) for testing conjunctions of quantified schemata for inconsistency. We shall make considerable use of these rules in what follows.

Firstly, no conjunction of type (*a*) can be inconsistent. For

$$U\alpha . U\beta . U\gamma$$

is equivalent to

$$U(\alpha . \beta . \gamma)$$

which, by Rule (ia) is inconsistent if and only if

$$\alpha' \cdot \beta' \cdot \gamma'^{1} \tag{2}$$

is inconsistent.

Now (2) contains exactly three propositional variables, and its matrix will therefore contain eight rows. Moreover, each of α', β' and γ' is an implication with different single variables (or their negations) as antecedent and consequent; therefore the truth-table for each of them will contain six 1's and two 0's. So the maximum number of 0's in the truth-table for (2) is 3×2 (i.e. 6); hence the truth-table must contain at least two 1s and therefore (2) cannot be inconsistent.

Secondly, no conjunction of type (*b*) can be inconsistent. For by Rule (iiia),

$$\exists\alpha \cdot \exists\beta \cdot \exists\gamma$$

is inconsistent if and only if at least one of α', β' and γ' is inconsistent. Each, however, consists of a conjunction of two distinct variables (or their negations), and no such conjunction can be inconsistent.

Thirdly, no conjunction of type (*c*) can be inconsistent. For by Rule (iva)

$$U\alpha \cdot \exists\beta \cdot \exists\gamma$$

is inconsistent if and only if one or other of $(\alpha' \cdot \beta')$ and $(\alpha' \cdot \gamma')$ is inconsistent. Neither, however, can be inconsistent. Consider $(\alpha' \cdot \beta')$. α' is an implication, whose truth-table contains two 0's and six 1's. β' is a conjunction of single variables, whose truth-table contains six 0's and two 1's. $(\alpha' \cdot \beta')$, therefore, could be inconsistent only if the 0's in the truth-table of β' coincided exactly with the 1's in the truth-table of α'. But if they did, β' would be (equivalent to) the negation of α'. This, however, is impossible, since only one of the variables which occurs in α' occurs in β'.

For the same reason, $(\alpha' \cdot \gamma')$ cannot be inconsistent.

The only conjunctions which can be inconsistent are therefore all of type (*d*). So the remaining question is, which conjunctions of type (*d*) are inconsistent?

The argument which will lead us to an answer to this question will run more smoothly if we revert to our former practice of writing

---

[1] Here, and throughout, α', β', ... are the PC wffs isomorphic with the wfpes α, β, ... respectively.

all the schemata with existential quantifiers; so we shall say that conjunctions of type (*d*) are of the form

$$\exists\alpha \, . \sim\!\exists\beta \, . \sim\!\exists\gamma \tag{3}$$

β and γ are now of course not implications but conjunctions, just as α is. (They are the negations of the implicative wfpes represented by 'β' and 'γ' in (*d*).)

Since $(\sim\!\exists\beta \, . \sim\!\exists\gamma)$ is equivalent to $U(\sim\!\beta.\sim\!\gamma)$, we can apply Rule (iva) to (3) quite simply: (3) will be inconsistent if and only if

$$\alpha' \, . \sim\!\beta' \, . \sim\!\gamma' \tag{4}$$

is inconsistent.

In (4), α', β' and γ' are all conjunctions of two distinct propositional variables. Moreover in each case the first variable is unnegated, but the second may be either negated or unnegated. Let us therefore re-write (4) as

$$(\alpha_1' \, . \, \alpha_2') \, . \sim\!(\beta_1' \, . \, \beta_2') \, . \sim\!(\gamma_1' \, . \, \gamma_2') \tag{5}$$

where each Greek letter with the subscript '$_1$' represents an unnegated variable, and each Greek letter with the subscript '$_2$' represents a variable which may be either negated or unnegated.

We have also to remind ourselves that (5) contains exactly three variables, each of which occurs in exactly two conjuncts.

Let us now reduce (5) to DNF. The details of the reduction are omitted here, but the final result is

$$\begin{aligned}
&(\alpha_1' \, . \, \alpha_2' \, . \sim\!\beta_1' \, . \sim\!\gamma_1') \\
\vee \, &(\alpha_1' \, . \, \alpha_2' \, . \sim\!\beta_1' \, . \sim\!\gamma_2') \\
\vee \, &(\alpha_1' \, . \, \alpha_2' \, . \sim\!\beta_2' \, . \sim\!\gamma_1') \\
\vee \, &(\alpha_1' \, . \, \alpha_2' \, . \sim\!\beta_2' \, . \sim\!\gamma_2')
\end{aligned} \tag{6}$$

A disjunction, as we know, is inconsistent if and only if each disjunct is inconsistent; and a conjunction of variables is inconsistent if and only if some variable occurs in it both negated and unnegated.

With this in mind, let us try to do some filling in. α_1' is an unnegated variable, so let us replace it by 'p'. α_2' is a variable distinct from α_1'; it can be either 'q' or '$\sim$q'. Moreover 'p' will occur either somewhere in β' or somewhere in γ', but not in both. It will not matter which of β' and γ' we choose to contain 'p'; let us say that it occurs in β'. Then 'q' will occur in γ', and the third variable, 'r', will occur in both β' and γ'.

Now firstly, no matter what positions we suppose 'r' to occupy in β' and γ', there is going to be one of the disjuncts in (6) which will read:

$$\text{p . q}(or \sim q) \text{ . } \sim r(or \sim\sim r) \text{ . } \sim r(or \sim\sim r) \tag{7}$$

Clearly the only way in which (7) can be inconsistent is for one of the last two conjuncts to be '$\sim r$' and the other to be '$\sim\sim r$'. So 'r' must occur in β' and '$\sim r$' in γ', or vice versa. We therefore have one of the conditions for the inconsistency of (4): the variable which occurs in both β' and γ' must be negated in one and unnegated in the other.

Secondly, no matter what positions we suppose 'p', 'q' and 'r' to occupy in β' and γ', there is going to be one disjunct in (6) which will read:

$$\text{p . q}(or \sim q) \text{ . } \sim p(or \sim\sim p) \text{ . } \sim r(or \sim\sim r) \tag{8}$$

The only way for (8) to be inconsistent is for the third conjunct to be '$\sim p$'. Therefore either β_1' or β_2' must be simply 'p'. I.e. 'p' (unnegated) occurs in β'.

Thirdly, no matter what positions we assign to 'p', 'q', and 'r' in β' and γ', there is going to be one disjunct in (6) which will read:

$$\text{p . q}(or \sim q) \text{ . } \sim r(or \sim\sim r) \text{ . } \sim q(or \sim\sim q) \tag{9}$$

(9) can be inconsistent only if the fourth conjunct is the negation of the second; and therefore either γ_1' or γ_2' must be identical with α_2'.

We have now discovered three conditions all of which must be fulfilled if (4) is to be inconsistent. We can summarize them as follows: the variable common to β' and γ' must be negated in one and unnegated in the other; and the variables in α' must occur in β' and γ' respectively exactly as they occur in α'. These conditions are in fact not only necessary but also sufficient. We can show this by making a list of all possible values of α', β' and γ' which are compatible with the stated conditions, and checking that, in each case, (4) – i.e. (α' . $\sim\beta'$. $\sim\gamma'$) – is inconsistent. There are five and only five ways in which the conditions can be fulfilled. They are

A	B	C	D	E
p.q	p.q	p.q	p.q	p.$\sim$q
p.r	r.p	p.$\sim$r	p.$\sim$r	p.$\sim$r
q.$\sim$r	q.$\sim$r	q.r	r.q	r.$\sim$q

Replacing 'p' by 'S', 'q' by 'P' and 'r' by 'M', and introducing quantifiers as in (3), we obtain the following inconsistent triads:

A	B	C	D	E
∃(S.P)	∃(S.P)	∃(S.P)	∃(S.P)	∃(S.P̄)
~∃(S.M)	~∃(M.S)	~∃(S.M̄)	~∃(S.M̄)	~∃(S.M̄)
~∃(P.M̄)	~∃(P.M̄)	~∃(P.M)	~∃(M.P)	~∃(M.P̄)

From each of these triads we can form a valid syllogism by taking any two of the schemata as premisses and the negation of the third as conclusion. To obtain the syllogism in its conventional form we re-letter the variables, if necessary, so as to make 'S' and 'P' occur in that order in the conclusion, and arrange the order of the premisses so that 'P' occurs in the first.

In this way we can form three valid moods from each triad. No duplicates arise in this process, so that exactly 15 valid moods emerge; and these turn out to be the 15 moods listed at the end of the previous chapter.

As an example, consider triad A. Let us take the negation of the second schema as the conclusion, which will therefore be '∃(S.M)'. This leaves '∃(S.P)' and '~∃(P.M̄)' as the premisses. We re-letter 'M' as 'P', and by consequence 'P' as 'M'. Writing the premiss containing 'P' first, we obtain the mood

$$\frac{\sim\exists(M.\bar{P})}{\exists(S.M)}$$
$$\overline{\exists(S.P)}$$

which is AII in Figure I.

You should not find it difficult to derive the other 14 valid moods in the same way.

The Antilogism Theorem

To draw the threads of our argument together: we have succeeded in proving that the only moods which are valid when Interpretation 1 is given to syllogistic schemata are the 15 listed at the end of the previous chapter; but in doing so we have also found a simple set of conditions for the validity of a mood under Interpretation 1. Expressed in terms of the symbolism we have been using, these conditions are:

A syllogistic mood is valid under Interpretation 1 if and only if its antilogism has all of the following three characteristics:

1. It consists of two universal propositions and one particular (i.e. two which begin with '∼Ǝ' and one which begins with 'Ǝ');

2. The variable common to the two universals is negated in one of these and unnegated in the other;

3. The remaining variables in the universals occur exactly as they do in the particular (negated if negated there, unnegated if unnegated there).

This is known as the *Antilogism Theorem*. It – or more accurately its analogue in the logic of classes – was first formulated by Mrs Christine Ladd-Franklin in a paper published in 1880.[1]

As a test for validity, the Antilogism Theorem is simplicity itself to apply. You take any properly constructed syllogism you choose, expressed in the symbolism we have used in this chapter, and place a '∼' before its conclusion (or delete one if there is one there already). About the group of three formulae you thus obtain – the distinction between premisses and conclusion has now vanished – you ask three questions, the answers to each of which will leap to the eye. 1. Do two of the formulae begin with '∼Ǝ' and the third with 'Ǝ'? 2. If so, does the variable which occurs in the two which begin with '∼Ǝ' have a bar over it in one case but not in the other? 3. Do the other variables in these two formulae occur exactly as they occur in the remaining one (the one beginning with 'Ǝ')? If the answer to all these three questions is 'Yes', the syllogism with which you started is valid; if not, it is invalid.

EXERCISES 44

44.1 Test the validity of the following moods by the Antilogism Method:

(*a*) EAE in Figure I.

(*b*) AAA in Figure II.

(*c*) EAO in Figure III.

(*d*) IAI in Figure IV.

44.2 Use the Antilogism Theorem to establish the following:

(*a*) No syllogism with two particular premisses is valid.

---

[1] 'On the Algebra of Logic' in *John Hopkins Studies in Logic*.

(*b*) No syllogism with two negative premisses is valid.

(*c*) No syllogism in which either premiss is particular and the conclusion is universal is valid.

(*d*) No syllogism in which either premiss is negative and the conclusion is affirmative is valid.

CHAPTER 45

Syllogistic and LPC1 :
Further Interpretations

We have found that when syllogistic schemata are construed in accordance with Interpretation 1, a considerable number of traditionally valid inferences have to be rejected as invalid. So it would appear that this interpretation, although it looked promising at first, does not turn out to be at all a good account of how traditional syllogistic is to be understood.

Nevertheless, there is more to be said about Interpretation 1 before we proceed.

In the first place, we should notice that the lines of demarcation between what remains valid and what is no longer valid under this interpretation correspond to distinctions which are already drawn in traditional syllogistic itself. Thus, traditional syllogistic distinguishes between weakened syllogisms, strengthened syllogisms, and syllogisms which are neither. The 15 valid moods coincide exactly with the third of these groups, and the 9 rejected moods are the weakened and strengthened ones. Moreover, in the case of Immediate Inferences, the equivalential inferences all continue to hold while the merely implicational ones all fail. And something analogous is true of the Square of Opposition; for the contradictory relations, which still hold, are equivalences of a sort, and the remaining relations, which fail to hold, are implications. (We expressed the sub-contrary relation as 'S i P v S o P', but we could equally well have written '∼(S i P) ⊃ S o P'). All this should at least suggest that it is not merely an *arbitrary* segment of traditional syllogistic which remains (or is excluded) when Interpretation 1 is given.

Secondly, the items in the traditional scheme which become invalid under Interpretation 1 consist of all those cases, and only those cases, in which a particular proposition is inferred from one or more universal propositions. A glance at the table on pp. 308–9 will show this as far as Immediate Inferences are concerned. Weakened and strengthened syllogisms all have two universal premisses and a particular conclusion, whereas all other valid syllogisms with a particular conclusion have one particular premiss. In the Square of Opposition the matter is clear in the case of subalternation, but a moment's thought will show that the contrary and sub-contrary relations exhibit the same features: we expressed the contrariety of A and E propositions by the formula 'S a P $\supset$ $\sim$(S e P)', but since '$\sim$(S e P)' is equivalent to 'S i P' it can rank as a particular; and in the case of the sub-contrary relation, since '$\sim$(S i P)' is equivalent to 'S e P', '$\sim$(S i P) $\supset$ S o P' will also count as the implication of a particular by a universal.

It is not difficult to see why all these implications should fail to hold. We have been interpreting A and E propositions *non-existentially*, i.e. we have regarded 'S a P' and 'S e P' simply as *denying* that there are any things of a certain sort, viz. S-not-P's and S-P's respectively, and not as asserting that there are any S's (or P's or not-P's for that matter). On the other hand, we have been interpreting I and O propositions *existentially*, i.e. we have regarded 'S i P' and 'S o P' as asserting that there *are* some S-P's and some S-not-P's respectively; and hence of course that there are S's and P's in the former case, and that there are S's and not-P's in the latter. It is therefore hardly surprising that no particular proposition should be validly inferable from any universal, or from any number of universals, alone. In fact, the items which we found to remain valid under Interpretation 1 constitute exactly what is left of traditional syllogistic if we add to it the single restriction that no universal proposition implies any particular one.

Existential interpretation of universal propositions

The natural next step would seem to be to try to recover what we have lost of the traditional scheme by giving an existential interpretation to A and E propositions as well as to I and O propositions, while still remaining within LPC1. We can do this by conjoining to our previous formulae for 'S a P' and 'S e P', the additional formula '$\exists$S' in each case. Then 'S a P' and 'S e P' would become respectively

$$\exists S \, . \, \sim\!\exists(S.\bar{P})$$
and $$\exists S \, . \, \sim\!\exists(S.P)$$

We could think of the former as meaning 'There are some S's, and none of them fail to be P's', and of the latter as meaning 'There are some S's, but none of them are P's'.

It may be as well to make it clear that the interpretation of A and E propositions we have in mind here consists in each case in adding to the previous interpretation the further assertion that there is at least one thing to which the subject-term applies, or that there is at least one thing which possesses the property represented by the *first* of the two variables in the predicate expression which occurs after '∼∃'. This variable need not, of course, be 'S'. Thus 'S e P̄' will be taken as

$$\exists \bar{S} \cdot \sim\exists(\bar{S}.\bar{P})$$

('There are some not-S's, but none of them are not-P's') and 'M a P' will be taken as

$$\exists M \cdot \sim\exists(M.\bar{P})$$

('There are some M's, and none of them fail to be P's') and so forth.

If we adopt this interpretation of A and E propositions, and retain our previous interpretation of I and O propositions, we have what we shall call *Interpretation 2*. How does the traditional scheme fare this time?

We shall not work through all the details – you should by now, not find this difficult to do – but simply present a summary of the results.

In the Square of Opposition we certainly achieve our first aim, since (A ⊃ I) and (E ⊃ O) are both valid. Moreover A and E are now contraries (A ⊃ ∼E). On the other hand, the contradictory relations have disappeared; as we might have expected, since we have changed the meanings of A and E propositions but left O and I propositions (their previous contradictories) alone. And of course, since I and O propositions remain unchanged, the sub-contrary relation still fails to hold.

In the table of Immediate Inferences, once again 12 of the traditional 20 inferences hold, but not the same 12 as with Interpretation 1. The following eight now *fail* to hold: (2) – the converse of E – (9), (11), (14), (17), (18), (19), (20). The remaining 12 hold.

22 of the traditional 24 syllogistic moods are valid. The only two that fail are AEE and AEO in Figure IV.

It is true that the list of valid items is somewhat longer this time. It does not, however, in any obvious way reflect any natural division within the traditional scheme, and we cannot claim to be any further forward.

At this point some logicians have been known to throw up their hands and declare that traditional syllogistic has been shown to be confused or inconsistent. The expressions 'All S is P' and 'No S is P', they have said, are ambiguous as between existential and non-existential interpretations. If we remove this ambiguity, as we can by translating them into a symbolism such as that of LPC1, in which all existential assertions are clearly indicated, then we find that if we construe them non-existentially certain elements in the traditional system are lost, whereas if we construe them existentially certain others are lost; and some elements – the sub-contrary relation, the Inverses, mood AEO in Figure IV – cannot be obtained in either interpretation.

This, however, is a hasty judgment. For one thing, there are further manoeuvres possible within LPC1. For another, it is not obvious that syllogistic requires to be given an interpretation within the Predicate Calculus at all; it may be a different kind of logical system, though clear and consistent within its own boundaries. But let us remain within LPC1 for the present.

Some other interpretations

With Interpretation 2, A and O propositions, and likewise E and I propositions, cease to form pairs of contradictories. The contradictory of '∃S . ∼∃(S.P̄)' is not '∃(S.P̄)' but, (applying the de Morgan Law) '∼∃S ∨ ∃(S.P̄)'. Similarly the contradictory of '∃S . ∼∃(S.P)' is '∼∃S ∨ ∃(S.P)'. We could therefore restore the contradictory relations by taking these new schemata as interpretations of 'S o P' and 'S i P' respectively.

For convenience we shall draw up a table of all the suggested LPC1 schemata we have had so far under consideration as interpretations of A, E, I and O propositions (including the two new ones) and assign a reference number to each.

(A): ∼∃(S.P̄)	(1)	∃S . ∼∃(S.P̄)	(1a)
(E): ∼∃(S.P)	(2)	∃S . ∼∃(S.P)	(2a)
(I): ∃(S.P)	(3)	∼∃S ∨ ∃(S.P)	(3a)
(O): ∃(S.P̄)	(4)	∼∃S ∨ ∃(S.P̄)	(4a)

Just as we can think of (1a) and (2a) as – to speak roughly – existential versions of (1) and (2) respectively, so we can think of (3a) and (4a) as non-existential versions of (3) and (4) respectively. What is meant by this will be clearer if we re-write e.g. (3a) as

'∃S ⊃ ∃(S.P)' – 'if there are any S's, there are some S-P's': it will then be seen that the existential assertion that there *are* some S's has been dropped.

With Interpretation 1 we tried to form a Square of Opposition out of (1), (2), (3) and (4), but failed. With Interpretation 2 we tried to form one out of (1a), (2a), (3) and (4), and again failed. Can we do better with our additional material?

The answer is that, as far as the Square of Opposition is concerned, we can. There are in fact three ways of selecting a quadruplet of schemata from our table, between which all the required six relations will hold. The three Squares of Opposition thus obtained are as follows:

I	II	III
(1a) (2a)	(1a) (2)	(1) (2a)
(3a) (4a)	(3) (4a)	(3a) (4)
Interpretation 3.	Interpretation 4.	Interpretation 5.

In Interpretation 3, universal propositions are interpreted existentially and particular ones non-existentially; in 4, affirmative propositions are interpreted existentially and negative ones non-existentially; in 5, negative propositions are interpreted existentially and affirmative ones non-existentially.

That I, II and III are all genuine Squares of Opposition (i.e. that all six relations hold in each of them) can be shown as follows. We have already seen that (1) and (4), (2) and (3), (1a) and (4a), and (2a) and (3a) are pairs of contradictories. We have also seen that (1a) implies (3) and (2a) implies (4). Now clearly (3) implies (3a) – by 'p ⊃ (q v p)' – and therefore (1a) implies (3a). From this material and a general theorem about Squares of Opposition (which we shall prove at the end of this chapter) to the effect that if the two contradictory relations and any one of the other four relations hold, the remaining three relations must also hold, it follows that all six relations hold in each of I, II and III.

None of these three interpretations, however, will save the whole traditional scheme. It would be tedious to go into all the details; the following will suffice. We have already seen that 'S e P', when interpreted as (2a), will not convert to 'P e S'; and this is enough to wreck Interpretations 3 and 5; and in the case of Interpretation 4 (and 5 also, for that matter), none of the obverses hold.

Nevertheless, Interpretation 4 comes nearer to success than either

3 or 5. For with it, all the 24 traditional moods are valid, and this is not the case with either 3 or 5. Moreover all the three converses hold with Interpretation 4; and this means that the only items in traditional logic which become invalid are some of those which involve negative terms.

If we want to do better with the Predicate Calculus than we have so far been able to do, we shall have to use more complex formulae. P. F. Strawson[1] gives the following formulae, which we shall refer to as Interpretation 6:

$$(A): \ \exists S \ . \ \exists \bar{P} \ . \ \sim\!\exists(S.\bar{P})$$
$$(E): \ \exists S \ . \ \exists P \ . \ \sim\!\exists(S.P)$$
$$(I): \ \sim\!\exists S \ v \ \sim\!\exists P \ v \ \exists(S.P)$$
$$(O): \ \sim\!\exists S \ v \ \sim\!\exists \bar{P} \ v \ \exists(S.\bar{P})$$

In this interpretation we regard an A proposition as asserting that there is something to which the subject term applies, something to which the predicate term does not apply, but nothing to which the subject term applies but the predicate term does not; and analogously for the other cases.

Strawson claims that under this interpretation the entire traditional syllogistic holds. And it is indeed true that if we translate syllogistic schemata following these patterns, the schemata representing all the relations in the Square of Opposition and all the traditionally valid immediate inferences and syllogistic moods, will turn out to be valid schemata in LPC1. There is, however, one item in traditional syllogistic which we have not mentioned so far but which perhaps presents a difficulty. Text-books of syllogistic commonly refer to what is known as the Law of Identity, which is usually stated in the form 'A is A'. It may be claimed that 'A' is here used not as a term variable but as an individual-variable, and that the Law therefore falls outside the field of syllogistic schemata. Yet it seems to be capable of being formulated as a syllogistic schema, and some logicians have in fact so formulated it. The schema in question is 'S a S' – 'All S is S' – to which we may add its subaltern 'S i S' – 'Some S is S' – which has a claim to be regarded as a kind of weakened form of the Law. Whether or not these schemata are accepted as formulations of the Law of Identity, they are at least well-formed, and a traditional logician would find it

---

[1] *Introduction to Logical Theory*, p. 173. We have translated his formulae into the symbolism we are using, and altered the order of conjuncts and disjuncts.

difficult to avoid regarding both of them as valid. Now 'S a S', when translated in accordance with Interpretation 6, turns out to be invalid; for it will then mean 'There is an S and also a non-S, but nothing is both S and non-S', and this is true only for those values of 'S' which have both an instance and a counter-instance. 'S i S', however (somewhat surprisingly perhaps), is valid. We may also add that 'S e S̄', which ought also to be valid, will be invalid, though 'S o S̄' will be valid. (You should construct the relevant LPC1 schemata and see why in each case.) These, however, are the only exceptions to the truth of Strawson's claim.

Suppose we waive the cases of 'S a S' and 'S e S̄' because they are not commonly given in traditional treatments of syllogistic. Let us ask: have we at last, in Interpretation 6, found a satisfactory interpretation of traditional syllogistic in predicate calculus terms?

This question is ambiguous. Each of the interpretations we have considered can be regarded as giving a comprehensive set of instructions which enable us to replace every wff of traditional syllogistic by a determinate wff of LPC1. When we ask whether such an interpretation is a satisfactory one, we may have in mind either of two quite distinct questions:

1. Are the logical relations which hold among the LPC1 formulae thus obtained, in all cases the same as those which traditional syllogistic asserts to hold among the formulae from which they are derived?

If this is what is meant, then the answer is that of the interpretations we have mentioned, the last (6), and only the last, is a satisfactory one. We have not, of course, proved that it is the only possible satisfactory interpretation in this sense; but at least it seems clear – though we have not proved this either – that no simpler one can satisfy the conditions in question.

We may however be asking a question which is not strictly one of *formal* logic at all:

2. Do the LPC1 formulae accurately express the meaning of the relevant traditional schemata? We know precisely what is meant e.g. by '∃S . ∃P . ~∃(S.P)'; is this what traditional logicians mean by 'S e P'? – and so forth in the other cases. If *this* is what is being asked, almost everyone is likely to have serious qualms, to say the very least, about calling Interpretation 6 a satisfactory one. It seems plain that traditional logicians have thought of A, E, I and O propositions as having a meaning at least very closely related to that

of some common, standard uses of English sentences of the forms 'All ......'s are ——'s', 'No ......'s are ——'s', 'Some ......'s are ——'s' and 'Some ......'s are not ——'s' (or their equivalents in other natural languages). But (1b)–(4b) seem bizarre if offered as analyses of any standard used of such sentences. No one, e.g., would be likely to maintain that some dragons speak Hungarian simply on the ground that there are no dragons at all; yet if there are no S's (if '∼∃S' is true), then (3b), which is taken to represent 'Some S is P', is thereby made true. Strawson himself rejects Interpretation 6 as giving a satisfactory account of syllogistic logic on just such grounds as these.

It would be only a little less unplausible to suggest that either Interpretation 3 or Interpretation 5 expresses the meaning of the traditional A, E, I and O propositions; though perhaps Interpretation 4 has rather more to be said for it. Our main reasons for introducing these Interpretations were firstly that it seemed to be a matter of some interest that a Square of Opposition could be constructed in each case, and secondly that they paved the way for the formulae given by Interpretation 6, which at least behave formally as A, E, I and O propositions should, except for the cases of 'S a S' and 'S e S̄'. The only groups of LPC1 schemata which seem to have some claim to intuitive reasonableness as expressing the meaning of the four traditional forms are those in Interpretations 1 and 2 (and possibly 4); but none of these will enable the whole traditional scheme to stand.

A theorem about squares of opposition

Earlier in this chapter we referred to and made use of a certain theorem about Squares of Opposition. We shall now state this theorem and show how it can be proved. It is a theorem of quite general applicability, not confined to syllogistic.

Informally stated, the theorem asserts that if any group of four propositions or schemata are such that when they are arranged in the form of a square the diagonal (contradictory) relations and any one of the other four relations hold, the remaining three relations must also hold.

More formally stated, the theorem runs: If p, q, r and s are propositions such that ($p \equiv \sim s$) and ($q \equiv \sim r$) are true, then

(a) if ($p \supset r$), then ($p \supset \sim q$), ($q \supset s$) and ($\sim r \supset s$);

(b) if ($p \supset \sim q$), then ($p \supset r$), ($q \supset s$) and ($\sim r \supset s$);

(c) if (q ⊃ s), then (p ⊃ r), (p ⊃ ∼q) and (∼r ⊃ s);
and

(d) if (∼r ⊃ s), then (p ⊃ r), (p ⊃ ∼q) and (q ⊃ s).

(a) may be proved by showing the validity of the schema:

$$((p \equiv {\sim}s) . (q \equiv {\sim}r)) \supset ((p \supset r) \supset ((p \supset {\sim}q) . (q \supset s) . ({\sim}r \supset s)))$$

A Reductio test will show this to be valid quite simply.

(b), (c) and (d) can be proved by showing the validity of the analogous schema in each case.

In virtue of this theorem, if we want to show that four propositions or schemata form a Square of Opposition, we need to test for only three relations, not six.

CHAPTER 46

Syllogistic and LPC1 :
Another Approach

Our attempts to find LPC1 interpretations of syllogistic schemata which will preserve the validity of the entire traditional system all seem to have broken down. There is, however, an alternative approach which, while still keeping within LPC1, will enable us to fare better.

Throughout this chapter we shall regard immediate inferences and syllogistic moods as implications (or equivalences), rather than as inferences. E.g. by mood AEE in Figure IV we shall understand not the inferential schema:

$$P \, a \, M$$
$$M \, e \, S$$
$$\therefore S \, e \, P$$

but the corresponding propositional schema:

$$(P \, a \, M \, . \, M \, e \, S) \supset S \, e \, P$$

or its appropriate translation into a wff of LPC1. Questions of validity will not, of course, be affected by this.

Our new approach begins with a return to Interpretation 1, viz.

$$S \, a \, P \quad : \quad \sim\!\exists(S.\bar{P}) \quad [or \; U(S \supset P)]$$
$$S \, e \, P \quad : \quad \sim\!\exists(S.P) \quad [or \; U(S \supset \bar{P})]$$
$$S \, i \, P \quad : \quad \exists(S.P)$$
$$S \, o \, P \quad : \quad \exists(S.\bar{P})$$

We have already discovered that a substantial segment of traditional syllogistic is valid under Interpretation 1. It consists of the contradictory relations, the equivalential immediate inferences, and 15 syllogistic moods: to which incidentally we may add 'S a S' and 'S e S̄'. Let us call this segment, *Syllogistic Part 1*. The remainder – including 'S i S' and 'S o S̄' – which is invalid under Interpretation 1, we shall call *Syllogistic Part 2*.

Let us make a survey of Syllogistic Part 2. We have seen that, e.g.

$$S\ a\ P \supset S\ i\ P$$

when interpreted as

$$\sim\!\exists(S.\bar{P}) \supset \exists(S.P) \tag{1}$$

is invalid; for if there are no S's, then '$\sim\!\exists(S.\bar{P})$' is true, but '$\exists(S.P)$' is false. On the other hand, if there *are* some S's, (1) will be bound to be true; for in that case, if no S's fail to be P's, there must be some S's which are P's. So although (1) is invalid, the following formula is valid:

$$\exists S \supset (\sim\!\exists(S.\bar{P}) \supset \exists(S.P))$$

(It is, indeed, simply the exported form of $(A \supset I)$ under Interpretation 2.)

The same holds for a great deal more of Part 2 as well: to be precise, for the other three relations on the Square of Opposition; for inferences (1), (8), (12) and (15), and the subaltern inferences corresponding to (4) and (5), in the Table of Immediate Inferences; for the five weakened syllogistic moods; and for the schemata 'S i S' and 'S o $\bar{S}$'. In each of these cases if we translate into LPC1 according to Interpretation 1 we obtain a schema, X, which is invalid; but in each case

$$\exists S \supset X$$

is valid.

The remainder of Part 2 cannot be handled in quite the same way. An example will show why. Consider immediate inference (18) – the Partial Inverse of E. Syllogistic logicians have in fact often expressed doubts about the validity of Inverses. H. W. B. Joseph[1] mentions the following example of inference (18): 'No men die twice; therefore some who are not men do die twice.' This indeed does not sound like the happiest piece of argumentation. Moreover, the assurance that there are some men does nothing to reconcile us to it. If, however, it is granted that there are some beings who die twice, the inference in question becomes safe: what we need to suppose in this case is not that there are some S's, but that there are some P's. So although the LPC1 schema which Interpretation 1 gives us for inference (18), viz.

$$\sim\!\exists(S.P) \supset \exists(\bar{S}.P)$$

is invalid,

---

[1] *An Introduction to Logic*, pp. 241–2.

$$\exists P \supset (\sim \exists (S.P) \supset \exists (\bar{S}.P))$$

is valid.

The following other items in Syllogistic Part 2 can be dealt with in the same way: immediate inference (20), the subaltern inferences corresponding to inferences (2) and (9), and the (strengthened) mood AAI in Figure IV. Let Y be the LPC1 schema for any of these under Interpretation 1; then Y is invalid, but

$$\exists P \supset Y$$

is valid.

The remaining immediate inferences – (17), (19) (the Inverses of A) and the subalterns corresponding to (11) and (14) can be gained by using '$\exists \bar{P}$' as an antecedent. I.e. if Z is the LPC1 schema for any of these under Interpretation 1, then Z is invalid (and so are '$\exists S \supset Z$' and '$\exists P \supset Z$'), but

$$\exists \bar{P} \supset Z$$

is valid.

Finally, the schemata for the remaining three strengthened moods – AAI and EAO in Figure III and EAO in Figure IV – require the antecedent '$\exists M$'. If W is the LPC1 schema for any of these moods, then although W is invalid (and so are '$\exists S \supset W$' and '$\exists P \supset W$')

$$\exists M \supset W$$

is valid.

This survey exhausts Syllogistic Part 2. It is worth noting, as a matter of some interest, that '$\exists \bar{S}$' is never required as an antecedent.

Let us introduce two pieces of terminology here which will prove useful. Firstly, if a schema of the form

$$X \supset Y$$

is valid, we shall say that Y is *valid under hypothesis X*. And secondly, if there are, say, no S's, we shall say that the term 'S' is *empty*; whereas if there is at least one S, we shall say that 'S' is *non-empty*; and analogously for other terms.

We can then sum up our recent discussion by saying that each schema in Syllogistic Part 2 (when translated according to Interpretation 1) is valid under the hypothesis of the non-emptiness of some one term (or the negation of one term) which occurs in it.

Moreover, if we conjoin all the antecedents we have mentioned into one schema, '∃S . ∃P . ∃P̄ . ∃M', and conjoin all the items in Syllogistic Part 2 into another schema which, since it is much too long to write down, we shall simply call A, then

$$(∃S . ∃P . ∃P̄ . ∃M) ⊃ A \qquad (2)$$

is valid. I.e. the whole of Syllogistic Part 2 is valid under the hypothesis '∃S . ∃P . ∃P̄ . ∃M'.

We can if we like go further. Every item in Syllogistic Part 1 (when translated according to Interpretation 1) is valid as it stands. But of course if Y is itself valid, (X ⊃ Y) is also valid, no matter what X may be. So there is no harm in saying (though it is a somewhat vacuous thing to say) that Y is valid under any hypothesis we care to choose. That being so, we can conjoin all the items in Syllogistic Part 1 to A in (2), and therefore say that not merely all of Part 2 but the whole of traditional syllogistic is (when translated according to Interpretation 1) valid under the hypothesis '∃S . ∃P . ∃P̄ . ∃M'. In other words, if B is the translation of *any* valid item in traditional syllogistic, or the conjunction of any, or even all, of such items, then

$$(∃S . ∃P . ∃P̄ . ∃M) ⊃ B$$

will be a valid schema in LPC1.

You should be careful about what the last statement means – or rather about what it does not mean. We are *not* asserting that the translation of every, or indeed any, item in traditional syllogistic is valid *only* under the hypothesis in question. For of course all the items in Part 1 are valid under any other hypothesis or under none at all; and even in Part 2 no single item *requires* more than one conjunct in the general hypothesis as its own hypothesis. All we are asserting is that if we are looking for a hypothesis under which the traditional system *as a whole* will retain its validity, then

$$∃S . ∃P . ∃P̄ . ∃M$$

is such a hypothesis.

The point of unifying the whole system under one hypothesis is that it enables us to claim to have solved the problem of finding a 'reflection' of traditional syllogistic in LPC1. Our method of tackling this problem in Chapters 43 and 45 was this: we tried to match each *subject-predicate schema* in traditional syllogistic with a certain wff of LPC1 in such a way that the result of replacing the subject-predicate schemata in any traditionally valid item in syllogistic logic by their matching LPC1 wffs would always be a valid formula in LPC1. The disappointments of those chapters strongly suggest – though they do not prove – that this cannot be done; at any rate in the present chapter we have worked on a different principle. This time we have given a systematic method of replacing each *complete item* in traditional syllogistic (such as a syllogistic mood or an immediate inference) by a determinate wff of LPC1. The wff in question is an implication whose antecedent is '∃S . ∃P . ∃P̄ . ∃M' and whose consequent is the translation of the traditional item into LPC1 by the rules of Interpretation 1. And validity is preserved by such replacement in every case.

In order, however, to be sure that we have found an exact reflection of traditional syllogistic in LPC1, we must face a further question. Have we perhaps by our method validated too much? Might there, that is, be syllogistic schemata which are not in the traditional list of valid ones, but which when translated according to Interpretation 1 and placed under the hypothesis '∃S . ∃P . ∃P̄ . ∃M' yield valid wffs of LPC1?

The answer is no. The formulae valid under the hypothesis in question are the translations of just the traditionally valid schemata and no others.

Such a statement of course requires proof. In the next chapter we shall give a proof of it as far as syllogistic moods are concerned. We shall leave it unproved as it applies to immediate inferences, but you could take it as an exercise to devise a proof of your own in this field.

CHAPTER 47

The Validity of Syllogisms Reconsidered: An Extension of the Antilogism Theorem

The problem we are to solve in the present chapter is this: what syllogistic moods are such that their translations into LPC1 formulae by Interpretation 1 are valid under the hypothesis '∃S . ∃P . ∃P̄ . ∃M'? We shall prove that the answer is: the 24 traditionally valid moods, and no others.

To avoid unnecessary complexity, we shall drop '∃P̄' from our hypothesis, as it is relevant only to certain immediate inferences and not to syllogistic moods. (Its restoration would not affect our results but would complicate parts of our argument.)

Let X, Y and Z be respectively the LPC1 schemata corresponding to the premisses of any syllogism and the *negation* of its conclusion. (Its conclusion will then be ∼Z.) To say that the syllogism is valid under the hypothesis in question is to say that

$$(\exists S . \exists P . \exists M) \supset ((X.Y) \supset \sim Z)$$

is valid in LPC1. This is valid if and only if its negation is inconsistent; and its negation, by simple transformations, is expressible as

$$\exists S . \exists P . \exists M . X . Y . Z \tag{1}$$

So our problem is: what values of X, Y and Z will make (1) inconsistent, it being stipulated that X, Y and Z form a syllogistic triad whose terms are 'S', 'P' and 'M'?

The conjunction of X, Y and Z must be of one or other of the following forms (see Chapter 44):

(*a*) Uα . Uβ . Uγ
(*b*) ∃α . ∃β . ∃γ
(*c*) Uα . ∃β . ∃γ
(*d*) Uα . Uβ . ∃γ

342

It is easy to see that in cases (*b*) and (*c*), (1) cannot be inconsistent. For in case (*b*), (1) is of the form

$$\exists S \cdot \exists P \cdot \exists M \cdot \exists \alpha \cdot \exists \beta \cdot \exists \gamma$$

which is inconsistent if and only if at least one of the wfpes is inconsistent[1] on its own. But this is clearly impossible.

And in case (*c*), (1) is of the form

$$\exists S \cdot \exists P \cdot \exists M \cdot U\alpha \cdot \exists \beta \cdot \exists \gamma$$

which is inconsistent if and only if the conjunction of α and some one of the other wfpes is inconsistent. We saw in Chapter 44 that α cannot be inconsistent with either β or γ. But it cannot be inconsistent with any single variable either, as reflection on the relevant truth-tables will show.

We are therefore left with cases (*a*) and (*d*). We need to show that the combinations of values for α, β and γ which will make either

$$\exists S \cdot \exists P \cdot \exists M \cdot U\alpha \cdot U\beta \cdot U\gamma \qquad \text{(case (}a\text{))}$$

or

$$\exists S \cdot \exists P \cdot \exists M \cdot U\alpha \cdot U\beta \cdot \exists \gamma \qquad \text{(case (}d\text{))}$$

inconsistent are exactly those which give us the antilogisms for the 24 traditionally valid moods. We consider case (*d*) first.

Triads with two universals and one particular

In case (*d*), (1) is of the form

$$\exists S \cdot \exists P \cdot \exists M \cdot U\alpha \cdot U\beta \cdot \exists \gamma \qquad (2)$$

In Chapter 44 we proved that there are exactly 15 combinations of values for α, β and γ which make ($U\alpha \cdot U\beta \cdot \exists \gamma$) – the last three conjuncts of (2) – inconsistent, and these give the antilogisms for the 15 valid moods in Syllogistic Part 1. Clearly these values will also make (2) inconsistent, since the conjunction of an inconsistent formula and any other formula is inconsistent.

By Rule (iva) in Chapter 27, the only other way in which (2) can be inconsistent is that the conjunction of ($\alpha \cdot \beta$) and *one* of the other existentially quantified wfpes (viz. 'S' or 'P' or 'M') should be inconsistent.

We shall now prove that such a conjunction could never be inconsistent.

---

[1] Strictly, the PC wff isomorphic with it; and analogously throughout.

To save three separate proofs for 'S', 'P' and 'M' in turn, we shall let '$\mathfrak{b}$' represent any one of them. Since α and β are both implicative, we shall represent them by '$\alpha_1 \supset \alpha_2$' and '$\beta_1 \supset \beta_2$' respectively.

Since $\mathfrak{b}$ is a term in the mood of which $(U\alpha \,.\, U\beta \,.\, \exists\gamma)$ is the antilogism, and since every term appears in exactly two of the propositions in every mood, $\mathfrak{b}$ must occur in either α or β or both, and two variables other than $\mathfrak{b}$ must occur in α and β taken together.

With this understood, we have to show that

$$\mathfrak{b} \,.\, (\alpha_1 \supset \alpha_2) \,.\, (\beta_1 \supset \beta_2) \tag{3}$$

cannot be inconsistent. We do so as follows:

To assign a truth-value[1] to one term only (antecedent or consequent) of an implication is never sufficient to show that that implication is false. I.e. when we know the truth-value of one such term, we can always suppose the implication to be true provided we are free to assign what truth-value we choose to the other term.

Suppose $\mathfrak{b}$ occurs in both α and β. Then the remaining variables in α and β must be distinct from each other as well as from $\mathfrak{b}$. Now let us in (3) put $\mathfrak{b} = 1$. This will give us the value of one and only one term in each of $(\alpha_1 \supset \alpha_2)$ and $(\beta_1 \supset \beta_2)$, and since we are free to assign what truth-value we choose to the other term in each, we can do so in such a way as to make each true, and therefore (3) as a whole true. So (3) cannot be inconsistent in this case.

Suppose now that $\mathfrak{b}$ occurs in one of α and β but not in the other. Again let us put $\mathfrak{b} = 1$. This will determine the value of one term of the implication in which $\mathfrak{b}$ occurs but we are still free to assign what value we choose to the variable which forms its other term, and thus to make this implication true. This second variable will in turn appear in the second implication as well; but the other term of *that* implication will be a third variable, to which we are free to assign what value we choose. Hence again it is possible to make (3) take the value 1.

This suffices to show that (3) cannot be inconsistent. In other words, $(\alpha \,.\, \beta)$ cannot be inconsistent with 'S' or with 'P' or with 'M'.

Hence the only combinations of values for α, β and γ which will make (2) inconsistent are the 15 which yield the valid moods in Part 1.

---

[1] It must be remembered that (3) represents a wff in PC, not a wfpe (see footnote on p. 343). To avoid notational complexity we use in this chapter the same meta-logical variables for wfpes and the PC wffs isomorphic with them.

You should note that if we were to restore '∃P̄' to our hypothesis, the only changes required in the foregoing argument would be that (2) would contain '∃P̄' as an additional conjunct and that 6 would represent any of 'S', 'P', 'M' and 'P̄'; but these changes would not affect the validity or our reasoning.

Triads with three universals

We turn now to case (*a*). (1) is now of the form

$$\exists S . \exists P . \exists M . U\alpha . U\beta . U\gamma \tag{4}$$

We proved in Chapter 44 that no syllogistic triad of the form (Uα . Uβ . Uγ) can be inconsistent. It is possible, however, to find values for α, β and γ which will make (4) inconsistent. Let us examine the conditions for doing so.

By Rule (iva) in Chapter 27, (4) is inconsistent if and only if the conjunction of α, β, γ and any *one* of 'S', 'P' and 'M' is inconsistent. Let us again use '6' to represent any one of these single variables; and since α, β and γ are this time all implicative let us represent them by '$\alpha_1 \supset \alpha_2$,' '$\beta_1 \supset \beta_2$' and '$\gamma_1 \supset \gamma_2$' respectively.

The problem then is: under what conditions can a wff of the form

$$6 . (\alpha_1 \supset \alpha_2) . (\beta_1 \supset \beta_2) . (\gamma_1 \supset \gamma_2) \tag{5}$$

be inconsistent?

We have to remember that each Greek letter with the subscript '$_1$' represents an unnegated variable, that 6 is likewise an unnegated variable and that each letter with the subscript '$_2$' represents a variable which can be either negated or unnegated. Moreover, 6 occurs in exactly two of α, β and γ,

Now if (5) is to be inconsistent, α_2, β_2 and γ_2 cannot all be *unnegated* variables. For if they were, for the first row of the (8-row) matrix for (5), in which each variable = 1, every conjunct in (5) would take the value 1 and therefore (5) itself would take the value 1 and so not be inconsistent.

Secondly, α_2, β_2 and γ_2 cannot all be *negated* variables. For if they were, then for that row of the matrix in which 6 = 1 and each of the other two variables = 0, the following situation would obtain: the implication in (5) which does *not* contain 6 would have a false antecedent and would therefore take the value 1; and each of the implications which do contain 6 would either have 6 (=1) as antecedent and a true consequent, or else have ∼6 (=0) as consequent and a false antecedent, and in either case would take the value 1. For that row, therefore, (5) itself would have the value 1 and so not be inconsistent.

Thirdly, α_2, β_2 and γ_2 cannot consist of two negated variables and one unnegated one. For in that case the implication with the unnegated consequent either (i) contains $\mathfrak{b}$, or (ii) does not contain $\mathfrak{b}$. In case (i), consider the row of the matrix in which $\mathfrak{b}$ and the other variable in that implication both take the value 1, and the remaining variable takes the value 0. For that row, the implication with the unnegated consequent will be evaluated as $(1 \supset 1) = 1$. Each of the other two implications will have an unnegated antecedent and a negated consequent and will contain a variable which $= 0$; each will therefore have either a false antecedent or a true consequent, and will therefore take the value 1. So (5) will take the value 1.

In case (ii) – where $\mathfrak{b}$ does not occur in the implication with the unnegated consequent – consider the row in which $\mathfrak{b} = 1$ and each of the other variables $= 0$. Then the implication with an unnegated consequent will be evaluated for that row as $0 \supset 0 = 1$. And each of the other implications will have an unnegated antecedent and a negated consequent and will contain some variable which $= 0$, and hence, as shown in the previous paragraph, will take the value 1. So for that row, (5) itself will have the value 1.

Therefore neither in case (i) nor in case (ii) can (5) be inconsistent.

The only remaining possibility is therefore that α_2, β_2 and γ_2 should consist of two unnegated variables and one negated one; i.e. that $U\alpha$, $U\beta$ and $U\gamma$ should consist of two A propositions and one E.

Fourthly, however – again if (5) is to be inconsistent – the two unnegated variables among α_2, β_2 and γ_2 must not be the same variable. For if they are, consider the row of the matrix in which $\mathfrak{b}$ and that variable (if other than $\mathfrak{b}$) $= 1$, and the remaining variable (or variables) $= 0$. For that row the two implications with unnegated consequents will each have a true consequent and will therefore have the value 1; and the remaining implication, which has a negated consequent, will contain at least one variable which $= 0$, and will therefore, as shown above, have the value 1. So (5) will once more not be inconsistent.

We can summarize the results of the foregoing argument as follows: If (4) is to be inconsistent, α, β and γ must be such that (*a*) $U\alpha$, $U\beta$ and $U\gamma$ will consist of two A propositions and one E, and (*b*) the two unnegated consequents (the predicates of the A's) must be distinct.

These conditions can be fulfilled only in three ways, which we can express as follows:

A	B	C
U(S ⊃ P)	U(P ⊃ S)	U(P ⊃ S)
U(P ⊃ M)	U(P ⊃ M)	U(M ⊃ P)
U(S ⊃ M̄)	U(S ⊃ M̄)	U(S ⊃ M̄)

Any other arrangement of variables which conforms with the conditions will coincide by simple re-lettering with one or other of A, B and C.

In fact each of these three sets of values for Uα, Uβ and Uγ *will* produce an inconsistency in (4); the conjunction of the formulae in A can easily be shown (by the rules given in Chapter 27) to be inconsistent with 'ƎS', while the conjunction of those in B is inconsistent with 'ƎP' and the conjunction of those in C is inconsistent with 'ƎM'. So the conditions turn out to be not merely necessary but sufficient as well.

Therefore if we take the negation of any formula in any one of the three triads as conclusion, and the other two formulae in that triad as premisses, we shall obtain a syllogistic mood which is valid under the hypothesis 'ƎS . ƎP . ƎM'. To bring the mood into the conventional form we shall, if necessary, re-letter the variables appropriately, and arrange the order of the premisses so that 'P' occurs in the first one. In this way we shall obtain three moods from each triad, and therefore nine in all. Our argument has established that this will be a complete list of syllogistic moods valid under the hypothesis in question, whose antilogisms consist of three universals.

From A we obtain moods AAI in Fig. I, AEO in Fig. II and EAO in Fig. III.

From B we obtain moods AAI in Fig. III, EAO in Fig. II, and EAO in Fig. I.

From C we obtain moods AAI, AEO and EAO, all in Fig. IV.

You can easily check that these are the nine traditional strengthened and weakened moods.

We have therefore proved that the moods valid under the hypothesis 'ƎS . ƎP . ƎM' are exactly the traditional 24 (15 moods in Syllogistic Part 1 and 9 in Part 2.)

An extension of the antilogism theorem

The distinction between the 15 moods and the 9 is an important one. As we said earlier, it is drawn in traditional syllogistic in the form of the distinction between moods which are neither weakened nor strengthened on the one hand, and those which are either weakened or strengthened on the other. When the schemata are translated in accordance with Interpretation 1, the distinction appears as that between the moods which are valid as they stand, and those which are invalid as they stand but valid under the hypothesis '$\exists$S . $\exists$P . $\exists$M'; or alternatively, between those which are valid whether or not any or all of their terms are empty, and those which are valid only when at least a certain one of their terms is presumed to be non-empty. Let us call the former, *valid Part 1 moods* and the latter, *valid Part 2 moods*.

One point of importance which emerges from our recent discussion of the conditions for inconsistency of (4) is that we now have a simple test for valid Part 2 moods, a test which forms a kind of extension of the Antilogism test for Part 1 moods which we expounded in Chapter 44. For what we have proved is that a syllogistic mood is a valid Part 2 mood if and only if its antilogism has the following two characteristics:

(*a*) It consists of two A propositions and one E; and

(*b*) The predicates of the two A propositions are not identical.

If we revert to our earlier practice of writing all the schemata with existential quantifiers ('S a P' as '$\sim\exists(S.\bar{P})$', etc), an alternative way of stating (*b*) is

(*b'*) The two negated variables are not identical.

Since, in traditional syllogistic, valid Part 1 and valid Part 2 moods are all equally regarded as valid, we can formulate a test for the validity of moods in traditional syllogistic by combining the antilogism test given at the end of Chapter 44, with the test we have just stated. We can then say that a syllogistic mood is valid in the traditional theory if and only if its antilogism, when translated according to Interpretation 1, has *either* all of the three characteristics listed at the end of Chapter 44 *or* both of the characteristics ((*a*) and (*b*)) mentioned above.

EXERCISES 47

47.1 Making use of the Antilogism Test and the Test stated at the end of Chapter 47, determine which of the following are valid Part 1 moods, which are valid Part 2 moods, and which are neither:

(a) AAI in Figure I.
(b) AII in Figure I.
(c) OAO in Figure II.
(d) OAO in Figure III.
(e) EIO in Figure III.
(f) AEE in Figure IV.
(g) EAE in Figure IV.

CHAPTER 48

Syllogistic :
An Axiomatic Presentation

In this chapter we shall make a new approach to Syllogistic. We shall not try either to analyse, or to find analogues for, syllogistic schemata within the Predicate Calculus (or any other Calculus), but shall take them simply as they are. We shall take the whole set of schemata traditionally regarded as valid, and present this entire system in an axiomatic form.

In our summary of traditional syllogistic in Chapter 42 we looked on immediate inferences and syllogistic moods as *inferential* schemata. This is in fact how they are set down in most books. In later chapters, however, we have for the most part used the corresponding *propositional* schemata instead. Questions of validity are of course unaffected by doing this, and we shall continue the practice here. We shall, that is, express a syllogistic mood as an implicative schema in which the antecedent is the conjunction of the premisses, and the consequent is the conclusion. Those immediate inferences which hold in one direction only we shall likewise express as implicative schemata; those which hold in both directions we shall express as equivalential schemata, for the pair of inferential schemata X ∴ Y, and Y ∴ X, are together valid if and only if the propositional schema (X ≡ Y) is valid.

In this way we shall be regarding syllogistic, like PC and the Predicate Calculus, as consisting wholly of a system of propositional schemata. It is perhaps worth noting that Aristotle, unlike most later logicians, usually expressed syllogistic moods as implicative, not as inferential, schemata.

Axiomatization: informal discussion

The first question is: what is the smallest number of primitive symbols we require? Every syllogistic wff is a truth-function of one or more schemata of the forms $S_1 a S_2$, $S_1 e S_2$, $S_1 i S_2$ and

S_1 o S_2, where S_1 and S_2 are term variables or the negations of term variables. We cannot dispense with term variables, or with a negation sign operating on them. We do not, however, require all the four operators 'a', 'e', 'i' and 'o' as primitives; two will suffice, for we can e.g. define S_1 e S_2 as the negation of S_1 i S_2, and S_1 o S_2 as the negation of S_1 a S_2. In order to express truth-functions we shall require operators from PC. We shall need '$\sim$' for the contradictory relations (and in fact elsewhere), '.' and '$\supset$' for syllogistic moods, and '$\equiv$' for the contradictory relations and some of the immediate inferences. '.', '$\supset$' and '$\equiv$' can, of course, be defined in terms of '$\sim$' and 'v'.

Next, how shall we obtain the theses of our system? Since A, E, I and O schemata (and truth-functions of them) are all propositional schemata, any uniform substitution of such schemata for the variables in a valid wff of PC will yield a valid formula. The most straightforward way of obtaining such formulae as theses is to proceed as we did in axiomatizing LPC1 (Chapter 29), and include the basis of PM in the basis of our axiomatized syllogistic. We can then introduce a transformation rule which will entitle us to regard any wff obtained by uniform substitutions of syllogistic schemata for all the variables in a thesis of PM, as a thesis. All the theses of PM will thus be theses of our present system, but we shall not explicitly derive any of them as theorems, since we are interested only in theorems of a distinctively syllogistic sort. The derived rules of PM will of course be available for use wherever we need them.

The theses which are substitution-instances of PM theses do not, however, include any of the traditional syllogistic schemata. We therefore require some additional axioms of a specifically syllogistic kind. Łukasiewicz, in his book *Aristotle's Syllogistic from the Standpoint of Modern Formal Logic*, has shown that all syllogistic theses, with the exception of those which contain negative terms, can be derived from a number of PC theses, together with four axioms which in our symbolism we can write thus:

$$(MaP . SaM) \supset SaP \quad (1) \quad (AAA, Fig. I)$$
$$(MaP . MiS) \supset SiP \quad (2) \quad (AII, Fig. III)$$
$$S \ a \ S \quad (3)$$
$$S \ i \ S \quad (4)$$

In addition to the rule permitting substitution in PM theses, two straightforward transformation rules are used: a substitution rule for terms, which allows any term variable in a thesis to be uniformly replaced by any other term variable; and the familiar rule of detachment.

Of the four Łukasiewicz axioms, the first three yield what we have called Syllogistic Part 1, and the addition of (4) enables Syllogistic Part 2 to be derived as well, in each case minus the theses which contain negative terms.

Suppose we wish to strengthen this basis in order to obtain the theses containing negative terms as well. There are several ways in which this can be done, one of which is the following: (*a*) We broaden our substitution rule for terms to allow term variables to be uniformly replaced by term variables or their negations; (*b*) we introduce a principle of double negation for terms, which is most easily stated as a transformation rule to the effect that, in any thesis, S_1 may be replaced by $\bar{\bar{S}}_1$ and *vice versa*; (*c*) we take the obverses of A and E, in their merely implicative (not equivalential) forms, as two new axioms, viz.

$$\text{SaP} \supset \text{Se}\bar{\text{P}} \qquad (5)$$
$$\text{SeP} \supset \text{Sa}\bar{\text{P}} \qquad (6)$$

It is possible, however, to shorten this addition to our axiom set by using the valid schema

$$\text{Se}\bar{\text{S}} \qquad (7)$$

('no S is non-S') in place of (5); for from (2), (3) and (7) we can obtain (5) as a theorem. So let us take (6) and (7) as our additional axioms, not (5) and (6). But now a further economy becomes possible, for from (6) and (7), with the help of the rule of double negation, we can derive (3) – 'SaS' – itself; so if we use (6) and (7) as axioms, we can drop (3). Moreover, once we obtain the obverses in their equivalential forms (which will not be difficult), we can even dispense with (1) as an axiom. The details of all the derivations we have referred to are set out below.

The special position of (4) is unaffected by this modification of the axiomatic basis: without (4), we can derive the whole of Syllogistic Part 1; with it, we can derive Part 2 as well.

We are thus led to what is probably as economical a set of special syllogistic axioms as we are likely to find:

A1. $(\text{MaP} \,.\, \text{MiS}) \supset \text{SiP}$
A2. $\text{SeP} \supset \text{Sa}\bar{\text{P}}$
A3. $\text{Se}\bar{\text{S}}$

with, as an additional axiom for Part 2,

    A4. SiS

Formal construction of the system

The System AS.   (Axiomatized Syllogistic.)

  1. Primitive symbols:

p, q, r, . . .	[propositional variables]
S, P, M	[term variables]
⁻	[negation sign for terms]
a ⎫ i ⎭	[dyadic operators]
∼	[negation sign for propositions]
v	[disjunction sign]
(,)	[brackets]

In stating definitions and rules, we shall use 'S_1' and 'S_2' as meta-logical variables which take term variables (with or without a superimposed bar or bars) as values, and 'X' and 'Y' as meta-logical variables which take wffs as values.

  2. Formation Rules:

The wffs of AS consist of all the wffs of PM, together with all the formulae specified by the following rules (*syllogistic wffs*):

   (1) A term variable standing alone is a well-formed term expression ('term' for short).

   (2) If S_1 is a term, $\bar{S}_1$ is a term.

   (3) If S_1 and S_2 are terms, S_1 a S_2 and S_1 i S_2 are wffs.

   (4) If X is a wff, ∼X is a wff.

   (5) If X and Y are wffs, (XvY) is a wff.

  3. Definitions:

   [e] S_1 e S_2 $=_{Df}$ ∼S_1 i S_2

   [o] S_1 o S_2 $=_{Df}$ ∼S_1 a S_2

   [.]   (X.Y) $=_{Df}$ ∼(∼Xv∼Y)

   [⊃]   (X ⊃ Y) $=_{Df}$ (∼X v Y)

   [≡]   (X ≡ Y) $=_{Df}$ ((X ⊃ Y) . (Y ⊃ X))

[Note that when a bar is superimposed on a term, its argument is that term only. But when '∼' immediately precedes a term (with no bracket intervening), its argument is the wff which consists of that term followed by 'a', 'e', 'i' or 'o', followed by a second term.]

4. Axioms:

$$(p \vee p) \supset p$$
$$q \supset (p \vee q)$$
$$(p \vee q) \supset (q \vee p)$$
$$(q \supset r) \supset ((p \vee q) \supset (p \vee r))$$

A1. $(MaP \cdot MiS) \supset SiP$ (AII, Fig. III)
A2. $SeP \supset Sa\bar{P}$
A3. $Se\bar{S}$
A4. SiS

The unnumbered axioms are those of PM.

5. Transformation Rules.

R1. *The Rule of Substitution for Propositional Variables.*

If X is a thesis containing propositional variables $p_1, \ldots, p_n$, and $Y_1, \ldots, Y_n$ are (not necessarily distinct) wffs, then X $(Y_1/p_1, \ldots, Y_n/p_n)$ is a thesis.

We apply R1 only when $Y_1, \ldots, Y_n$ are either all wffs of PM or all syllogistic wffs; and in the latter case only when $p_1, \ldots, p_n$ are the totality of the propositional variables which occur in X.

R2. *The Rule of Substitution for Term Variables.*

The result of uniformly replacing any term variable in a thesis by any term is also a thesis. More than one such uniform substitution may be made in the one operation.

R3. *The Rule of Detachment.*

If X and $(X \supset Y)$ are theses, Y is a thesis.

R4. *The Rule of Double Negation.*

If S_1 is any term, the result of replacing any occurrence of S_1 by $\bar{\bar{S}}_1$, or any occurrence of $\bar{\bar{S}}_1$ by S_1, in any thesis, is also a thesis.

The use of the Rules of Substitution and Detachment will be indicated in the usual way; that of R4 by '$\times$DNT' ('Double Negation for Terms').

The Rule of Substitution of Equivalents will be available as a derived rule, and its use will be indicated as in Part II.

We shall assume that the following PM theses have been proved, and shall refer to them by the names attached to them:

$$p \equiv p \hspace{4em} \text{[Id]}$$
$$(p \equiv q) \supset (\sim q \equiv \sim p) \hspace{2em} \text{[Transp]}$$
$$p \equiv \sim\sim p \hspace{4em} \text{[DN]}$$
$$((p.q) \supset r) \supset (p \supset (q \supset r)) \hspace{1em} \text{[Exp]}$$
$$(p.q) \equiv (q.p) \hspace{3em} \text{[Comm]}$$
$$((p.q) \supset r) \supset ((p.\sim r) \supset \sim q) \hspace{1em} \text{[Ant]}$$
$$(p \supset q) \supset ((q \supset r) \supset (p \supset r)) \hspace{1em} \text{[Syll]}$$
$$p \supset (q \supset (p.q)) \hspace{3em} \text{[Adj]}$$

(The second of these theses is not the Transp of earlier chapters but an analogue of it for equivalence. The sixth is labelled 'Ant' because it is closely connected with the principle of the Antilogism. The remaining theses and their names are already familiar.)

These PM theses are used chiefly to transform syllogistic theses by means of D or Eq. To indicate this use we adopt the abbreviating conventions employed in Parts II and III. Thus '$T_j \times$ Comm' (where T_j contains some conjunctive part) will mean: 'reverse the order of the conjuncts within T_j'. And '$T_k \times$ Exp' (where T_k is of the form '$(p.q) \supset r$') will mean: 'replace the whole of T_k by the corresponding formula of the form "$p \supset (q \supset r)$" '.

Proofs of theorems

A. Syllogistic Part 1.   (Using A1, A2 and A3.)

T1. $S \, o \, P \equiv \sim S \, a \, P$

PROOF: Id(SoP/p) $\times$ Def o.

T2. $S \, a \, P \equiv \sim S \, o \, P$

PROOF: T1 $\times$ Transp, $\times$ DN

T3. $S \, e \, P \equiv \sim S \, i \, P$

PROOF: Id(SeP/p) $\times$ Def e

T4. $S \, i \, P \equiv \sim S \, e \, P$

PROOF: T3 $\times$ Transp, $\times$ DN

T1–T4 express the contradictory relations in the Square of Opposition.

T5.   S a S

PROOF:

A2($\bar{S}$/P), A3 $\times$ D   :   S a $\bar{\bar{S}}$ (1)

(1) $\times$ DNT   :   T5.

T6.   S i P $\equiv$ P i S   (Conversion of I)

PROOF:

A1 (S/M, S/P, P/S) $\times$ Exp   :   S a S $\supset$ (S i P $\supset$ P i S)   (1)

(1), T5 $\times$ D   :   S i P $\supset$ P i S   (2)

(2), (2)(P/S, S/P) $\times$ Adj, $\times$ Def $\equiv$:   T6.

T7.   S e P $\equiv$ P e S   (Conversion of E)

PROOF: T6 (P/S, S/P) $\times$ Transp $\times$ Def e

T8.   (M a P . S i M) $\supset$ S i P   (AII, Fig. I)

PROOF: A1, T6(M/P) $\times$ Eq

T9.   (M i P . M a S) $\supset$ S i P   (IAI, Fig. III)

PROOF:

A1 (S/P, P/S), T6 $\times$ Eq   :   (M a S . M i P) $\supset$ S i P   (1)

(1) $\times$ Comm   :   T9

T10.   (P i M . M a S) $\supset$ S i P   (IAI, Fig. IV)

PROOF: T9, T6(M/S) $\times$ Eq

T11.   (P e M . S a M) $\supset$ S e P   (EAE, Fig. II)

PROOF:

A1 $\times$ Ant.   :   (M a P . $\sim$S i P) $\supset$ $\sim$M i S   (1)

(1)(S/M, M/P, P/S), $\times$ Def e, $\times$ Comm   :   T11

T12.   (M e P . S a M) $\supset$ S e P   (EAE, Fig. 1)

PROOF: T11, T7(M/S) $\times$ Eq

T13.   (P a M . S e M) $\supset$ S e P   (AEE, Fig. II)

PROOF:

T11 (P/S, S/P) $\times$ Comm   :   (P a M . S e M) $\supset$ P e S   (1)

(1), T7 $\times$ Eq   :   T13

T14.   (P a M . M e S) $\supset$ S e P   (AEE, Fig. IV)

PROOF: T13, T7 (M/P) $\times$ Eq

T15. $(M e P . S i M) \supset S o P$ (EIO, Fig. I)

PROOF:

A1(M/S) S/M, × Comm	: $(S i M . S a P) \supset M i P$	(1)
(1) × Ant	: $(S i M . \sim M i P) \supset$	
	$\sim S a P$	(2)
(2), × Def e, × Def o, × Comm	: T15.	

T16. $(P e M . S i M) \supset S o P$ (EIO, Fig. II)
PROOF: T15, T7(M/S) × Eq

T17. $(M e P . M i S) \supset S o P$ (EIO, Fig. III)
PROOF: T15, T6(M/P) × Eq

T18. $(P e M . M i S) \supset S o P$ (EIO, Fig. IV)
PROOF: T16, T6(M/P) × Eq

Before deriving the remaining three syllogistic moods in Part 1, we derive the Obverses.

T19. $S e \bar{P} \supset S a P$
PROOF: A2 $(\bar{P}/P) \times$ DNT

T20. $S a P \supset S e \bar{P}$
PROOF:

| T12 (P/M, $\bar{P}$/P) × Exp | : $P e \bar{P} \supset (S a P \supset S e \bar{P})$ | (1) |
| (1), A3(P/S) × D | : T20. | |

T21. $S a \bar{P} \supset S e P$
PROOF: T20 $(\bar{P}/P) \times$ DNT

T22. $S a P \equiv S e \bar{P}$ (Obversion of A)
PROOF: T20, T19 × Adj, × Def $\equiv$

T23. $S e P \equiv S a \bar{P}$ (Obversion of E)
PROOF: A2, T21 × Adj, × Def $\equiv$

T24. $S i P \equiv S o \bar{P}$ (Obversion of I)
PROOF:

| T22 ($\bar{P}$/P) × Transp, × DNT | : $\sim S e P \equiv \sim S a \bar{P}$ | (1) |
| (1), T4, T1 × Eq | : T24. | |

T25. $S o P \equiv S i \bar{P}$ (Obversion of O)

PROOF:

T23 ($\bar{P}/P$) $\times$ Transp, $\times$ DNT $\sim S a P \equiv \sim S e \bar{P}$ (1)

(1), T1, T4 $\times$ Eq   : T25.

T26. $(M a P . S a M) \supset S a P$ (AAA, Fig. I)

PROOF:

T12 ($\bar{P}/P$)   : $(M e \bar{P} . S a M) \supset S e \bar{P}$ (1)

(1), T22 (M/S) $\times$ Eq, T22 $\times$ Eq : T26

T27. $(P a M . S o M) \supset S o P$ (AOO, Fig. II)

PROOF: T26 (M/P, P/M) $\times$ Ant, $\times$ Def o

T28. $(M o P . M a S) \supset S o P$ (OAO, Fig. III)

PROOF:

T26 $\times$ Comm, $\times$ Ant   : $(S a M . \sim S a P) \supset$

$\sim M a P$ (1)

(1)(M/S, S/M), $\times$ Def o, $\times$ Comm : T28

We now complete the proofs of the Part 1 immediate inferences.

T29. $S e P \equiv P a \bar{S}$ (Obverted Conversion of E)

PROOF: T23 (P/S, S/P), T7 $\times$ Eq

T30. $S i P \equiv P o \bar{S}$ (Obverted Conversion of I)

PROOF: T24 (P/S, S/P), T6 $\times$ Eq

T31. $S a P \equiv \bar{P} e S$ (Partial Contrapositive of A)

PROOF: T22, T7($\bar{P}/P$) $\times$ Eq

T32. $S o P \equiv \bar{P} i S$ (Partial Contrapositive of O)

PROOF: T25, T6($\bar{P}/P$) $\times$ Eq

T33. $S a P \equiv \bar{P} a \bar{S}$ (Full Contrapositive of A)

PROOF: T31, T23($\bar{P}/S$, S/P) $\times$ Eq

T34. $S o P \equiv \bar{P} o \bar{S}$ (Full Contrapositive of O)

PROOF: T32, T24 ($\bar{P}/S$, S/P) $\times$ Eq

B. Syllogistic Part 2: theses additional to those in A. (Using A1, A2, A3 and A4.)

T35.   S a P ⊃ S i P   (Subalternation A – I)

PROOF:

A1(S/M) × Comm, × Exp   :   S i S ⊃ (S a P ⊃ S i P)   (1)
(1), A4 × D   :   T35.

T36.   S e P ⊃ S o P   (Subalternation E – O)

PROOF:

T17 (S/M) × Comm, × Exp   :   S i S ⊃ (S e P ⊃ S o P)   (1)
(1), A4 × D   :   T36.

T37.   S a P ⊃ ~S e P   (Contrariety A – E)

PROOF: T35, T4 × Eq

T38.   ~S i P ⊃ S o P   (Sub-contrariety I – O)

PROOF: T36, T3 × Eq

T35–38 are the remaining relations in the Square of Opposition.

T39.   S a P ⊃ P i S   (Conversion of A)

PROOF: T35, T6 × Eq

T40.   (M a P . S a M) ⊃ S i P   (AAI, Fig. I).

PROOF: T26, T35 × Syll

By similar proofs, using T36 and Syll, we can derive the other four weakened moods from T11–14. Thus we have

T41.   (P e M . S a M) ⊃ S o P   (EAO, Fig. II)
T42.   (M e P . S a M) ⊃ S o P   (EAO, Fig. I)
T43.   (P a M . S e M) ⊃ S o P   (AEO, Fig. II)
T44.   (P a M . M e S) ⊃ S o P   (AEO, Fig. IV)

The four strengthened moods can be derived as follows:

T45.   (P a M . M a S) ⊃ S i P   (AAI, Fig. IV)

PROOF:

T44(S/M, P/S, M/P) × Ant   :   (M a S . ~P o M) ⊃ ~S e P   (1)
(1), T2, T4 × Eq, × Comm   :   T45

T46. $(M a P . M a S) \supset S i P$ (AAI, Fig. III)

PROOF:

T41 × Comm, × Ant   : $(S a M . \sim S o P) \supset$
$$\sim P e M \quad (1)$$

(1)(M/S, P/M, S/P), T2, T4 × Eq   :   T46.

T47. $(M e P . M a S) \supset S o P$ (EAO, Fig. III)

PROOF:

T43 × Comm, × Ant   : $(S e M . \sim S o P) \supset \sim P a M$ (1)
(1)(M/S, P/M, S/P), T2, T1 × Eq   :   T47

T48. $(P e M . M a S) \supset S o P$ (EAO, Fig. IV)

PROOF: T47, T7 (M/S) × Eq

T49. $S a P \supset P o \bar{S}$ (Obverted Conversion of A)

PROOF: T35, T30 × Syll

T50. $S e P \supset \bar{P} i S$ (Partial Contrapositive of E)

PROOF: T36, T32 × Syll

T51. $S e P \supset \bar{P} o \bar{S}$ (Full Contrapositive of E)

PROOF: T36, T34 × Syll

T52. $S a P \supset \bar{S} i \bar{P}$ (Full Inverse of A)

PROOF: T33, T39($\bar{P}$/S, $\bar{S}$/P) × Syll

T53. $S a P \supset \bar{S} o P$ (Partial Inverse of A)

PROOF: T52, T25($\bar{S}$/S) × Eq

T54. $S e P \supset \bar{S} i P$ (Partial Inverse of E)

PROOF: T39(P/S, $\bar{S}$/P), T29 × Eq

T55. $S e P \supset \bar{S} o \bar{P}$ (Full Inverse of E)

PROOF: T54, T24($\bar{S}$/S) × Eq

The schemata for the subaltern immediate inferences can be readily derived from the relevant theorems together with T35 or T36 ('S a P $\supset$ S i P' or 'S e P $\supset$ S o P') as the case may be.

For the sake of completeness we add

T56. S o S̄

PROOF: T36 (S̄/P), A3 × D

One fact which emerges from these deductions seems worth commenting on. Part 1 is the non-controversial segment of syllogistic; all the schemata whose validity has been questioned occur in Part 2. What emerges is that the schemata in Part 2 are 'all of a piece': all can be derived from the non-controversial schemata in Part 1 together with 'S i S' (or alternatively 'S a P ⊃ S i P');[1] and in particular it seems impossible to regard only the inverses as invalid, although they have occasioned more controversy than the other inferences. More exactly, if we admit the validity of the schemata in Part 1, accept 'S a P ⊃ S i P' as valid, and grant that the transformation rules are validity-preserving, we cannot deny the validity of the inverses.

[1] (S a P ⊃ S i P)(S/P), T5 × D : S i S

CHAPTER 49

On the Meta-logic of AS

Consistency

We show that AS is consistent with respect to negation; i.e. that where X is any wff of AS, X and $\sim$X are not both derivable.

All wffs of AS are either wffs of PM or wffs of syllogistic.

The basis of PM is contained in the basis of AS. The transformation rules do not permit the derivation of any PM formulae other than those which are derivable within PM itself. Therefore, since PM is consistent with respect to negation, if X and $\sim$X are wffs of PM, they are not both derivable in AS.

It remains to show that if X and $\sim$X are wffs of syllogistic, they are not both derivable. We prove this as follows.

Suppose that in every syllogistic wff of AS we bracket each expression of the form $S_1 a S_2$, $S_1 e S_2$, $S_1 i S_2$ or $S_1 o S_2$, and then replace every occurrence of 'a' or 'i' by '$\equiv$', every occurrence of 'e' or 'o' by '$\equiv\sim$', every occurrence of 'S', 'P' and 'M' by 'p', 'q' and 'r' respectively, and every occurrence of a bar over a variable by '$\sim$' written immediately before that variable. Then

1. As reference to the Formation Rules will show, every syllogistic wff of AS will become a wff of PM.

2. Every syllogistic axiom of AS will become a thesis of PM.

3. Every theorem of AS will become a thesis of PM.

The last assertion (3) can be proved by a survey of the transformation rules. R1 (so far as it concerns syllogistic wffs) and R2 will both become limited forms of the PM rule of substitution; the Rule of Detachment (R3) is stated exactly as in PM in any case; and the application of R4 will coincide with that of '$\sim\sim p \equiv p$' by substitution of equivalents.

(Many invalid syllogistic wffs – e.g. 'S i P $\supset$ S a P' – will also become theses of PM, but this is irrelevant.)

Therefore:

4. If there were two syllogistic wffs, X and $\sim$X, which were both theses of AS, these would become two wffs, X' and $\sim$X', which were both theses of PM.

5. But, as was proved in Part II, no such pair of wffs can both be theses of PM

It follows that X and $\sim$X cannot both be syllogistic theses of AS.

An extension of AS

Although we have confined ourselves to proving those theorems in AS which find a place in traditional syllogistic, the theorems derivable from our axioms are by no means confined to these. Nevertheless, AS is a limited system in one important way, in which no other system discussed in this book has been limited; for we have restricted ourselves to a limited number of term variables – in fact to a bare three – while in the other systems we have had at our disposal an unlimited number of variables of each type used. We have restricted ourselves in this way because all the syllogistic schemata we were trying to derive as theses can be formulated with three term variables only. But the restriction, though convenient, is quite unnecessary, and if we wish to remove it we have only to make a simple alteration in the list of Primitive Symbols to bring it into line (in this respect) with the corresponding list in the other systems (e.g. by using 'A', 'B', 'C', . . . as term variables); everything else in AS could remain as it is. We should then have an extended system (which we may call AS') in which many more theorems can be proved. For example, we should be able to derive the schemata for what are known as *polysyllogisms*, which are similar to syllogisms except that they contain four or more terms. An example is:

$$(A \, a \, B \, . \, B \, a \, C \, . \, C \, a \, D) \supset A \, a \, D$$

Polysyllogisms have certainly a claim to be called traditional, for they were studied in antiquity; if we have not provided a place for them in AS, it is not in order to deny this fact, but because it is also a traditional doctrine that they can be analysed as chains of syllogisms of the ordinary type. Most text-books of syllogistic logic will explain how this is done. Nevertheless, it can hardly be denied that AS' would open up a wide field of valid formulae (both traditionally recognized and otherwise), on which we have barely touched here. Jan Łukasiewicz' book *Aristotle's Syllogistic from the Standpoint of Modern Formal Logic* sets out a system similar to AS', but without negative terms, using the axiom set mentioned near the beginning of Chapter 48, though expressed in a different symbolism.

It is clear that AS' is consistent: the consistency proof we have given for AS will run equally smoothly if we suppose ourselves to have an unlimited number of term variables.

Strong completeness

Neither AS nor AS′ is strongly complete. The formula

$$S\,i\,P \supset S\,a\,P$$

for example, cannot be derived from the axioms, yet it is consistent with them, as our Consistency Proof has in effect shown.

Weak completeness

We could define the weak completeness of an axiomatic basis for syllogistic in either of two ways.

(*a*) We could say that such a basis was to count as complete if all the traditionally valid schemata listed in Chapter 42 could be derived from it. In this sense we have of course already proved the completeness of AS, since we have derived all of these schemata.

(*b*) In a more important sense, however, a basis for syllogistic will be said to be complete only if from it can be derived all valid formulae which can be constructed from the materials of the system. The completeness of AS in this sense raises issues which lie beyond the scope of this book. For a discussion of this topic you could not do better than consult the work by Łukasiewicz to which we have already referred. It is a book which has made important contributions to Aristotelian scholarship as well as to logic itself; to it our discussion of the axiomatization of syllogistic owes a very considerable debt.

The Conjunctive Normal Form Theorem

We now give the proof, foreshadowed in Chapter 11 of Part I, that every wff of PC can be put into CNF.

In what follows, a wff is called *elementary* if it consists of a single propositional variable or the negation of a propositional variable. A part of a wff is called an *elementary part* if the part is an elementary wff.

A wff is said to be in *reduced form* (or to be a reduced wff) if it contains no dyadic operators other than 'v' and '.' and no negations except in its elementary parts.

CNF THEOREM: Given any wff of PC, we have an effective method for finding another wff equivalent to the given wff and of the form

$$D_1 . D_2 . . . . . D_n$$

where $n \geq 1$ and each D_i is an unnegated disjunction (possibly degenerate) of elementary wffs. I.e. every wff of PC can be put into CNF.

PROOF:

1. Every wff of PC can be put into reduced form.

This is so because the definitions allow the elimination of all other dyadic operators in favour of 'v' and '.'; and successive applications of the Law of Double Negation and De Morgan's Laws allow the removal of

  (i) multiple negations
  (ii) occurrences of '∼' outside brackets – i.e. negations not in elementary wffs.

2. Reduced wffs can be graded in *order of complexity*.

A wff of *1st order* consists of an elementary wff.

A wff of *2nd order* consists of the disjunction or conjunction of two wffs of 1st order.

Where n > 2, a wff of *nth order* consists of the disjunction or conjunction of two wffs, at least one of which is of (n–1)th order and neither of which is of more than (n–1)th order. E.g., a wff of 3rd order is a disjunction or conjunction of two wffs, at least one being of 2nd order and neither being of more than 2nd order.

Since every reduced wff is built from elementary wffs and the dyadic operators 'v' and '.', it is of some order of complexity. And since every wff of PC is of finite length, each reduced wff is of some *finite* order of complexity.

3. Every wff of 1st order is a degenerate disjunction and is therefore in CNF already.

4. Every wff of 2nd order is either a degenerate conjunction (being a disjunction of elementary wffs) or a conjunction of degenerate disjunctions, and is therefore in CNF already.

5. Every wff of 3rd order has one of the forms

$$\text{(i) } X \,.\, Y$$
$$\text{(ii) } X \vee Y$$

where X and Y are of at most 2nd order.

Now in case (i) the wff is already in CNF since a 2nd order conjunct must be either a disjunction or a conjunction of elementary parts. Thus the wff will have one of the forms:

$D_1 \,.\, D_2$	(X and Y both disjunctive)
$D_1 \,.\, D_2 \,.\, D_3$	(X conjunctive, Y disjunctive; or X disjunctive, Y conjunctive)
$D_1 \,.\, D_2 \,.\, D_3 \,.\, D_4$	(X and Y both conjunctive)

In case (ii), the wff is already in CNF if both X and Y are disjunctions. If, however, at least one of X and Y is a conjunction, then application (repeated if necessary) of the Distributive Law

$$(p \vee (q \,.\, r)) \equiv ((p \vee q) \,.\, (p \vee r))$$

together with the Commutative Law if required, yields a wff in CNF. E.g., if the wff has the form:

$$(X_1 \,.\, X_2) \vee (Y_1 \,.\, Y_2)$$

we obtain

$$(X_1 \lor Y_1).(X_2 \lor Y_1).(X_1 \lor Y_2).(X_2 \lor Y_2)$$

Thus the result will have one of the forms:

$$D_1$$
$$D_1 . D_2$$
$$D_1 . D_2 . D_3 . D_4$$

Therefore, every wff of 3rd order is either already in CNF or can be put into CNF.

6. We can generalize the argument on wffs of 3rd order.

For $n > 2$, a wff of nth order is either a conjunction or a disjunction of wffs of lower order, each of which can be put into CNF. A conjunction of wffs in CNF is evidently itself in CNF. And a disjunction of such wffs is either in CNF already (for if D_1 and D_2 are degenerate conjunctions, so is $(D_1 \lor D_2)$) or can be put into CNF by successive applications of the Distributive and Commutative Laws.

7. Thus, since every reduced wff is of finite order, and every wff of PC can be put into reduced form, every wff of PC can be put into CNF.

Parallel to the CNF Theorem we have

DNF THEOREM: Given any wff of PC, we have an effective method for finding another wff equivalent to the given wff and of the form:

$$C_1 \lor C_2 \lor \ldots \lor C_n$$

where $n \geq 1$ and each C_i is an unnegated conjunction (possibly degenerate) of elementary wffs. I.e., every wff of PC can be put into DNF.

The proof of the CNF Theorem given above can be turned into a proof of the DNF Theorem simply by reading 'disjunction (disjunct, disjunctive)' for 'conjunction (conjunct, conjunctive)', and vice versa, throughout, and by consequence replacing '.' by 'v' and vice versa, 'D' by 'C', and 'CNF' by 'DNF', wherever they occur.

APPENDIX 2

A Bracket-Free Notation

During the past half-century many alternative notations for PC and LPC have appeared. Most have been variations on the notation used by Whitehead and Russell in *Principia Mathematica* (which in turn was developed from that of the Italian, Peano). The notation we have used is one of these variants, the principal change being the employment of brackets for punctuation in place of a system of dots. Some other notations have involved more substantial deviations, especially in the matter of signs for operators. One example is the use of '→' in place of '⊃' (usually associated with the use of the very suggestive '↔' in place of '≡'). Another is the use of '∼', the Russellian symbol for negation, as a material equivalence sign; in this case, of course, '∼' is a dyadic operator, so that '∼p' is ill-formed.

It is characteristic of all of this family of notations that they require some punctuation devices to prevent ambiguity. However there has also appeared an entirely different notation in which no brackets or equivalent devices are necessary. This is the so-called Polish notation, devised by J. Łukasiewicz, and widely used by those taking part in or influenced by the important logical work carried on in Poland, especially between the two World Wars. The essential feature of this notation is that all operators (dyadic as well as monadic) are placed immediately *before* their arguments. It is this which eliminates the need for brackets. A more accidental feature is that all truth-functional operators are symbolized by letters of our alphabet, while Greek letters are used in quantifiers and (normally) as predicate variables.

The following table gives the elements of the Polish notation as translations of the signs used in Parts I–III of this book.

∼p	Np
p ∨ q	Apq
p ⊃ q	Cpq
p . q	Kpq

368

p ≡ q	Epq
p ∨ q	Jpq
Uxfx	Πxφx
∃xfx	Σxφx
x = y	Ixy

The rule that operators precede their arguments applies whether or not the arguments are single variables. Thus, '∼(p.q)' is written as 'NKpq'; '(p.q) ⊃ (p∨q)' is written as 'CKpqApq'; and '(p⊃q) ⊃ ((q⊃r) ⊃ (p⊃r))' becomes 'CCpqCCqrCpr'. It is an immediate consequence of this rule that the main operator of any wff always occurs in the left-most position in the wff, whether or not the wff is part of another wff. Thus a wff beginning with 'K' is immediately identified as a conjunction. A wff beginning with 'NK' is immediately seen to be a negated conjunction, while one beginning with 'KN' is seen to be an unnegated conjunction in which the first argument is negated. In reading a wff written in the Polish notation, the essential point to bear in mind is that each argument of any occurrence of an operator must be well-formed. Thus, 'Cp' cannot be the argument of any operator, since it is not well-formed.

The following selection of formulae set out in both notations will illustrate these points.

CpNNp	p ⊃ ∼∼p
CNNpp	∼∼p ⊃ p
CpCqp	p ⊃ (q ⊃ p)
CCpqp	(p ⊃ q) ⊃ p
CCCpqpp	((p ⊃ q) ⊃ p) ⊃ p
CpCqCpp	p ⊃ (q ⊃ (p ⊃ p))
KNpp	∼p . p
NKpp	∼(p . p)
EAApqrApAqr	((p ∨ q) ∨ r) ≡ (p ∨ (q ∨ r))
CCpqCNqNp	(p ⊃ q) ⊃ (∼q ⊃ ∼p)
CCpqNCqNp	(p ⊃ q) ⊃ ∼(q ⊃ ∼p)

ENEpqJpq	$\sim(p \equiv q) \equiv (p \lor q)$
$\Pi x C\varphi x\psi x$	$Ux(fx \supset gx)$
$C\Pi x\varphi x\psi x$	$(Uxfx) \supset gx$
$EN\Pi x\varphi x\Sigma xN\varphi x$	$\sim Uxfx \equiv \exists x \sim fx$
$C\Pi xC\varphi x\psi xC\Pi x\varphi x\Pi x\psi x$	$Ux(fx \supset gx) \supset (Uxfx \supset Uxgx)$
$\Pi xC\varphi xN\Sigma y\psi yx$	$Ux(fx \supset \sim\exists y(gyx))$
$\Sigma xKK\varphi x\Pi yC\varphi yIyx\psi x$	$\exists x(fx \, . \, Uy(fy \supset y=x) \, . \, gx)$

We could easily devise a simplified Polish notation for LPC1 and LPC2, analogous to the notation used in Chapters 23–35, by omitting all bound occurrences of individual-variables and writing the quantifiers as 'Π' and 'Σ'.

Answers to Exercises

Answers are provided for most of the exercises in the text, though usually in the form of a brief sketch only. They may range from sufficient instructions for constructing the proof, etc., required, to substantial hints on procedure, to a simple statement of result (e.g. 'Valid') or of a key result to be used in proving a theorem.

It is however important that your own answers should be set out in the full form explained in the text. This will prevent self-deception. And it hardly needs to be said that indiscriminate use of the answers as a crib will defeat the purpose of the exercises.

[To a few of the Exercises no answers are provided. Most, though not all, of these are questions of the more discursive type, to which satisfactory answers can vary considerably. In the case of some Exercises we give answers only to a selection of the examples; but these should provide a sufficient clue to the remainder.]

4.1 Tables for (a), (b), (c) have 2 rows; tables for (d), (e) have 4 rows; tables for (f), (g), (h) have 8 rows. All are valid except (b) and (g).

N.B. $(g) = 0$ when p = 0, q = 0, r = 1.

4.3 Propositional schema: $((p \supset q) . {\sim}p) \supset q$
Invalid.

4.4 Propositional schema: $(((p \supset (q.r)).(r \supset {\sim}q)).r) \supset {\sim}p$
Valid.

4.5 To obtain the inferential schema,
put 'p' for 'I am in Armidale'
  'q' for 'I am in Wellington'
and get:

> If p then not q
> If q then not p
> ∴ not (p and q)

Propositional schema is: $((p \supset {\sim}q).(q \supset {\sim}p)) \supset {\sim}(p.q)$
Valid.

5.1　Table for (*a*) has 2 rows; table for (*c*) has 8 rows; all others have 4 rows.

　　　All schemata are valid except (*e*) and (*h*)

5.2　Result: both schemata are valid.

5.3　To obtain inferential schema,

　　　put 'p' for 'The Greeks took the city'
　　　　　'q' for 'The Persians took the city'
　　　　　'r' for 'The inhabitants were killed'

　　　and get:
　　　If (either p or q) then r

$$\frac{\quad p \quad}{\therefore r}$$

　　　Reading 'either . . . or . . .' as disjunction, the propositional schema is: $(((p \vee q) \supset r).p) \supset r$
　　　Result: Valid.

　　　[N.B. If alternation is used instead of disjunction the inference will turn out invalid; and the counter-intuitive nature of this result seems a good reason for preferring disjunction here.]

6.1　All valid except (*f*).
　　　(*f*) = 0 in the two cases in which both p = 0 and r = 0.]

6.3　Propositional schema of form:

$$(((p \supset q) \supset r).{\sim}q) \supset ({\sim}p \vee {\sim}r)$$

　　　Invalid.

　　　[N.B. 'but only if' = 'only if'. 'But' has no conjunctive force here. 'If p then q, only if r' = 'Only if r, then if p then q' = 'If (if p then q) then r'.]

6.4　Invalid.

8.2　In each sequence let the wffs be $W_1, W_2, W_3, \ldots$ and let the propositional variables in alphabetical order be $a_1, a_2, a_3, \ldots$ (so $p = a_1$, $q = a_2$, etc.)

　　　(*a*) Rules: (1) $W_1 = a_1$
　　　　　　　　　(2) $W_{n+1} = (W_n) \vee a_{n+1}$

　　　(*b*) Rules: (1) $W_1 = a_1$
　　　　　　　　　(2) $W_{n+1} = {\sim}(W_n) \vee a_{n+1}$

8.3 *Sketch of a solution.* Since every wff can be expressed in terms of negation and disjunction only, and for present purposes negations are irrelevant, we may consider only disjunctive wffs.

Case (a). n = 1. Single variable case. The rule holds.

Case (b). Suppose the rule holds when n = k (for k > 1), and consider the transformation of a wff for which n = k (call this wff 'K') into one for which n = k + 1, by the 'addition' of one more variable (say, p_{k+1}).

To effect this transformation we must *either*

    (i) disjoin p_{k+1} to K

or (ii) disjoin p_{k+1} to some disjunct in K.

In either case the new variable brings with it exactly one more occurrence of 'v'. Thus if the rule holds when n = k, it holds when n = k + 1. Therefore since the rule holds when n = 1, it holds for all values of n.

8.4 Rather than introduce eleven new symbols here, we shall use the numbers at the head of the column as operators. [Thus 'p5q' = 'p⊃q'.]

$$(p1q) \equiv ((p{\supset}q){\vee}(q{\supset}p))$$
$$\equiv ((\sim p{\vee}q){\vee}(\sim q{\vee}p))$$

Whence the definition: $(X1Y) =_{Df} ((\sim X{\vee}Y){\vee}(\sim Y{\vee}X))$

Similarly the following equivalences give rise to definitions:

$$(p3q) \equiv (q{\supset}p) \qquad\qquad (p4q) \equiv (p.(q{\vee}\sim q))$$
$$\equiv (\sim q{\vee}p) \qquad\qquad\qquad \equiv \sim(\sim p{\vee}\sim(q{\vee}\sim q))$$
$$\equiv (p{\vee}\sim q)$$
$$(p6q) \equiv (q.(p{\vee}\sim p))$$
$$\equiv \sim(\sim q{\vee}\sim(p{\vee}\sim p))$$

$$(p9q) \equiv \sim(p8q),\text{ and so on to}$$
$$(p16q) \equiv \sim(p1q)$$

9.2 All are valid except (*c*), (*l*) and (*m*).

9.3 (*a*) Valid.

    (*b*) Invalid. (Consider p, q, r, s, t = 1, u = 0.)

9.4 Valid.

10.1 (*a*) Apply Def ⊃ throughout left-hand side, then Double

Negation within each of the resulting disjuncts to allow use of De Morgan.

(*b*), (*c*): Begin with LHS, use De Morgan and Associative Laws.

(*d*) Beginning with RHS: Def ⊃, Commutative Law (v), De Morgan [on '(p.∼q)'], Double Negation, Def ⊃ twice.

(*e*) To LHS apply Def ⊃, Commutative Law, Double Negation, Def ⊃.

[N.B. Other methods of solution than those listed are possible.]

10.2 Let H be the propositional schema corresponding to Affirming the Antecedent, A and B be those corresponding to (*a*) and (*b*) respectively. Then show that 'H ≡ A' and 'H ≡ B' are valid.

11.1 All are valid except (*c*) and (*f*).

11.2 (*f*) alone is inconsistent.

11.3 (*a*) If the CNF obtained is

$$(pv\sim pvqvr).(pvqv\sim qvr).(pv\sim pvrv\sim r).(pv\sim qvrv\sim r)$$

then the only conjunct not containing all three variables is the third. The perfect CNF is then obtained by replacing the third conjunct by:

$$(pv\sim pvqvrv\sim r).(pv\sim pv\sim qvrv\sim r)$$

If the DNF obtained is:

$$(\sim p.\sim q.r)v(q.\sim r)vpvr$$

(the last two disjuncts being degenerate conjunctions) then every disjunct fails to contain all three variables. The perfect DNF is:

$$(\sim p.\sim q.r) \lor (\sim p.\sim q.\sim r) \lor (p.q.\sim r) \lor (\sim p.q.\sim r) \lor$$
$$(p.q.r) \lor (p.\sim q.r) \lor (p.q.\sim r) \lor (p.\sim q.\sim r) \lor$$
$$(p.q.r) \lor (p.\sim q.r) \lor (\sim p.q.r) \lor (\sim p.\sim q.r)$$

in which the 7th, 9th, 10th and 12th disjuncts are redundant and may be dropped out (although written in here for illustrative purposes).

[These answers should provide sufficient guide for checking (*b*), (*c*) and (*d*).]

15.1 A1($\sim$p/p) $\times$ Def $\supset$

15.2 A3($\sim$p/p, $\sim$q/q) $\times$ Def $\supset$

15.3 A3($\sim$q/p, $\sim$p/q) $\times$ Def $\supset$

15.4 A2(q/p,p/q), A3(p/q,q/p) $\times$ Syll

15.5 15.4($\sim$p/p) $\times$ Def $\supset$

15.6 15.5 $\times$ Perm

15.7 T19(p/q), A1 $\times$ Syll

15.8 15.4 $\times$ Transp

15.9 A2 $\times$ Transp

15.10 15.9, A2($\sim$p/p, $\sim$q/q) $\times$ Syll

15.11 15.10($\sim$p/p) $\times$ Def $\supset$

15.12 T10 ($\sim$pv$\sim$q/p) $\times$ Def.

16.1 15.2 ($\sim$p/p, $\sim$q/q), T30 $\times$ Eq

16.2 16.1 (q/p, p/q)

16.3 A4(rvs/r), T32 $\times$ Eq

16.4 Id [T36]((q.p) $\supset$ r/p) $\times$ Def . :

$$(\sim(\sim qv\sim p) \supset r) \equiv ((q.p)\supset r) \qquad (1)$$

Use the following for successive Eq operations on the left-hand equivalent:

T39, T37 $\times$ Eq; Assoc*; Def $\supset$.

* Derive '((pvq)vr) $\equiv$ (qv(pvr))' from T41, T42.

16.5 Id (pv(q.r)/p), then use T32, T34.

16.6 Simp (r/p, q/r), T22(q/p, r/q) $\times$ Syll (1)
T2(q.r/q, q$\supset$r/r), (1) $\times$ D (2)
T2(p$\supset$r/p, p$\supset$(q.r)/q, p$\supset$(q$\supset$r)/r), (2) $\times$ D (3)
(3), Comp $\times$ Syll

16.7 T22, Simp (q/p, p/q) $\times$ Syll.

16.8 A5 × Perm (1)

Simp ((1)/p, q⊃r/q), (1) × D × Perm.

16.9 Hint: Prove ∼(pvq) ⊃ (p⊃q) (1)

and ∼(pvq) ⊃ (q⊃p) (2)

and use Comp. To prove (1), apply the principle of A2 to 15.8; to prove (2), use 15.9 similarly.

17.1 Obtain '(p⊃(q.r)) ⊃ (∼p v (q.r))' by Id and Def ⊃. Then use Distrib.

17.2 Use A5(p⊃q/q, p/r) × Perm

17.3 Use Syll [T3] × Imp, and Syll (r/q, s/r)

17.4 Syll [T2](q⊃(r⊃s)/q, r⊃(q⊃s)/r). Use Perm to detach.

17.5 Perm (r⊃s/r); Syll [T2] — cf. 17.4; Perm.

17.6 Syll [T2](s/p, p/q, q⊃r/r) (1)

(1) (q⊃r/p, r⊃s/q, q⊃s/r, p/s) (2)

(2),Perm × Eq (3)

17.7 T50 (r/q, q/r, r/s); reduce antecedent to 'p⊃q' [see proof of T54]; use 16.7.

17.8 *Hint*: use T21, T22 to get 'Antecedent ⊃ (p⊃q)' and 'Ant ⊃ (q ⊃ r)'; thence 'Ant ⊃ (p⊃r)' by the thesis derived thus: use Simp to obtain

p⊃(Syll[T3](q/p, r/q, s/r))

to which apply T25 twice.

Similarly, obtain 'Ant ⊃ (r⊃p)' and use Comp.

17.9 Similar to 17.8

20.1 Simp (p⊃p/q)

20.2 A2(p/q)

20.3 Substitute in A2

20.4 Simp

20.5 Syll

20.6 Syll, Perm

20.7 Simp (p⊃p/p, q⊃p/q), Id × D

20.8 Id((p⊃q) ⊃ q/p) × Perm

20.9 Simp (p⊃s/p), Perm, Syll

20.10 Θ18 × Θ14

20.11 Θ16(p⊃q/p, q⊃r/q, p⊃r/r, (r⊃s) ⊃ ((s⊃t)⊃(p⊃t))/s)
Use Θ18 to detach.

20.12 Θ8, Syll

20.13 Θ1 (r/p, p⊃q/q, q/r), Θ18 (r/q, q/r)

21.1 (a) Θ23(∼0/p), Θ21 × D
    (b) Simp (∼0/p, 0/q)
    (c) Simp, Θ20
    (d) Syll Θ (0/q, q/r), A4, Def ∼
    (e) Syll [A1] (p⊃0/p, p⊃q/q, q/r), (d) above
    (f) Syll Θ (∼q/q, q⊃s/r)
    (g) Comp, Id
    (h) Θ34, (g) above
    (i) Θ25; A2(p/q) × Perm
    (j) Θ35, A4
    (k) Θ16 (p.q/r, r/s), Adj × D
    (l) Syll (∼r/r) × Transp × Def .

21.2 (a) Begin with A6(r.q/p)
    (b) Θ7 × Def v
    (c) Simp (q/p, p⊃q/q) × Def v
    (d) A5, Simp (q/p, p⊃q/q)
    (e) A4(p.q/p, r/q)
    (f) Similar to (e) above
    (g) Use A6 ((p.q).r/p, p/q, q.r/r) and A6 ((p.q).r/p)
    (h) Use A6 (p/q, q/r) and Simp (q/p, p/q)

22.2 For Peirce in PM, see 17.2.

22.3 For Meredith's Axiom 2, see 15.5.

22.4 For Church's Axioms 2 and 3, see Θ31 and Θ24.

23.1 (Formulae only are given here. Variables are assigned in alphabetical order to predicates in the order of their appearance, or first appearance, in the examples.)

(*a*) U(f⊃g) (*b*) ∃(f.g.h) (*c*) ∼U(f⊃g) (*d*) U(f⊃g) [*not*: ∃(f.g)] (*e*) ∼∃f . ∃g (*f*) U((f . ∼h) ⊃ g) (*g*) ∃(f.g) . ∃(f.∼g) (*h*) U(∼(f.g) ⊃ ∼h) (*i*) ∼∃(f.∼(gvh)) (*j*) (U(f⊃g).∼∃(h.g)) ⊃ ∃(i.j) (*k*) U(f⊃g) v ∼∃(f.g) (*l*) U((fvg) ⊃ (hvi)) [*or*: U((f⊃(hvi)).(g⊃(hvi)))]; but *not*: U((f.g)⊃ (hvi))]

25.1 (We give the fully reduced forms here, using 'A', 'B', 'C', and 'D' for the basic formulae as in the example on p. 188. As explained in the text, the full reduction need not always be undertaken.)

(*a*) ((CvD).∼B) ⊃ (BvD)   Invalid.

(*b*) (∼B.(BvD)) ⊃ ((∼A.∼B) v (∼C.∼D.∼A))   Invalid.

(*c*) (∼B.∼A) ⊃ (∼A.∼B)   Valid.

(*d*) (∼A.∼B) ⊃ ((∼A.∼C) ⊃ (∼B.∼C))   Valid.

(*e*) ((CvDv(∼B.∼D)) ⊃ (AvBvD)) v ((∼A.∼B.(AvC)) ⊃ B)   Invalid.

(*f*) (∃(f.∼f.g) v ∃(f.∼f.∼g) v C v A) ⊃ (∼A⊃C)   Valid.

27.1 (*a*) Valid. (*b*) Invalid. (*c*) Invalid. (*d*) Valid. (*e*) Invalid. (*f*) Invalid. (*g*) Valid. (*h*) Invalid. (*i*) Valid. (*j*) Invalid.

27.2 (Variables in alphabetical order are assigned to predicates in the order of their first appearance in the examples.) Inferential schemata:

(*a*) ∼∃(f.∼(g.h)); ∃(g.∼i); ∃(h.∼j); ∴ ∼U(f⊃(ivj)) Invalid.

(*b*) U(f⊃(g.h)); U(i⊃g).∃(i.∼h); ∴ U(f⊃i)   Invalid.

(*c*) U((f.g)⊃h) ⊃ ∃(g.∼f); U(i⊃(h.f)) v ∼∃(g.i); ∴ U((g.∼i)⊃h) ⊃ ∃(h.∼f) Valid.

27.3 (*b*), (*c*) and (*e*) are inconsistent; (*a*) and (*d*) are not.

28.1 (*a*) ∃(f.∼g.h) v ∃(f.∼g.∼h) v ∃(∼f.∼g.h) v ∃(∼f.∼g.∼h)

(*b*) ∃(f.∼g.h) v ∃(f.∼g.∼h) v ∃(f.∼f.g.h) v ∃(f.∼f.g.∼h) v ∃(f.∼f.∼g.h) v ∃(f.∼f.∼g.∼h)

The other examples follow a similar pattern.

28.2 If and only if a wff is valid, its negation is inconsistent. By Rule (i), ∃∼α is valid if and only if ∼α' is valid. Therefore ∼∃∼α is inconsistent if and only if ∼∼α' is inconsistent. Rule (ia) then follows easily. Similar reasoning yields the other Rules.

28.3 (a) If $(\alpha' \supset \beta')$ is valid, $(\sim\alpha' \vee \beta')$ is valid. Therefore by Rule (iv), $(\exists\sim\alpha \vee U\beta)$ is valid; and this is equivalent to $(U\alpha \supset U\beta)$. (b) and (c) have similar solutions.

29.1 (a) '$\sim p \supset (p \supset q)$', DQ1, T2. (b) Transp, T3. (c) T22, Comm. (d) T8, Def $\equiv$, '$(p.q) \supset q$', Def $\supset$, deM. (e) T20, A2, Syll, Def $\supset$, deM, T3. (f) T17, Perm. (g) '$(p \supset \sim q) \supset ((p.r) \supset (\sim q.r))$', DQ1, T17, Syll, T1, Imp. (h) Distrib, DQ3, T6, T8. (i) '$(p.(p \supset q)) \supset q$', DQ3, T6; T22, Exp, T2; Syll. (j) '$(p \supset (q.r)) \supset ((p \supset q).(p \supset r))$', DQ2, T19, T15.

31.1 (a) fx.$\sim$fy (b) (f.$\sim$g)x . (g.$\sim$f)y (c) $\exists$f $\supset$ fx (d) (fx.fy) $\supset$ U(g$\supset$h) (e) (fx.$\sim\exists$(f.g)) $\supset$ $\exists$(h.$\sim$g) (f) U(f$\supset$g).U(h$\supset\sim$g); (i.$\sim$(gvh))x; $\therefore$ $\exists$(i.$\sim$(fvh))

32.1 (a) 8 EBF's as in LPC1, plus fx, gx, hx, fy, gy, hy. (b) 4 EBF's as in LPC1, plus fx, gx, fy, gy, fz, gz, fw, gw, fu, gu.

32.2 80.

32.3

	$\exists$(f.g)	$\exists$(f.$\sim$g)	$\exists$($\sim$f.g)	$\exists$($\sim$f.$\sim$g)
(a)	1	1	1	1
	1	1	1	0
	0	1	1	1
	0	1	1	0
(c)	1	1	1	1

(one row only).

There are 8 rows for example (b).

32.4 (a) $((\sim\exists(f.g).\sim\exists(f.\sim g).\sim\exists(\sim f.g)) \vee (fx.\sim gx)) \supset$
$(\exists(f.g).(\sim gx \supset fx))$

(b) $[(fx \supset (gy \vee hy)) \supset (\sim\exists(\sim f.\sim g.h).\sim\exists(\sim f.\sim g.\sim h).$
$\sim\exists(\sim f.g.h).\sim\exists(f.g.\sim h))] \supset [\sim fx \vee \sim hy \vee \exists(f.g.h) \vee$
$\exists(f.g.\sim h) \vee \exists(\sim f.g.h) \vee \exists(\sim f.g.\sim h)]$

33.1 (a) Valid. (b) Invalid. (c) Valid. (d) Invalid. (e) Invalid. (f) Valid.

33.2 Inferential schemata:
(a) $\sim fx \supset U(g \supset h)$; (fx.fy)$\supset\exists$(i.h); (fx.$\sim$fy)$\supset$hx; $\therefore$ $\exists$h
Invalid in this form; but if the first premiss is taken to include

the assertion that there are some men (at the party), and the relevant formula amended accordingly, the inference is valid. (b) U(f⊃g) ⊃ ((h.i)x ∨ (h.j)y); ~∃(i.h); ~jy; ∴ ∃(f.~g) Valid.

35.1 (a) A4, A3. (b) A4, T50(PM). (c) T3(PM), T32; T3(PM), A4; Syll, Exp. (d) '(p⊃q)⊃((r⊃s)⊃((q⊃r)⊃(p⊃s)))', A4, A4, Transp. (e) T37, T37, T50(PM), Adj. (f) T27, T27, T50(PM), T6, Comp.

36.1 (a) Invalid in both. (b) Valid in LNEU only. (c) Valid in both. (d) Valid in LNEU only. (e) Valid in both. (f) Invalid in both.

36.2 (a) Unstarred. T25b, A4, PM thesis. (b) Unstarred. Obtain 'U~g ⊃ (~fx ⊃ (~fx.~gx))' from (a) by PM thesis; apply A3, deM, T2, Imp. (c) Starred. (b), *A6, PM thesis. (d) Starred. Obtain 'Uf ⊃ (fvg)x' by *QI1, whence obtain '(Uf.((fvg)x⊃Ug)) ⊃ (Uf.Ug)' by PM thesis; obtain '(Uf.Ug) ⊃ (f.g)y' by T5 and *T25; Syll, Exp.

40.1 ('Univ' = 'Universe of Discourse'.)

(a) (Univ: buildings. fx_1 – x_1 is in Greece; gx_1 – x_1 is in England; hx_1x_2 – x_1 is older than x_2.) ∃x(fx.Uy(gy ⊃ hxy))

(b) (Univ: numbers. fx_1 – x_1 is prime; gx_1x_2 – x_1 is greater than x_2.) ~∃x(fx.Uy((fy.(y≠x)) ⊃ gxy))

(c) (Take 'end' to mean 'what is aimed at'. fx_1 – x_1 is an action; gx_1x_2 – x_1 aims at x_2. Same key for (d) and (e).) Ux∃y(fx ⊃ gxy)

(d) ∃yUx(fx ⊃ gxy)

(e) ∃yUx[fx ⊃ (gxy . Uz(gxz ⊃ (z=y)))]

(f) (fx_1 – x_1 is a sailor; gx_1 – x_1 is a port; hx_1x_2 – x_1 is wife of x_2; ix_1x_2 – x_1 is in x_2.) UxUy∃z((fx.gy) ⊃ (hzx.izy))

(g) (Univ: human beings. $fx_1x_2x_3$ – x_1 loves x_2 more than he loves x_3. Same key for (h).) UxUy((x≠y) ⊃ fxxy)

(h) ∃xUy((x≠y) ⊃ fxyx)

(i) (fx_1 – x_1 is a candidate; gx_1 – x_1 is a question in the examination; hx_1x_2 – x_1 answered x_2; ix_1x_2 – x_1 is more difficult than x_2.)

∃x[gx . Uy((gy.(y≠x)) ⊃ ixy) . UzUwUu((fz.fw.fu. hzx.hwx.hux) ⊃ ((z=w) ∨ (w=u) ∨ (u=z)))]

(j) (Univ: buildings in the city. $fx_1 - x_1$ is a skyscraper; $gx_1 - x_1$ has architectural merit.)

$\exists x \exists y [fx \cdot fy \cdot Uz(fz \supset ((z=x) \lor (z=y))) \cdot gx \cdot gy \cdot$
$Uw(gw \supset ((w=x) \lor (w=y)))]$

(k) (Univ: human beings. $fx_1x_2 - x_1$ wants to make x_2 happy. 'Only some' = 'some but not all'; 'others' = 'at least one other'.)

$Ux(fxx) \cdot \exists x \exists y(x \neq y \cdot fxy) \cdot \sim Ux \exists y(x \neq y \cdot fxy)$

(l) ($fx_1 - x_1$ is a play at the Opera House; $gx_1 - x_1$ is a film in town; $hx_1x_2 - x_1$ is better than x_2.)

$\exists x(fx \cdot Uy(fy \supset (y=x)) \cdot Uz(gz \supset hxz))$

(m) (Univ: human beings. x – Mary; y – Tom; $fx_1x_2 - x_1$ is aunt of x_2; $gx_1x_2 - x_1$ is brother of x_2; $hx_1x_2 - x_1$ is father of x_2; $ix_1x_2 - x_1$ is sister of x_2; $jx_1x_2 - x_1$ is mother of x_2.)

$fxy \equiv \exists z((gzx \cdot hzy) \lor (izx \cdot jzy))$

(n) (Univ: human beings. $fx_1x_2 - x_1$ is first cousin of x_2; $gx_1x_2 - x_1$ is grandparent of x_2.)

$UxUy\exists z(fxy \supset (gzx \cdot gzy))$

(o) (x – Jill; $fx_1 - x_1$ is a man; $gx_1x_2 - x_1$ is in love with x_2.)

$\exists y \exists z \exists w(fy.fz.fw.gyx.gzx.gwx.y \neq z.z \neq w.w \neq y)$

(p) (Univ: fleas. $fx_1x_2 - x_1$ is greater than x_2; $gx_1x_2 - x_1$ is on the back of (and bites) x_2.)

$Ux \exists y \exists z(fxy \cdot gyx \cdot fzx \cdot gxz)$

40.2 Hint: there are 47 such sequences, making 48 equivalent sequences in all. In each, 'x' is the first variable, but 'y', 'z' and 'w' can occur in any order; there are thus 6 possible orders of the variables. The last quantifier is always existential; each of the others may be universal or existential; thus there are 8 possibilities for each order of the variables. The position of the negation signs is determined by R1.

(This assumes that an expression ending with '$\sim$' is not to count as a sequence. If such expressions are admitted, the last quantifier may be either existential or universal, and the total is 96.)

40.3 (a) $\equiv$ (b); (c) $\supset$ (a); (d) $\supset$ (a); (a) $\supset$ (e); (c) $\supset$ (b); (d) $\supset$ (b); (b) $\supset$ (e); (c) $\supset$ (e); (d) $\supset$ (e).

40.4 (a) $\sim \exists x \exists z \sim \exists y \sim \exists w [\sim(\sim fxy \cdot \sim gzy) \cdot \sim(\sim(hwx \cdot \sim fyz) \cdot$
$\sim(fyz \cdot \sim hwx))]$

(b) $\exists y Ux \exists w Uy \sim((fx \supset \sim gyx) \supset \sim(\sim hxz \supset gwy))$

40.5   Where Q_j is any one of $Q_1, \ldots, Q_n$, let R_j be the *other* quantifier containing the same individual-variable as Q_j. By R1, Q_1 may be replaced by $\sim R_1 \sim$. Q_2 is now prefixed by '$\sim$'; so $\sim Q_2$ may be replaced by $R_2 \sim$. We continue until we reach $\sim Q_n$, which we replace by $R_n \sim$. Double negations are cancelled if necessary at the beginning and end.

40.6   Outlines of arguments:

1. Let x be any object which stands in the relation f to some object y. Then fxy; and since f is symmetrical, fyx also. Therefore since f is transitive, fxx.

2. Let f be asymmetrical. Then for any x and y, fxy $\supset$ $\sim$fyx. Therefore by (y/x), fxx $\supset$ $\sim$fxx. Whence by '(p$\supset$$\sim$p)$\supset$$\sim$p', $\sim$fxx.

3. Let f be transitive. Then for any x and y, (fxy . fyx) $\supset$ fxx. But f is irreflexive, therefore $\sim$fxx. Therefore $\sim$(fxy . fyx); i.e. fxy $\supset$ $\sim$fyx.

40.7   Examples are: (*a*) implies; (*b*) distinct from; (*c*) and (i.e. joint truth of both arguments).

40.8   (*b*) $\sim$1 v $\sim$2 v $\sim$3 v $\sim$4 v $\sim$5 v $\sim$6 v $\sim$7 v $\sim$8 v $\sim$9

(*c*) ($\sim$1 v $\sim$2 v $\sim$3) . ($\sim$4 v $\sim$5 v $\sim$6) . ($\sim$7 v $\sim$8 v $\sim$9)

(*d*) (1 . 2 . 3) v (4 . 5 . 6) v (7 . 8 . 9)

(*e*) ($\sim$1 v $\sim$4 v $\sim$7) . ($\sim$2 v $\sim$5 v $\sim$8) . ($\sim$3 v $\sim$6 v $\sim$9)

(*f*) (1 . 4 . 7) v (2 . 5 . 8) v (3 . 6 . 9)

(*g*) 1 v 2 v 3 v 4 v 5 v 6 v 7 v 8 v 9

(*h*) $\sim$1 . $\sim$2 . $\sim$3 . $\sim$4 . $\sim$5 . $\sim$6 . $\sim$7 . $\sim$8 . $\sim$9

(*i*) ($\sim$1 . $\sim$2 . $\sim$3) v ($\sim$4 . $\sim$5 . $\sim$6) v ($\sim$7 . $\sim$8 . $\sim$9)

(*j*) (1 v 2 v 3) . (4 v 5 v 6) . (7 v 8 v 9)

(*k*) ($\sim$1 . $\sim$4 . $\sim$7) v ($\sim$2 . $\sim$5 . $\sim$8) v ($\sim$3 . $\sim$6 . $\sim$9)

(*l*) (1 v 4 v 7) . (2 v 5 v 8) . (3 v 6 v 9)

40.9   (*a*) Every student prefers every subject to some game or other. (I.e. in the case of each student there is some game – not necessarily the same game in the case of each student – to which he prefers all subjects without exception.)

(*b*) There is at least one game to which every student without exception prefers every subject whatsoever.

(*c*) Every game is such that at least one student prefers it to some subject or other.

(*d*) There is a subject which no student prefers to any game whatsoever.

40.10

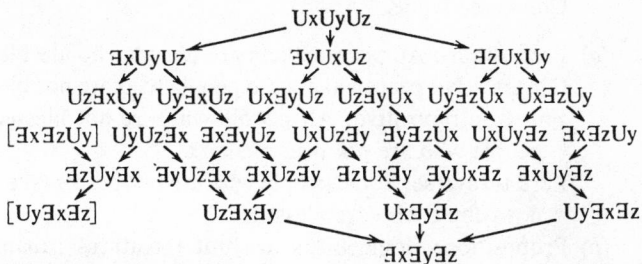

The sequences in brackets are identical with those on the extreme right of the same lines. Strictly a three-dimensional figure is needed; e.g. a model of the earth, with 'UxUyUz' at the North Pole and '∃x∃y∃z' at the South.

40.11 (*a*) x is a sister of y $=_{Df}$ (Fx . x≠y . ∃z(Pzx.Pzy))

(This definition admits half-sisters as sisters. If only full sisters are to be admitted, the definiens will have to be more complicated.)

(*b*) x is an uncle of y $=_{Df}$ (Mx . ∃z∃w(Pzx.Pzw.Pwy.x≠w))

(*c*) x is a brother-in-law of y $=_{Df}$
[Mx . (∃z∃w(Pzx.Pzw.Swy) v ∃z∃w(Pzy.Pzw.Swx))]

(*d*) x is a step-sister of y $=_{Df}$
(Fx . ∃z∃w(Pzx.Pwy.Szw) . ~∃z(Pzx.Pzy))

41.3 (*a*) ∃x∃yUz((fx.~gxy) v hzx)

(*b*) ∃xUy∃z∃w(fxy . gzx . gyw . fwx)

(*c*) UxUy∃z∃u[((~fy v ~gyx) . ~fz . ~gzw) v (~fu . ~hu)]

(*d*) ∃w∃u∃t((fxy . gw . ~fyw) v fuz v gt)

42.1 (*a*) Contrary: No Italians are Europeans.
Contradictory: Some Italians are not Europeans.
Converse: Some Europeans are Italians.

(*b*) Sub-contrary: Some acts of lying are not morally justified acts.
Contradictory: No acts of lying are morally justified acts.
Converse: Some morally justified acts are acts of lying.

(c) Subcontrary: Some people who confess to crimes are guilty people.

Contradictory: All people who confess to crimes are guilty people.

Converse: None.

42.2 (a) Proposition: All peacemakers are people who are blessed.

Obverse: No peacemakers are people who are not blessed.

Full Contrapositive: All people who are not blessed are people who are not peacemakers.

Partial Inverse: Some people who are not peacemakers are not people who are blessed.

(b) Proposition: Some birds are not (creatures capable of flying).

Obverse: Some birds are (creatures incapable of flying).

Full Contrapositive: Some (creatures incapable of flying) are not (creatures other than birds).

Partial Inverse: None.

(d) Proposition: Some human beings are (being capable of running a mile in less than four minutes).

Obverse: Some human beings are not (beings incapable of running a mile in less than four minutes).

No Full Contrapositive or Partial Inverse.

42.3 (a) True (Obverted Converse). (b) Truth-value undetermined. (c) False (Contradictory of Converse). (d) Truth-value undetermined.

42.4 (a) AEE, Fig. I. Invalid. (b) OAO, Fig. III. Valid. (c) AEE, Fig. IV. Valid. (d) AII, Fig. II. Invalid. (e) EAO, Fig. III. Valid.

43.1 (a) $\sim\exists(S.\bar{P}) \equiv \sim\exists(\bar{P}.S)$ Valid. (b) $\sim\exists(S.P) \supset \exists(\bar{S}.\bar{P})$ Invalid. (c) $\exists(S.P) \equiv \exists(P.\bar{\bar{S}})$ Valid.

(d) $\sim\exists(M.P), \sim\exists(S.\bar{M}), \therefore \exists(S.\bar{P})$ Invalid.

(e) $\sim\exists(P.M), \exists(S.M), \therefore \exists(S.\bar{P})$ Valid.

(f) $\sim\exists(P.\bar{M}), \sim\exists(M.\bar{S}), \therefore \exists(S.P)$ Invalid.

44.1 (a) Valid. (b) Invalid. (c) Invalid. (d) Valid.

44.2 (a) If both premisses are particular, the Antilogism contains at most one universal proposition. Hence Condition 1 is violated.

(b) In an inconsistent syllogistic triad, the two universals must contain at least one negated variable between them (Condition 2); hence not more than one can be an E. If they are E and A, the variables not common to them are both unnegated. Hence the particular is an I (Condition 3). Therefore no inconsistent triad can contain more than one negative proposition. But the premisses of a valid syllogism must be selected from such a triad. Hence (b) follows.

(c) and (d) should now present little difficulty.

47.1 (a) Valid Part 2. (b) Valid Part 1. (c) Invalid. (d) Valid Part 1. (e) Valid Part 1. (f) Valid Part 1. (g) Invalid.

Some Suggestions
for Further Reading

The following lists name a few of the books which will provide useful collateral or more advanced reading and thus give the student a foothold on a rapidly growing mountain of logical literature.

List A contains books mainly of an elementary type that provide alternative treatments of, or amplifications on, topics treated in this book. The occurrence of a Roman numeral as an annotation indicates that Part of this book to which the listed work is relevant. ' + other' indicates that some topic outside the range of our own book receives substantial treatment. In addition, we indicate the fact if the notation or terminology used is markedly different from our own.

List B contains a few works which will provide more advanced material once the elements have been mastered.

List A

BLANCHÉ, R. *Axiomatics* (London: Routledge and Kegan Paul, 1962). II (on axiomatics in general).

BOCHEŃSKI, J. M. *A Précis of Mathematical Logic* (Dordrecht, Holland: Reidel, 1959). I, II, III, IV + other. Russellian and Polish notations.

CARNAP, R. *Introduction to Symbolic Logic and its Applications* (New York: Dover, 1958). I, III + other. Substantial differences in terminology.

FARIS, J. A. *Truth-functional Logic* (London: Routledge and Kegan Paul, 1962). I.

ŁUKASIEWICZ, J. *Aristotle's Syllogistic from the standpoint of modern formal logic* (2nd edition [enlarged]. Oxford: Clarendon Press, 1957). IV + other. Polish notation.

PRIOR, A. N. *Formal Logic* (2nd edition. Oxford: Clarendon Press, 1962). I, II, III, IV + other. Polish notation.

QUINE, W. V. O. *Methods of Logic* (London: Routledge and Kegan Paul, 1952). I, III.

REICHENBACH, H. *Elements of Symbolic Logic* (New York: Macmillan, 1948). I, III, IV, + other.

STRAWSON, P. F. *Introduction to Logical Theory* (London: Methuen, 1952). I, III, IV + other.

SUPPES, P. *Introduction to Logic* (Princeton, N.J.: Van Nostrand, 1957). I, III + other.

An exposition of traditional syllogistic logic is given in

KEYNES, J. N. *Studies and Exercises in Formal Logic* (4th edition. London: Macmillan, 1906).

or, more briefly, in

STEBBING, L. S. *A Modern Elementary Logic* (Revised edition. London: Methuen, 1952).

List B

Anyone wishing to pursue logic further should become acquainted at least with the nature and structure of

WHITEHEAD, A. N. and RUSSELL, B. *Principia Mathematica* (2nd edition. Cambridge: CUP, Vol. I, 1925, Vols. II and III, 1927). [*Principia Mathematica to *56* (Cambridge: CUP, 1962) includes those sections of the above which are specially relevant to the present book.]

A comprehensive treatment of the propositional and predicate calculi is contained in

CHURCH, A. *Introduction to Mathematical Logic, Vol. I* (Princeton, N.J.: Princeton University Press, 1956).

A more condensed exposition of the propositional and predicate calculi is given in

HILBERT, D. and ACKERMANN, W. *Principles of Mathematical Logic* (New York: Chelsea, 1950) [Original German edition, 1928, 1938].

For an extended treatment of the history of the subject, see

KNEALE, W. and KNEALE, M. *The Development of Logic* (Oxford: Clarendon Press, 1962).

The Journal of Symbolic Logic Vol. I (1936) contains a bibliography, compiled by A. Church, for the period 1666–1935. This Journal also reviews all relevant literature (articles as well as books), and thus provides a continuing and exhaustive bibliography of modern formal logic and associated fields.

INDEX

Bold face type indicates a definition or explanation of the term in question.

389

Abbreviations and Special Symbols

PART I

Basic Truth-tables

p	$\sim$p		p	q	p.q	pvq	p⋎q	p⊃q	p≡q
1	0		1	1	1	1	0	1	1
0	1		1	0	0	1	1	0	0
			0	1	0	1	1	1	0
			0	0	0	0	0	1	1

Formation Rules for PC

1. A variable standing alone is a wff.
2. If X is a wff, $\sim$X is a wff.
3. If X and Y are wffs, then X and Y with a dyadic operator between them, and the whole enclosed in brackets, is a wff.

Rule for Substitution of Equivalents

If X is a well-formed part of a wff W, and Z is the result of replacing X by Y, then if (X ≡ Y) is valid, then W is equivalent to Z.

PART II

Transformation rules for PC systems, PM, TB and W

1. **Substitution.** If X is a thesis containing propositional variables, $p_1, \ldots, p_n$, and $Y_1, \ldots, Y_n$ are (not necessarily distinct) wffs, then $X(Y_1/p_1, \ldots, Y_n/p_n)$ is a thesis.
2. **Detachment.** If X and (X ⊃ Y) are theses, then Y is a thesis.

Axioms

PM: 1. (pvp) ⊃ p

2. q ⊃ (pvq)

3. (pvq) ⊃ (qvp)

4. (p v (qvr)) ⊃ (q v (pvr))

5. (q⊃r) ⊃ ((pvq) ⊃ (pvr))

TB: 1. (p⊃q) ⊃ ((q⊃r)⊃(p⊃r))

2. ((p⊃q) ⊃ p) ⊃ p

3. p ⊃ (q⊃p)

W: TB + 4. 0 ⊃ p

400

Important theses

(N.B. When an implication and an equivalence are both proved in the text, only the latter is listed here.)

$(p \supset (q \supset r)) \supset (q \supset (p \supset r))$	[Perm]
$(q \supset r) \supset ((p \supset q) \supset (p \supset r))$	[Syll]
$(p \supset q) \supset ((q \supset r) \supset (p \supset r))$	[Syll]
$p \supset (q \supset p)$	[Simp]
$p \vee \sim p$	[Excluded Middle]
$(p \supset (q \supset r)) \supset ((p \cdot q) \supset r)$	[Imp]
$((p \cdot q) \supset r) \supset (p \supset (q \supset r))$	[Exp]
$(p \cdot q) \supset p$	T21, Θ34
$(p \cdot q) \supset q$	T22, Θ35
$p \supset (q \supset (p \cdot q))$	[Adj]
$(p \supset q) \supset ((p \supset r) \supset (p \supset (q \cdot r)))$	[Comp]
$p \equiv \sim\sim p$	[Double Negation]
$(p \supset q) \equiv (\sim q \supset \sim p)$	[Transp]
$(p \vee q) \equiv (q \vee p)$	[Comm (Disjunction)]
$(p \cdot q) \equiv (q \cdot p)$	[Comm (Conjunction)]
$p \equiv (p \vee p)$	T33
$p \equiv (p \cdot p)$	T35
$p \equiv p$	[Id]
$(p \equiv q) \equiv (\sim p \equiv \sim q)$	T38
$(p \vee q) \equiv \sim(\sim p \cdot \sim q)$	[De Morgan]
$(p \vee (q \vee r)) \equiv ((p \vee q) \vee r)$	[Assoc]
$(p \vee (q \vee r)) \equiv (q \vee (p \vee r))$	[Assoc]
$(p \cdot (q \cdot r)) \equiv (q \cdot (p \cdot r))$	[Assoc]
$((p \cdot q) \cdot r) \equiv (p \cdot (q \cdot r))$	[Assoc]
$(p \cdot (q \vee r)) \equiv ((p \cdot q) \vee (p \cdot r))$	[Distrib]
$(p \vee (q \cdot r)) \equiv ((p \vee q) \cdot (p \vee r))$	[Distrib]
$p \equiv ((p \cdot q) \vee (p \cdot \sim q))$	T54
$(\sim p \supset p) \supset p$	[Consequentia Mirabilis]

PART III

Distributive Laws for Quantified Schemata

$$\exists(\alpha \lor \beta) \equiv (\exists\alpha \lor \exists\beta) \qquad \text{[LED]}$$

$$U(\alpha \cdot \beta) \equiv (U\alpha \cdot U\beta)$$

Rules for Testing Disjunctions/Conjunctions of Quantified Schemata

Wff is valid if and only if PC wff on right is valid.		Wff is inconsistent if and only if PC wff on right is inconsistent.	
*i. $\exists\alpha$	α'	*ia. $U\alpha$	α'
ii. $U\alpha$	α'	iia. $\exists\alpha$	α'
iii. $U\alpha \lor U\beta$	At least one of	iiia. $\exists\alpha \cdot \exists\beta$.	At least one of
$\lor \ldots$	$\alpha', \beta' \ldots$	$\ldots$	$\alpha', \beta' \ldots$
iv. $\exists\alpha \lor U\beta_1 \lor$	$\alpha' \lor \beta_j'$, where β_j is	iva. $U\alpha \cdot \exists\beta_1 \cdot$	$\alpha' \cdot \beta_j'$, where β_j is
$\ldots \lor U\beta_n$	one of $\beta_1 \ldots \beta_n$	$\ldots \cdot \exists\beta_n$	one of $\beta_1 \ldots \beta_n$

Rule for validity of disjunctions containing IS's (N.B. No individual-variable may occur more than once in any disjunction.)

In every IS replace the individual-variable at the end by 'U' at the beginning, and apply Rules i.–iv.

Transformation rules for LPC systems, PM+LPC1 and PM+LPC2

1. Uniform substitution of wffs for propositional variables.

2. If α' is a thesis, then $U\alpha$ is a thesis.   (Q)

3. Uniform substitution of wfpes for predicate variables.

4. Detachment (as for PC systems).

5. (PM+LPC2 only) Uniform substitution for individual-variables.

Axioms for LPC Systems

PM+LPC1: PM axioms 1,2,3,5+

A1. $U(f \supset g) \supset (Uf \supset Ug)$

*A2. $Uf \supset \exists f$

PM+LPC2: PM axioms 1,2,3,5+

A1. $U(f \supset g) \supset (Uf \supset Ug)$

A3. $(f.g)x \equiv (fx.gx)$

A4. $fx \supset \exists f$

Rules concerning Quantifiers

R1. **Quantifier transformation.** A universal quantifier may be replaced by an existential one (containing the same variable), or vice versa, provided '$\sim$' is inserted or deleted immediately before and after it. [For LPC1–2 omit phrase in brackets.]

R2. **Quantifier rearrangement.** Quantifiers in an adjacent group, if all universal or all existential, may be rearranged in any order. (N.B. A '$\sim$' preceding the group remains where it was.)

Rules of relative strength (applicable only to sequences of *affirmative* quantifiers at the *beginning* of a wff):

R3. Replacing any occurrence of 'U' by '$\exists$' weakens the wff.

R4. Moving an existential quantifier to the right of a universal quantifier weakens the wff.

PART IV

Interpretations of Syllogistic Schemata in LPC1

	1.	2.	3.	4.	5.
SaP	(1)	(1a)	(1a)	(1a)	(1)
SeP	(2)	(2a)	(2a)	(2)	(2a)
SiP	(3)	(3)	(3a)	(3)	(3a)
SoP	(4)	(4)	(4a)	(4a)	(4)

Key:

(1): $\sim\exists(S.\bar{P})$ (1a): $\exists S.\sim\exists(S.\bar{P})$

(2): $\sim\exists(S.P)$ (2a): $\exists S.\sim\exists(S.P)$

(3): $\exists(S.P)$ (3a): $\sim\exists S \lor \exists(S.P)$

(4): $\exists(S.\bar{P})$ (4a): $\sim\exists S \lor \exists(S.\bar{P})$

For Interpretation 6 see p. 333.